Hints & Kinks
for the Radio Amateur

Edited By
Stuart Leland, W1JEC

The American Radio Relay League, Inc.
Newington, CT 06111

Foreword

How can you find a solution to a tricky problem in your amateur radio workshop or station? Has some other amateur experienced a similar problem? Chances are someone *has* already grappled with a like problem and has devised a workable solution. It shouldn't be surprising. Inventiveness has always been an outstanding quality of the radio amateur.

This booklet contains a collection of such tricks of the trade, written by several hundred amateurs. Many of their ideas were published originally in *QST,* the monthly journal of the League.

A sincere effort has been made to touch upon a wide area of interests with the intention of offering something for everyone. And should you find your own experiments producing a handy answer to a common problem, send it to *QST.* You may be among the authors of the next volume of *Hints & Kinks for the Radio Amateur.*

Richard L. Baldwin, W1RU
General Manager

Contents

Chapter 1

Aids for the Station and Shop

SOME IDEAS ON STATION LAYOUT AND HELPFUL ACCESSORIES

Desk drawers with stops: "Second" or "reject" doors, finished and mounted on legs, with flaws underneath, have come into common use as desks. Two-drawer filing cabinets on each end, beside the legs or in place of them, further extend the usefulness of the gimmick. There is a need for more carpentry to make shallow drawers for installation under the length of the front of the desk. An easy trick is to use shallow aluminum baking pans of the type that are made with a rolled lip around the top. Strips of wood can be grooved, then glued and screwed underneath the door. The pans are simply slipped by the lip into the grooves. For a nice finishing touch, varnished strips of wood are secured to the front side of the "drawers." Both front and back slide stops are made by placing a stick-on rubber foot on the underside of the table. For the inside stop, simply reach inside the open drawer at its intended maximum pull, and stick the stop in place.

Step-to-talk: For those who haven't discovered the ease of using a foot switch, here's a quick application for a relay from the junkbox. Select one that will sit flat on the floor, wire the push-to-talk circuit through a length of line cord to the contacts, and place the assembly on the floor under your operating table. A mic on a boom makes for hands-off operation in the absence of VOX as well as the professional studio look for the station.

Centralize your switches: A friend of mine, K9KXP, told me how he stops worrying about wearing out the switches in his various units. He has them wired through a master control panel which can be rigged to include master switch, fused circuits and the individual circuit switches

labeled for various pieces of equipment. Wire such a unit with a three-wire system for maximum shock protection. The installation might also include a voltage-monitor meter, and the position would be

This operating position features many of the hints described, including a relay for the foot switch, power panel, boom mic and Kleenex box speaker cabinet as well as the custom-crafted baking pan drawers under the table.

a good place to put your SWR meters.

Speakers the easy way: New poly-planar foam cone speakers are being marketed by Lafayette Radio Electronics in a 5 × 8-inch (127 × 203 mm) size and will fit marvelously into a plastic Kleenex tissue box, the oval opening serving as the cabinet sound exit. Drill four holes in the front, spaced to fit the speaker mounts; mount the speaker with a double layer of

grill cloth, and drill two more holes in back, where you prefer, for hanging the speaker cabinet on the wall.

Doorstop/bookend: I just can't bring myself to throw out that old transformer that burned out in my af amplifier. It makes a fine bookend or doorstop. Be sure to put a strip of felt on the feet so you don't mar the bookshelf. — *Harrison Leon Church, WØKXP*

HOLDING LIGHTWEIGHT EQUIPMENT IN PLACE

Years ago, amateur equipment would stay put by sheer weight alone. Today, light-weight transceivers and the like will scoot off the desk with just a slight nudge.

I have found that a piece of indoor-outdoor carpeting will hold them in place. The equipment feet nestle down into the nap of the carpet. The rubber backing holds the carpet material firmly to the desk top or other surface.

When stacking gear, put a piece of carpeting under the feet of the top unit. This should not be used on a vented cabinet of course, but is great for solid ones, such as speaker enclosures. — *Ed Heubach, W9AO*

BEWARE OF PROTECTIVE DIODES

A word of caution regarding the use of protective diodes across the antenna input terminals of solid-state receivers is in order. If separate antennas are used for transmitting and receiving, severe TVI can be created by the diodes rectifying the transmitted signals and reradiating them on many frequencies in the rf spectrum. I discovered this while experimenting with my solid-state receiver. I was attempting to see if the diodes really protected the front-end rf transistor stage by leaving the receiver connected to its own antenna while transmitting with a 350-watt rig nearby. I was impolitely informed by the XYL that I was raising havoc with the television set. As soon as the receiver was disconnected from its antenna, the problem disappeared. If the same antenna is used for transmitting and receiving, such a problem should not exist. — *Glen Benskin, K6UH*

GMT "HOUR HAND"

A homemade "hour hand" of thin sheet metal fixed to the same shaft as the hour hand of your clock, and set to the proper number of hours ahead (or behind) will show GMT, while the original hand will show local time. — *Tom Chaudou, WN9FLD*

HAM SHACK TABLE

For about $30, a handsome desk that will support heavy equipment can be built by following some simple steps. This information is offered as a guide for any amateur interested in constructing his own table (see drawing).

1) Two 4 × 4-inch, (102 × 102 mm) 8-foot (2.44 m) lengths are cut into the following dimensions: four pieces 22 inches (558 mm) long, two pieces 33 inches (838 mm) long.

2) Half-moon shaped cuts are made 6-1/2 (615 mm) and 7-1/2 inches (190 mm) from each end of the 33-inch-long pieces. These cuts should be 2 inches (51 mm) deep. A jigsaw is handy for this type

of work. While not necessary, the ends of these pieces were curved to improve the appearance.

3) Place the 22-inch pieces (legs) over these half-moon cuts and mark the legs so starting holes can be made. Four 4-inch No. 14 wood screws should be sufficient to hold the legs in an upright, stationary position.

4) Next, place two 1 × 6-inch pieces over the ends of the legs and drill four starting holes at the four positions. Secure the two 1 × 6 pieces with four No. 14 wood screws. This completes the base for the table.

5) Set a door or a sheet of plywood 1/2- or 3/4-inch (13 to 19 mm) thick on top. Drill two holes through the 1 × 6 at each end, so that they enter the top. Secure to top with 1-1/2 inch No. 14 wood screws. This completes the table.

6) A 2 × 4 is placed on the back side, about halfway down, to give the table lateral stability and to support electric outlets and cabling. A piece of plywood will do very nicely, too.

7) A large shelf on top gives additional room for equipment. A 2 × 12 was used here. The end supports (also made from 2 × 12 stock) for this shelf should be centered over the 4 × 4 legs of the table. L-shaped brackets hold the shelf together.

The overall dimensions used will make the surface of the table about 28-1/4 inches (717 mm) high, which is quite comfortable for myself. The height can be adjusted by making the legs different lengths. The table can be disassembled into its basic components, if necessary. — *Mike Greenway, K4TBN*

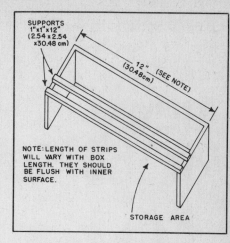

An orange-crate transceiver stand.

ORANGE-CRATE STAND

For those who have a small operating table, a wooden orange crate makes an excellent stand for a transceiver. One of the long sides of the crate is removed to provide a small storage space below. I have a keyer, bug, and small lamp stored underneath with room to spare. If additional support is desired, wooden strips about 1 × 1 × 12 inches (25 × 25 × 305 mm), attached as shown in the drawing, should do nicely. — *Robert Zagorac, WN9QYU*

LATCHING RELAY SOURCE

For your latching relay requirements, I have found VW electrical systems a good source of supply. They use a latching relay to control high- and low-beam headlight switching with a single pulse button. My last trip to the local junkyard netted me four relays for two dollars. The quality is excellent and the size is about 1-inch cube. Older VWs are 6 V and newer ones are 12 V. — *Walter LeForet, WA3VCY*

GROUNDING AC LINES

Howard M. Berlin's (K3NEZ) "Danger Lurks!" article in February, 1976, *QST* was excellent. Because of Berlin's familiarity with the subject, I think he may have overlooked supplying information which some hams do not have.

When a receptacle is properly mounted in a wall box, the pin hole GROUND is at the bottom. The line ground (NEUTRAL) is at the left side of the two slots. It is larger than the hot side slot in some receptacles.

The GROUND pin hole is frequently connected to the conduit or BX cable and like many other "pipe" conductors, does not provide the most perfect ground. In nonmetallic sheathed cable (Romex) installations, the ground is simply a bare wire.

Modern two-lead (two connections) wiring devices will show different colors

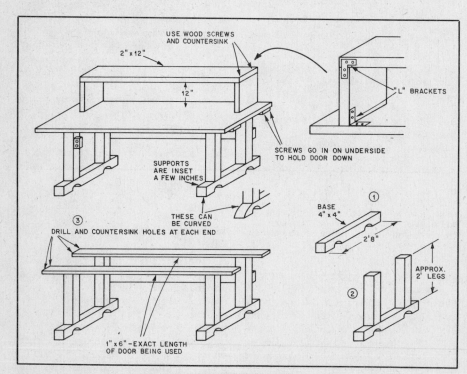

Plans for a homemade table that can be disassembled easily and is large enough to handle most of the equipment in one's shack. The builder can modify accordingly to suit his own needs.

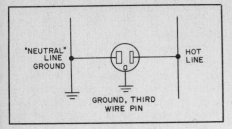

Standard circuit for 117-V ac receptacle.

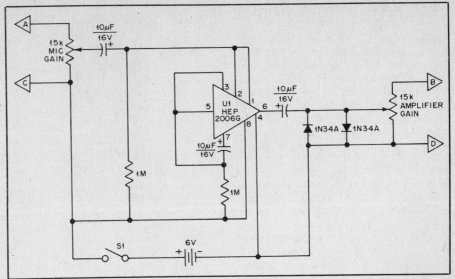

Schematic diagram of IC pre-amp for use with desk microphone.

of metal at connections. The natural brass is the HOT side. The light-colored connection (tinned, nickel, cadmium, etc.) is the NEUTRAL (line ground) side. If there is a third connection, as in plug receptacles, it is the ground connection, screw head daubed bluish-green.

In devices with pigtails, the white lead is neutral ground. In ac power wiring, white is almost always neutral ground. It must never be broken with switches, fuses, etc. The hot lead is black or any color except white. — *B. H. Hansen, W6HOZ*

PUTTING YOUR BUG OR PADDLE IN ITS PLACE AND KEEPING IT THERE

I keep my bug in place by applying a small amount of rubber cement on the feet and pressing the key down on the desired spot on the table. When I wish to move the key, I just pry it loose from the table. The old cement rubs off easily, leaving no marks on the table. — *M. Crosby Bartlett, K4EU*

DUAL-PURPOSE CARBON MICROPHONE REPLACEMENT

Some of the fm transceivers coming into service in the vhf amateur band still use carbon microphones. A vast improvement in audio quality can be achieved by the use of a dynamic microphone replacement cartridge.

Shown is a simple transistor circuit that can be used to adapt a dynamic element to a carbon circuit. The voltage required for the transistor is derived from the same source that originally was used by the carbon element. To make the adaptation, simply open up your microphone case and determine the positive and negative leads

to the carbon element. Remove the carbon element and install a dynamic element. One with approximately 500 ohms impedance is satisfactory; however, I have not found any element that won't work.

Distribute the rest of the parts around the inside of the microphone case. Practically any pnp transistor will work in this circuit. Any of the general replacement audio types should do. A drop or two of cement or liquid rubber will hold the parts in place. Connect points B and D to the dynamic element.

For use as a desk mic, add the IC circuit shown. Connect the output of the IC points B and D to the input of the transistor circuit, points B and D. Connect the dynamic element to the input points A and C.

The output waveform is clipped by the 1N34A diodes to prevent overmodulation. Careful adjustment of the input and output potentiometers will result in a distortion-free signal. If the input level is too high, severe clipping will occur. Adjust the input so that normal voice level will just start clipping.

A small 6-volt battery supplies the

power for the IC. A switch should be installed in the circuit to prevent running the battery down when the preamplifier is not in use. — *Robert D. Shriner, WAØUZO*

DUAL-GATE MOSFET OFFERS AN UNUSUAL CRYSTAL-CONTROLLED OSCILLATOR CONCEPT

This unusual crystal-controlled oscillator circuit offers some interesting possibilities for application as the LO in vhf and uhf converter design. No trimming or tuning is required to get the overtone frequency. Should the fundamental frequency of the crystal be desired as the output, raise the value of RFC1 to 100 µH or replace it with a 1000-ohm resistor.

The stability of the oscillator is excellent. Actually the circuit works well with as little as four volts applied to it. — *G. Tomassetti, I4BER*

[Editor's Note: The circuit is similar to the modified Pierce oscillator, which uses the crystal between grid 1 and grid 2 of a tetrode tube. Depending upon the resonant frequency of the output network of the oscillator, overtone or fundamental crystal-mode operation can be obtained.]

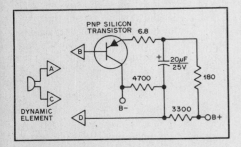

Schematic diagram of simple transistor adapter for dynamic element to carbon microphone circuit.

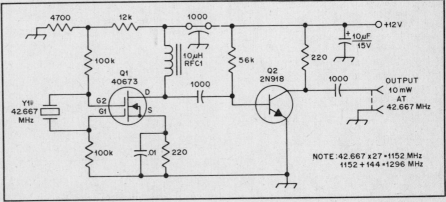

A crystal-controlled oscillator with interesting possibilities.

ADJUSTMENT OF POLAR RELAYS FOR RTTY

Almost nobody uses polar relays these days in connection with amateur RTTY operation, but there are still hundreds of them available as surplus, and at comparatively low prices. They have many possible uses besides RTTY. The most common type is the Western Electric 255A, and there are several equivalents manufactured by other companies. If you have one of these relays that you wish to adjust, try this simple procedure. It isn't as precise as you could do with a polar-relay test set, but is plenty good enough for most purposes. You will need an oscilloscope for finest adjustment, although fair results can be obtained using only a dc voltmeter. A small nail or the pointed tip of a soldering aid can be used for the adjustment tool. A feeler gauge might also be helpful.

The circuit for testing the relay is shown in the accompanying diagram. If you plan to check relay adjustments frequently, the circuit can be built into a 3 × 4 × 5-inch (76 × 102 × 127 mm) chassis box with insulated binding posts provided for scope or meter connections. With S1 closed, the armature (moving contacts) of the relay will move back and forth between the fixed contacts 60 times per second. That's just a bit slower than you would get with an RTTY signal at 100 wpm. The output from pin 1 (through the 100-ohm resistor) will alternate in square-wave fashion, going from +1.5 V to —1.5 V.

Begin the adjustment by disconnecting the ac power. Back off the contacts and the pole pieces (those round-shaped things below the contacts) and check to see that the armature is centered inside the coil opening. If not, loosening some screws on the bottom of the relay should allow you to position the coil for best alignment. After you get the coil set so the armature is centered, tighten all screws. Adjust one contact screw until it just makes contact.

A polar relay such as this may be adjusted by means of the test circuit shown below.

Use the dc meter or watch for a shift in the position of the baseline on the scope. After contact is made, back off thirty degrees or 1/12 turn on the contact screw. This should give a .002-inch clearance. Then adjust the other contact in the same manner. You should end up with a symmetric arrangement, with .002-inch clearance on either side of the armature contacts.

Now turn one pole piece until the armature just touches the *opposite* contact. Then back off on the pole piece slightly less than a half turn and tighten the tension nut. Then adjust the second pole piece so that the armature stands midway between the two pole pieces and tighten its tension nut. The armature should flip to either contact and remain, or else return to center, when moved manually. Slight readjustment of the second pole piece should help if needed here.

Now apply ac power. Look at the waveform on the scope, or use the voltmeter set on a low-value dc range. You should see a symmetric signal on the scope. It will not be a perfect square wave, because some time is required for the armature contact to move from one side to the other. During the travel time, you will see a small part of the waveform where the signal is neither positive nor negative. During contact, the signal should be positive or negative 1.5 volts. Any nonsymmetry can be corrected by a *very slight* readjustment of the *pole pieces* (not the contacts). If you are using a meter for indication, the meter should read zero. Slight pole-piece adjustment should bring the reading to zero, if needed. On the oscilloscope you may observe some amount of contact bounce, as a broken-up portion of the square wave. A very slight readjustment of the contacts may correct this. You won't be able to detect any contact bounce using a meter only.

That's all there is to it. Just a word of caution: Once you apply the ac and make readjustments, go very slowly and do not make adjustments of more than a small fraction of a turn. Usually with surplus relays, if they can't be adjusted by very slight trimming, something is defective in the relay. Even if this is the case, compromise settings can sometimes be found which will give quite satisfactory relay operation. — *K1TD*

COLOR CODING CIRCUIT DIAGRAMS

Numbered triangles showing connections between parts of a schematic clean up the diagram, but make it difficult to find the companion number of a pair. I color them around the outside, using a different color for each pair. — *Temple Nieter, W9YLD*

[Editor's Note: This is a handy hint for matching up sections of multifunction ICs.]

TV BACKDROP

With more amateurs using SSTV and fast (regular) scan television, the need for a white backdrop becomes important for the production of high-contrast pictures. The installation of a white roll-type window shade hanging from the ceiling, mounted a few feet behind the subject, provides a suitable background for this purpose. — *Robert W. Gervenack, W7FEN*

CATV TVI

This information should be of interest to any ham operating in a community or condominium complex served by cable television. After being informed that I was

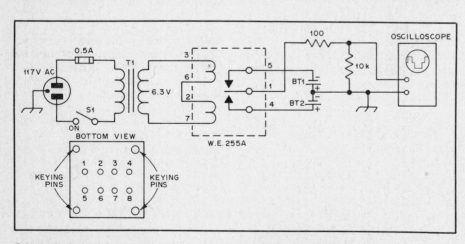

Schematic diagram for adjusting polar relays. Resistances are in ohms.
S1 — Spst slide or toggle switch.
T1 — Filament transformer, 6.3 V at 0.6 A (Halldorson 21F21 or equiv.)
X1 — W. E. 255A relay socket (circuit shown with relay plugged in).
BT1, BT2 — 1.5-V penlight cells. A Keystone Electronics no. 140 or equiv. battery holder may be used.

causing TVI on several occasions, some investigatory work seemed necessary. The problem stemmed from the loss of continuity in the outer shield conductor on the CATV feed line from their main feeder to the subscribers' sets. In each case, the connectors joining the feed line to the main line had corroded to the point where the resistance between the feeder and the main line was on the order of 40,000 ohms. The subscribers still received reasonably good quality pictures, but ignition noise and other forms of interference were also present. The CATV people were advised of the situation and have been most cooperative in resolving the problem. — *Richard M. Purinton, W1SX/4*

COLOR-BURST OSCILLATOR CRYSTAL HELPS VISUALLY HANDICAPPED LOCATE W1AW

Even when using a 100-kHz calibrator, it is difficult to know what frequency a receiver is tuned to if you can't see the dial. The color-burst generator in a color television set operates on approximately 3.579 MHz, close to the W1AW bulletin and code practice frequency in the 80-meter band. A color-burst crystal was purchased from a local TV repairman for $2, and the circuit shown was constructed. Now my sightless friend can easily locate W1AW. — *Steven A. Licht, WB2CZC*

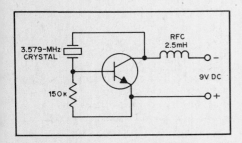

A crystal oscillator for locating W1AW on 80 meters.

KEY DOWN

Maybe your XYL won't like you drilling holes in that maple operating desk so you can mount your new electronic keyer paddle or "bug." Two-way carpet tape placed on the bottom of the "keys" will hold them quite well; also the tape is useful for wall maps and other items that require hanging. — *Larry Baine, W8GBR*

RUBBER FEET FOR EQUIPMENT

Many hobby shops stock a large supply of rubber stoppers intended for use with test tubes and flasks. They come in many sizes and are usually slightly tapered. Some have holes drilled through them lengthwise, which would facilitate mounting with sheet-metal screws. The type

without holes could simply be glued to the bottom of the piece of equipment. — *Ray Bass, W7YKN*

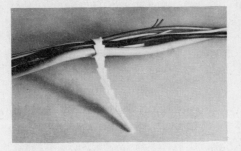

Economical cable ties.

PLASTIC-BAG TIES MAKE NEATER CABLE HARNESSES

The serrated plastic ties supplied with disposable plastic bags are useful around the shack and mobile installation to hold the various cables together. Unlike the commercial version, they may be unfastened when a wire must be added or removed. — *Mack Beal, W1PNR*

WEATHERPROOFING LOW-VOLTAGE CONNECTORS

Salt finally corroded one of the taillights on the boat trailer. The price of a new light was more than offset by discovering the trick that the manufacturer used to prevent the problem. The sockets for the bulbs were liberally smeared with grease, which effectively weatherproofed the metal parts, while not interfering with the pressure-contact electrical connectors. While a more suitable compound is recommended (such as Dow Corning DC-4, which is also good at rf), the author used ordinary marine grease (the kind used for pressure fittings and steering linkages) on the other lights, and with good results. The method could be used to advantage by amateurs where low-voltage connectors may be exposed to moisture. It definitely *should not* be used on ordinary rubber, since reaction between the grease and rubber will ruin the insulation. However, most modern plastics will not be affected. — *W1YNC*

CERAMIC TUBE CLEANER

I had a problem in trying to keep the lint and dust out of the cooling fins on the plates of the 8122 final amplifier tubes in my linear. They are the ceramic types like the 4CX250 family.

My solution was to solder an automotive inner-tube valve stem to the 4-inch spout of an oil can, using a 1-inch section of copper tubing as a coupler between the two. The end of the spout has an opening of about 1/16 inch and when this arrangement is connected to a tire

pump, and an "armstrong" energy source applied, I have a variable-velocity air jet that is cheap and easy to build, which does the job very well. — *Ben Fidler, W7PZ*

ADDED SWITCH FOR CONVENIENT OPERATION OF HM-102 WATTMETER

I recently purchased a Heath HM-102 wattmeter, and have noticed that it is easy to change the position of the sensitivity control when pulling out and pushing in the switch that selects forward and reverse indication. I replaced the original switch with a miniature spdt toggle switch. If the switch is centered on the panel just below the meter, it does not affect the appearance of the instrument. — *Robert Werner, W8BTD*

A STABLE CAPACITOR ROTOR CONNECTION

Electrical connection to the rotor of an air-variable capacitor is usually made through the use of small brushes which rub on the shaft or through contact between the shaft and the bearings. There are times when corrosion or dirt will cause the connection to become intermittent. This becomes an important factor when building any circuit requiring good frequency stability, such as a tunable oscillator.

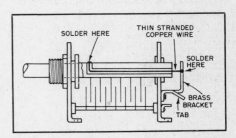

Modification of air-variable capacitor to make a stable rotor connection.

A remedy is shown in the drawing. First drill a hole through the shaft; then drill a hole at right angles into the shaft near the front of the capacitor. Use a No. 34 to No. 40 drill size depending on the shaft diameter. Fish a length of small-diameter, stranded copper wire (usually 27 gauge) into the hole in the end of the shaft and out through the egress hole. Solder the wire onto the shaft at the egress hole. Next, make a small brass bracket as shown in the drawing with a mounting hole and a soldering tab for a connection. Attach the bracket to the capacitor frame by means of a nut and screw. Solder the wire coming out of the shaft onto the bracket. This completes the installation. — *Gene Pearson, W3OY*

[Editor's Note: This type of connection should be used primarily with an air-variable capacitor with a stop.]

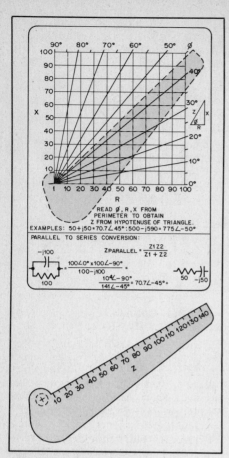

A simple vector calculator.

WB2NAG POLAR TO RECTANGULAR CONVERTER

When calculating ac circuit behavior, the use of polar and rectangular form representation of the vector relationships is almost indispensable. The "impedance-triangle" relationship between X, R, Z, and the phase angle ϕ can be worked out from the trigonometric relationships in a number of ways. A picture is worth a thousand words, so the Chinese say, and often mathematical relations are clearer when expressed graphically as in the simple vector calculator in the illustration.

The calculator can be fashioned from poster board. Measure off the 10 × 10-cm grid into 1-cm squares using a ruler. Set up the phase angles with a protractor. Pin the rotating Z member to the bottom left corner of the calculator with a thumbtack. Flatten the protruding tip against the back and put a piece of masking tape over it to fix it into place. Mark off the Z scale in 1-cm divisions. — *John Carlini, WB2NAG*

KEEPING THE KEY IN PLACE

If the operating table has a smooth surface, keeping the key or paddle in place can be a problem. Removing dust from the rubber feet often helps, but the heavy-fisted operator still might have problems. An easy cure is to cut a piece of fine-grained sandpaper to the size of the keyer base and fasten it to the operating table (rough side up of course) with a few pieces of wide masking tape. If the operator wants to change the position of the key, he can simply move the sandpaper.

The same system can be used to keep the rotor control box, lamps, and other items from walking around the desk. — *W1FBY*

USING STILL-CAMERA LENSES ON SSTV CAMERAS

Many SSTV cameras are designed to use lenses having a "C-mount." This type of mount is used on many 16-mm motion picture cameras, and dealers often stock adapters allowing various 35-mm still-camera lenses to be fitted to a C-mount. In addition to allowing the use of lenses which may be already available, still-camera lenses are usually of higher optical quality than those commonly supplied for use on video cameras. — *Bill Levy, WA2ROD/5Z4PI/VQ9BL*

AMSAT-OSCAR 7, MODE B OPERATION MADE EASIER

One way to generate a signal of any mode at 420 MHz is to high-level mix two signals in the final amplifier stage of a Motorola, RCA, General Electric or any of the other commercially manufactured 460-MHz business-band equipment. These units are usually rated for a minimum output power of 15 watts, with the final output stage operating in the Class C mode. A very cooperative unit for conversion is the RCA CMU-15 which uses a 5894 as the output tube.

Here is one procedure for converting this type of rig for use as a high-level mixer:

1) Secure a copy of the manufacturer's instruction manual for the tuning procedure and general information on the particular piece of equipment to be modified.

2) Obtain a crystal of the proper fundamental frequency so that the unit can be tuned up on 460.45 MHz, the original design center frequency.

3) A power supply which will provide 330 volts at 400 mA, 330 volts regulated (for use with the oscillator) and —105 volts for bias is required.

4) Remove the modulator-limiter tubes from their sockets.

5) Tune the "strip" as if for operation on 460 MHz; about 18 watts of 28.3-MHz energy will be required for proper mixing. Mixing can be accomplished by applying the 28.3-MHz signal to the 5894 grid or cathode circuit. The circuits at A show two methods for mixer input. The cathode circuit is suggested since it is the easiest of the two methods.

6) Apply a 28.3-MHz signal as shown and readjust the output at 432 MHz. A strip-line filter should be used to attenuate the unwanted mixer products. Under key-up conditions the 5894 output circuit is out of resonance since the plate tank circuit is tuned to 432 MHz and the excitation to the tube is at 460 MHz. To minimize damage to the strip (and for cooler operation) the circuit shown at B provides for the last three stages of the strip to be biased to cutoff during key-up conditions.

The CMU-15 provided about 10 watts of output power after the above modification was performed. This output power is used to drive a 4CX250B linear amplifier for use with OSCAR 7. It has performed very satisfactorily. — *Ben Stevenson, W2BXA*

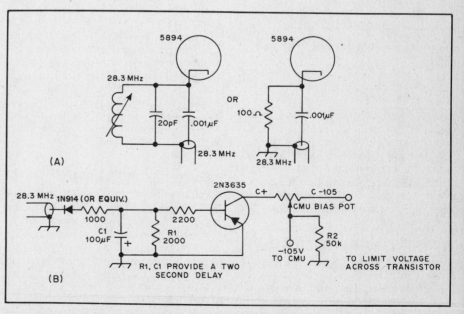

Circuits for converting the RCA CMU-15 460-MHz business-band unit for OSCAR 7, mode B at 420 MHz. Tuned and untuned cathode mixer inputs are illustrated in A. Biasing is provided by the circuit at B.

NAIL POLISH
IN THE HAM SHACK

1) I use red nail polish to mark dials and points on cabinets for rotary switches.

2) Red for the "off" button or switch on all equipment so the XYL and harmonics will know what to push if I leave something on when I am out.

3) I use red and white (other colors are available) to identify mating male and female connectors as in the case of the leads on a stereo or tape deck.

4) If you have a screw or nut that tends to work loose with vibration, a dab of polish under it will hold it solid.

5) Don't overlook nylon cord and rope; a little polish on the cut end stops the raveling.

6) Clear nail polish is ideal for waterproofing labels on equipment and electrical connections that tend to corrode. — *Max Pierce, K8DYI via DARA Bulletin*

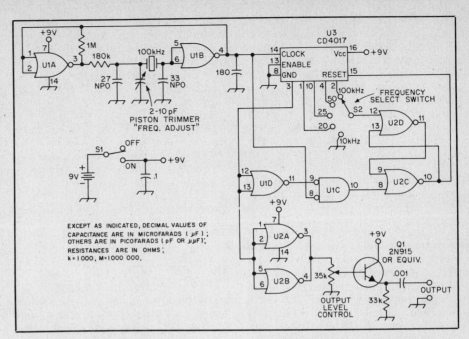

A secondary frequency standard.
U1, U2 — CMOS quad 2-input *NOR* gate ICs, type CD4001 or equiv.

U3 — CMOS decade counter-divider IC, type CD4017 or equiv.

CQ CONTEST

Using a prerecorded tape to call CQ during a contest is nothing new, but many vhf rigs don't have VOX, and manually switching the PTT line is tedious. This circuit will automatically activate the PTT function of the transmitter while the tape is playing. C1 and R1 determine the delay time before the relay drops out, and exact values will depend on the relay used. T1 is connected to step up the voltage before application to the voltage doubler. S1 is used to select the microphone or tape input. The TAPE IN connection is made to the speaker of the tape recorder. Layout

isn't critical but the unit should be built in a metal enclosure to provide rf shielding. — *Bill Radice, K2OWR*

VHF SECONDARY FREQUENCY STANDARD IS INEXPENSIVE AND BATTERY OPERATED

The secondary frequency standard shown here provides accurate calibration markers for vhf fm channels in the 144- to 225-MHz bands. Battery operation and

low cost are achieved by using CMOSs integrated circuits and a minimum number of components.

Fm receivers and transmitters operating in the vhf range are typically crystal controlled, and they use a small value trimmer capacitor to "net" the unit on the specified channel. Without a frequency counter, it is difficult to accomplish this to any degree of accuracy. By using a secondary frequency standard with switch-selectable outputs every 100, 50, 25, 20 and 10 kHz, it is possible to set the transmitter or receiver on frequency quickly.

The frequency standard uses two CMOS quad 2-input *NOR* gates and a 100-kHz crystal oscillator. The CD4017 counter is wired in a divide-by-X configuration by connecting two *NOR* gates as an RS flip-flop to reset the counter after X counts. The output level of the 10-kHz markers is on the order of 15 to 30 μV at 150 MHz. — *Alan D. Wilcox, W3DVX/WB4KRE*

HINTS AND MORE HINTS

I've noticed quite a few hints on ways to keep one's hand key from moving about on the table. The best and least expensive method I've found is to use loops of masking tape between the key base and the table. Two loops are formed with about two inches of masking tape. The top half of each loop is secured to the base of the key, and the key is then pressed down on the operating table. This method keeps the key firmly in place, yet it may be removed without leaving any gummy residue on the table.

I recently built a shelf for my operating

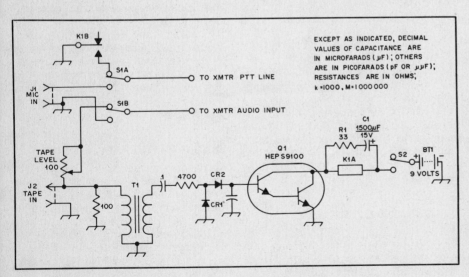

Schematic diagram of the contest accessory.
BT1 — 9-volt transistor-radio battery (RCA VS323 or equivalent).
C1 — See text.
CR1, CR2 — Silicon diode (1N914 or equivalent).
J1 — Connector to mate with station microphone.
J2 — RCA-type phono jack.
K1 — Sensitive dc relay with 6-volt coil and spst contacts.
Q1 — Darlington pair (Motorola HEP semiconductor).
R1 — See text.
S1 — Dpdt toggle or slide switch.
S2 — Spst toggle or slide switch.
T1 — Audio transformer, 8-Ω to 10Ω ratio.

table to hold all my equipment about six inches above the surface of the table. This permits me to store my hand key, bug and keyer in the space beneath the shelf. With the keyer under the shelf, I am no longer able to see the indicator knob for adjusting keyer speed. I cemented a small piece of plastic to the knob, to protrude above the edge of the knob. By locating the position of the plastic with my fingers, I am able to determine the setting of the speed control, and thus control keyer speed without looking at the knob. This might be a useful accessory for sightless hams.

I have always envied owners of transceivers equipped with "spinner" knobs on the VFO. After seeing the frequency control knob on the Heath SB-104, I considered purchasing such a knob from Heath. Instead, I found a button with a recessed center in my XYL's sewing box, and cemented it to the edge of the knob on my SB-102. The button was selected to provide a good fit to my fingertip, and also to match the color of my rig. I can now shift effortlessly from one end of the band to the other. — *Stu Levens, WBØOGK*

WIRE SOURCE

A handy source for No. 14 through No. 6 solid copper wire is the wire sold for house wiring. Most hardware and Sears stores stock two-conductor plastic covered wire and it can be purchased in any length required. — *W1ICP*

MORE ON DIGITAL CLOCKS FOR THE AMATEUR STATION

For those who may have constructed the digital clock described in the November, 1974, issue of *QST* (by Bert Kelly, K4EEU) using the 60-Hz time base, you may have found to your dismay that it gained time radically. This is due to noise

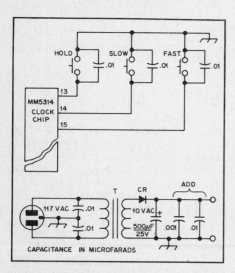

Adding capacitors as shown reduces digital-clock noise problems.

pulses getting into the chip and upsetting its normal operation. The following procedure was used with success to solve this problem in six different clocks:

1) Bypass each of the *set* and *hold* switches (pins 13, 14 and 15 of the clock chip) to ground with a .01-µF disk capacitor.
2) Bypass each side of the ac line to ground with a .01-µF capacitor.
3) Parallel a .001-µF and a .01-µF disk capacitor and place this combination across the 500-µF filter capacitor in the power supply. Your clock should then be essentially noise immune and a nice asset to the ham shack. — *Leland R. Shultz, KØRAB*

THAT OFT-NEEDED "THIRD HAND"

It can be frustrating when trying to solder several leads together at one time. If only someone were near at hand to hold those elusive wires together until they were soldered! Well, here's a simple remedy for the problem. Simply encircle the handles of your long-nose pliers with a good sturdy rubber band, then grip the leads to be soldered with the tips of the jaws, thus freeing one of your hands.

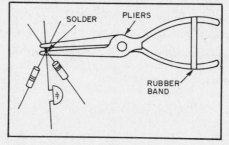

Long-nose pliers used as a clamp.

Long-nose pliers work nicely as a heat sink when soldering solid-state devices. Simply clamp the jaws of the pliers over the pigtail of the transistor, diode, or IC (between the point to be soldered and the body of the semiconductor) before doing the soldering. (This idea was borrowed from the Heath HW-101 manual.) — *WN1LZQ*

A TIP ON SOLDERING-IRON TIPS

The tip on my 30-watt soldering iron never seemed too massive until I tried soldering a 24-pin IC socket to a circuit board. The old trick of wrapping a piece of copper wire on the tip as a thin extension was an unwieldy arrangement. I removed the tip from the soldering iron, chucked it in my electric drill and "turned" the tip down against a file. The best shape for my purpose was a thin section, terminating in a long tapering point.

This ruined the tip for other uses, but soldering-iron tips are relatively inexpensive to replace. — *Julian N. Jablin, W9IWI*

SOLDERING VISE FOR SMALL PARTS

A spring-type wooden clothespin makes a handy vise for soldering small work. Mount it in a vertical position on the workbench. — *K1ZZ*

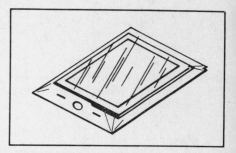

A film-pack battery.

RECYCLED BATTERIES

Used film packs from Polaroid SX-70 cameras contain a flat-plate, Ray-O-Vac, 6-volt battery that is still good even after taking ten pictures with the camera. The battery is enclosed in a cardboard and plastic envelope which measures 3-1/2 × 4-1/2 × 1/8 inches. These batteries can be connected in series, parallel or series-parallel to provide a variety of voltages and ampere-hour ratings, and thus are ideal for powering portable, low-power equipment. Removal of the battery is easy. Simply break off the plastic end of the container and slip the battery out of the case. Individuals should pay attention to the warning stamped on the battery: *Do not cut, take apart or burn the battery.* So don't throw those SX-70 film-pack batteries away — recycle them! — *R. W. Johnson, W6MUR*

SEALANTS FOR AMATEUR USE

Many radio amateurs will find uses for one-part silicone rubber sealer that is sold under such names as RTV, Silastic, and bathtub and tile sealer. On exposure to the air, the material forms a waterproof rubbery substance. This type of sealer has been used at WB6GNM for over two years, and no deterioration of the material is apparent.

One use of the material is to seal antenna connectors. I have also used it to form non-skid feet for a keyer-paddle base. Clean the base with alcohol to remove any grease or oil; then put a dab of the silicone rubber on a sheet of waxed paper and allow to cure or set overnight. — *Paul Zander, WB6GNM*

MORE ON SILICONE SEALANTS

In "Hints and Kinks" for May, 1976, WB6GNM described several uses for one-part silicone rubber sealants. If sealants are to be used near electronic components or connections in an enclosed area, the sealant used should be one that gives off alcohol, rather than a corrosive substance as it cures. One alcohol-cure sealant I have used successfully is Dow-Corning 738, available from their distributors. — *Roger Halstead, K8ZKF*

CIRCUIT-BOARD HOLDER

After only a brief exposure to working with circuit boards and the problems of supporting these unwieldy lightweights, it became obvious that some holding device was an absolute must. The commercially available clamps are beautiful, but they are expensive, and who needs all those universal joints?

The device I use was built from parts readily available and simple enough for a one-evening project. My unit has a width capacity of 6 inches, but this can be increased by using longer threaded rods. For the ham with limited working space, this clamp has the advantage of being stored easily when not in use, freeing the operating position or kitchen table for other uses.

The 1-1/2 × 1-1/2 × 6-inch (38 × 38

× 152 mm) aluminum tubing used as a base for the clamp is available — usually as scrap — from any aluminum-awning fabricator. The material I found had a wall thickness heavy enough to be tapped for the No. 6-32 screws that hold the plastic jaws. Wooden blocks could be substituted for the aluminum tubing at some sacrifice in weight and appearance.

The screws, nuts, washers, and threaded rod are available at any hardware store. The 1/4-inch rod comes in 36-inch lengths at about 60 cents per length, so your total investment should not be more than a couple of dollars. The plastic jaws were cut from 3/16-inch sheet stock (2 pieces 1 × 5 inches) (25 × 127 mm). However, there is nothing sacred about these dimensions. The tapered clamping edge should be worked with care to obtain a true straightedge and a uniform taper from end to end. This is not as difficult as it sounds. Place a sheet of sandpaper on a perfectly flat surface and hand lap the edge while checking at intervals with a known straightedge.

The holes in the aluminum tubing to pass the 1/4-inch rods should be drilled for minimum clearance. This will permit smooth adjustment while avoiding sloppy action at the jaws. With a little effort and minimum expense you can roll your own circuit-board clamp for near-perfect working conditions on that next solid-state project. — *Dave Adams, W6DRM*

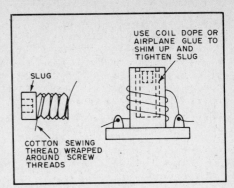

Two ways to tighten coil slugs.

TWO METHODS FOR TIGHTENING LOOSE SLUG-TUNED COILS

Here is a way to solve a minor problem. If you should have a loose iron core in a coil, two methods for tightening it again are shown. I have used both methods and it saves a lot of trouble when critical tuning is necessary. *One word of caution;* use the glue carefully and avoid getting any on the coil turns; it may affect coil Q. — *Franklin Rosenberg, W6NYG*

REPLACEMENT SOLDERING-IRON TIP

Unable to locate a tip for my Ungar no. 4035 soldering iron, I used a copper boat nail that is threaded with a no. 5-32 die. — *J. Edward Goervey, WA2VTG*

SOURCES OF FERRITE MATERIAL FOR CHOKES AND COILS

If you plan on winding your own rf choke or coil and the design calls for the use of ferrite as core material, where can it be found? One source of ferrite cores is older portable radios. These radios usually have ferrite rod antennas. The existing wire can be either unwound or cut off. Another source of ferrite cores is the horizontal output (flyback) transformer in television receivers. Use a hacksaw to remove the windings.

Many of the cores, whether from television sets or radios, are approximately 1/2 inch (13 mm) in diameter. This dimension is satisfactory for most bifilar choke designs, but sometimes a smaller diameter is required. These cores can be cut and ground to size, but caution must be exercised since they are brittle. If breakage does occur, not all is lost. These cores can be glued or taped together. — *Warren MacDowell, W2AOO*

[Editor's Note: Ferrite material obtained from horizontal output transformers and loop antennas from portable radios may be usable up to 10 MHz. One particular ferrite sample tested gave good performance up to 7 MHz. In general, these ferrite cores can be used in equipment that covers the 160- through 40-meter bands.]

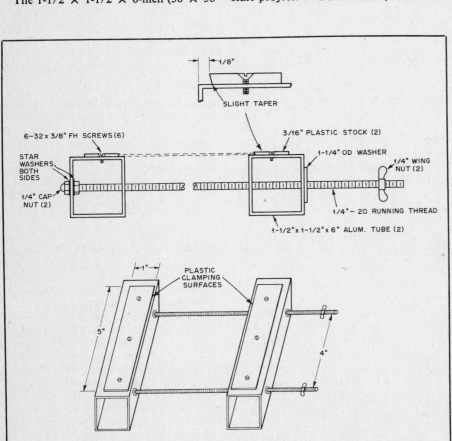

Printed circuit-board rig. Wooden blocks can be used instead of aluminum tubing.

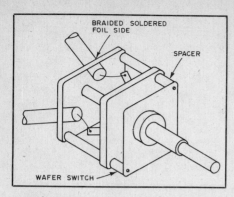

Connecting coaxial cable to a wafer switch is simplified by the method described below.

WIRING COAXIAL CABLE TO A WAFER SWITCH

Here is a useful way of getting rid of the horrible mess that occurs when trying to wire up a 3-pole, 3-position, rotary switch with RG-58/U coaxial cable. Cut a small piece of copper-clad, phenolic board more or less in the shape of the switch wafer. Drill a couple of holes in it to match the distance between the screws that hold the switch assembly together. Then with the foil side of the board facing away from the switch, drill three holes which will accommodate the shields of the cable (a No. 30 drill is about right.) Then solder the center conductors to the appropriate lugs, and the shields to the copper-clad board. This scheme results in a very neat jog, and also provides a good ground for the braid through the frame of the switch. — *M. Crosby Bartlett, W9MC/WB4OBF*

COILED CORD FOR THE SOLDERING IRON

There must be a special section of Murphy's Law covering soldering irons. No matter how carefully you set the iron down, you always end up burning holes in its cord — or the schematic that you are working on. One cure is to replace the present cord on your soldering iron with one of the coiled appliance cords available at electrical supply houses. The cords stretch out to five feet, but coil up to about nine inches when the iron is not in use. — *W1KLK*

REVITALIZING NICAD BATTERIES

Nickle-cadmium batteries of the kind used in Motorola P-33 hand-carried fm transceivers are prone to becoming relatively lifeless after a few years of charging and discharging. Though the old batteries will take a charge, the capacity of the units is very small. A tired battery will reveal its condition by allowing only a few minutes of transmitting time after being fully charged. However, the receiver will perform fine under the same conditions, mainly because the dc-to-dc converter which supplies operating voltage to the transmitter strip consumes considerable current.

Those wishing to renew battery life can place a pellet of industrial potassium hydroxide (ACS pellets) in each cell bank of the batteries, after removing the plugs. The chemical carries the number FW-56.11, and sells for approximately $1 per pound in most areas of the USA. — *W1FB*

NON-SLIP DIP-SOCKET IDEA

Of several methods suggested for securing DIP IC sockets to perfboard for wire wrapping (with a drop of glue, by bending one pin, etc.) WA3LLJ seems to have found the most convenient.

Electrical tape prevents an IC chip from shifting or falling.

As depicted in the photograph, apply a piece of black vinyl electrician's tape to the top of the perfboard, sticky side down. Then simply push the socket pins through the tape and the perfboard holes from the top of the board. The tape will keep the socket from shifting position or falling off the board during wiring. The socket can be removed easily or repositioned. — *Edward Kalin, WA1JZC*

ETCHING ALUMINUM

Recently, I built a version of McCoy's Transmatch. Unfortunately, the aluminum shows scratches and fingerprints. So, I etched the material in a solution of washing soda and hot water. I used two tablespoons of sal soda per gallon. The aluminum to be etched *must* be clean. Immerse the parts in the solution for three to five minutes, then remove and dry them. — *Geoffrey S. Vore, W9QBJ/WA9MZH*

REMOVING SOLDER FROM TERMINAL STRIPS AND PC BOARDS

Although commercially manufactured tools are available for the purpose, the method shown is handy when removing

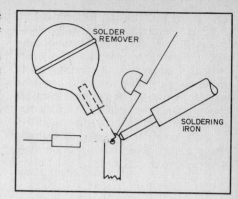

A syringe for removing solder.

components from either pc boards or terminal strips. Cut the tip off a small syringe and insert a short length of Teflon tubing into the end. It should be approximately 2 inches (51 mm) long and 1/16-inch (1.5 mm) OD. If Teflon tubing is unavailable, the metal insert from a ball-point pen could be substituted. Wrap the metal part that goes into the syringe with masking tape to prevent burning. The only difficulty with using a metal tube is that solder tends to stick to the walls and will have to be drilled out after a few operations.

Heat the terminal strip and squeeze the syringe before the solder starts to melt. When the solder starts to flow, bring the tip of the tube up to the joint and release the pressure on the bulb quickly. The molten solder will flow up into the bulb, leaving the terminal relatively free. — *W1NPG*

SOLDER PLATING — CHEAP!

Many experimenters have told me that they are tired of looking at their work sitting on ugly old oxidized copper circuit boards. The general comment is, "Sure would be nice to either tin or silver plate our circuit boards, but who can afford silver powder or a solder-flow pot?" The solution to this problem is simple. One need not look any further than his soldering iron.

Hand tinning is really nothing new; it just seems to be one of those things that is not often passed on to others. Previously, I sent out all my board work to be tin dipped and did so at great expense. As the bills mounted up, I decided it was time to find a less expensive solution. The one I finally came up with was hand tinning.

Hand tinning requires only some good rosin-core solder, a flat-tipped 60-watt soldering iron, and for best results — some liquid solder flux. Superior no. 30 or equivalent will do nicely. The liquid flux aids the flow of solder onto the copper.

In the case of double- or single-sided boards, apply a generous amount of solder onto the board. Next, hold the circuit board upright with some pliers and slowly run the excess solder off the board with the soldering-iron tip. Once the excess solder has been removed, the board may be cleaned. Freon TMC or isopropyl alcohol and a small brush will do the job.

Small wattage soldering irons should be used and care should be taken so as not to lift the copper off the board. The excess solder may be removed by the same method as before, or it can be done more safely by using a solder-wick. Remember that on small surface areas it is easy to destroy the bond between epoxy and copper with too much heat.

After you have practiced this a few times, you will not only get more proficient (and less destructive), but will probably find ways of improving on this technique to suit your own needs. — *Rick Olsen, WA7CNP*

STEEL PIPE SIZES AND STRENGTHS

In "Hints and Kinks," May, 1976, *QST*, page 36, W5LW describes a good foldover tower he built from galvanized steel pipe. Hams wishing to duplicate the tower may misinterpret the pipe sizes. For example, standard pipe, referred to as being of 2-inch size, has an actual outside diameter of 2.375 inches (6 mm), and an inside diameter of 2.067 inches (52.5 mm). Standard 1-1/4-inch pipe is 1.66 inches (42 mm) in outside diameter, with an inside diameter of 1.38 inches (35 mm). Schedule 80 or extra-strong pipe may be used for added load-bearing capability and wind resistance. This heavier pipe has the same outside diameter as the standard grade, but has a thicker wall, resulting in inside diameters of 1.939 inches (49 mm) for 2-inch pipe, and 1.278 inches (32.5 mm) for 1-1/4-inch pipe. I also suggest that consideration be given to the pipe fittings. Cast-iron fittings often crack under stress, while malleable iron fittings have a tendency to stretch. A better choice would be cast steel or the more expensive forged-steel fittings. The fittings used should be the extra-heavy type, as opposed to the standard strength. Either size fitting will accept both standard and extra-strong pipe sizes. — *Henry Spang*

RESTORING NICAD CELLS AND BATTERY HOLDERS

The failure mode in NiCad cells is caused by fine conducting whiskers which grow between the electrodes and prevent the cell from accumulating a charge. A momentary high-current through the cell will sometimes disintegrate the whiskers, allowing the cell to charge normally.

I have successfully restored several cells by charging a 35,000-μF capacitor from a 12-volt supply and discharging the capacitor across the cell. After two discharges of the capacitor, each cell was recharged according to the manufacturer's recommendations.

The spring clips in battery holders lose their gripping ability after about a year and should be replaced. A poor connection will result in a small resistance in series with each cell, causing a significant voltage drop when current is drawn from the battery pack. — *Ed Piller, W2KPQ*

GROUNDING STRAP SUBSTITUTE

Copper-plated pipe-clamping strips, sold in hardware stores, make cheap and sturdy ground straps for the shack. — *Leo Finkelstein, Jr., WA4AOL/WB4ONY*

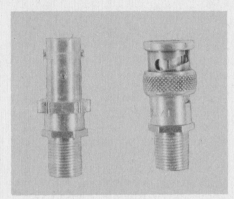

F connector becomes a BNC.

TYPE-F TO BNC ADAPTERS

It is often necessary to adapt from a type-F connector to a BNC fitting. Adapters from type-F female connectors to BNC male or female connectors may be easily made from type-F chassis female connectors available from TV sales stores and any of the BNC variety of connectors with bodies threaded to receive 3/8-32 clamping nuts. Before assembling, trim the solder lug on the type-F connector to allow the center pin of the BNC connector to just contact the lug when the connectors are assembled. It is only necessary to solder the pin and lug together and reassemble the pair (see photo). — *Harold S. Eisley, W3NET*

EXTRACTING HARD-TO-REACH TUBES

In my Collins 75A3 receiver, one of the tubes, a 6BA6 (V-5), defies extraction. It is located where only the tips of the fingers can touch the top of the tube, and unless one risks damage to the tube by using a pad type of instrument reaching to the bottom, removal for testing or replacement of the tube is virtually impossible.

The problem was solved with the use of air-conditioning "duct" tape. The tape is made of heavy cloth and has an adhesive that grips well to most anything it touches. Cut two strips of duct tape 1/4 × 3-inches (6 × 76 mm). Have a coffee stirrer (wood or plastic) or any stiff sliver of wood handy. Lower the tape strip alongside the tube, leaving enough of the tape above the top of the tube to allow the ends to be pressed together. Do this to both sides of the tube, using the stirrer to gently press the tape to the sides of the tube. An easy pull on the strips will release the tube from its socket. Leave the tape in place on the tube until after the tube has been replaced in the receiver. Using the same coffee stirrer, pry the adhesive away from the tube. Although this technique was used on my receiver, it could be applied to any piece of equipment which uses tubes. — *Mack O. Santer, W2ZPW*

REMOVING HARD-TO-REACH PA TUBES

In many modern transmitters and transceivers, it is difficult to grasp the final amplifier tubes to remove them from their sockets, due to the tight compartment surrounding the tubes. A modern version of the Chinese finger grip, manufactured by the Kellems Division, Harvey Hubbell Inc., of Stonington, CT, greatly simplifies tube removal. The device, used for industrial applications, is compressed slightly and pushed down over the tube. When pulled up, the braid compresses around the tube envelope, allowing the tube to be removed from its socket. The braid may be removed from the tube by compressing it once again. — *David Higgins, K1BCG*

ALUMINUM TAPE FOR SHIELDING

In the 1950s we learned that extreme filtering and shielding of our communications equipment was required to avoid creating TVI. Yet today we see manufactured and homemade gear housed in non-metallic or poorly shielded metal enclosures.

The author has found a heavy-gauge aluminum tape manufactured by Spartan Plastics, Inc., P. O. Box 67, Holt, MI 48842, very helpful in fabricating easy and convenient shielding. It is sold under the name "Trim Brite Custom Trim Metal-Mend Tape no. 11822," and is intended primarily for repair of auto bodies. The author bought a 3-3/4-inch (95 mm) by 5-foot (1.524 m) roll for $1.37 in a local auto shop. It should not be confused with Mylar tapes which appear metallized, but are really plastic.

As far as the author knows, the adhesive used is nonconducting, so this should be taken into account in any shielding project. Seams should be closed with metal-to-metal covering or 3M Scotch tape no. X-1170, an RFI tape which does have conductive adhesive. The latter is designed for the purpose, but may not be obtained as easily as the Spartan product, especially in the greater width. Obviously, the wider tape should be used for large areas, and the narrow X-1170 with conductive adhesive should be used for corners, seams, etc.

The author has used both tapes in shielding a transistor rig in a partly plastic case, as well as a uhf converter in a plastic case, both of which caused TVI before treatment. — *Edward F. Erickson, W2CVW*

CLEANING CAPACITANCE-ACTIVATED KEYER PADDLES

Capacitance-activated keyer paddles, such as the Data Engineering Electronic Feather Touch, become erratic in operation when dirt and oxide build up on the metal grid. The dirt may be removed with a soft cloth moistened with denatured alcohol. — *Wayne E. Whitman, W9HFR*

RESISTOR ADDED TO 5-CENT TRANSISTOR TESTER MAY SAVE THE LIFE OF AN FET

A 1000-ohm resistor in series with the battery of the five-cent transistor tester (Brophy, "A 5-Cent Transistor Tester," *QST* for November, 1975, page 24) may prevent accidental destruction of a field-effect transistor, should the battery leads be improperly polarized when connected to the transistor. — *Franklin Swan, W9SIA*

SLIPPING DIAL DRIVE

I had an old receiver in which the dial cord on the tuner was slipping. I tried a variety of things to put some traction into the line, and finally tried alum. A simple wetting of thumb and forefinger on the alum and running the fingers along the line did the trick.

That was twelve years ago and that was the end of the trouble; it has not slipped since. — *A. P. McMonigal, WB8VZW*

TEST POINTS

In planning the construction of equipment it is desirable to give consideration to providing useful test points for measuring voltages. Small loops of tinned wire may be soldered to appropriate points in circuits to serve as test-probe connections. — *Carlos H. Daniels, WB4FIR*

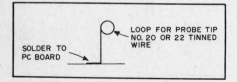

Small loops of tinned wire are soldered to appropriate points in the receiver circuitry to serve as test-probe connections.

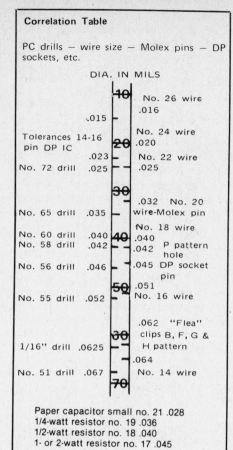

Correlation Table
PC drills — wire size — Molex pins — DP sockets, etc.

DIA. IN MILS

Drill	Dia.	Other
		No. 26 wire
	.015	.016
		No. 24 wire
Tolerances 14-16 pin DP IC		.020
	.023	No. 22 wire
No. 72 drill	.025	.025
		.032 No. 20 wire-Molex pin
No. 65 drill	.035	
No. 60 drill	.040	No. 18 wire .040
No. 58 drill	.042	.042 P pattern hole
No. 56 drill	.046	.045 DP socket pin
		.051
No. 55 drill	.052	No. 16 wire
		.062 "Flea" clips B, F, G & H pattern
1/16" drill	.0625	
		.064
No. 51 drill	.067	No. 14 wire

Paper capacitor small no. 21 .028
1/4-watt resistor no. 19 .036
1/2-watt resistor no. 18 .040
1- or 2-watt resistor no. 17 .045

Drill-bit correlation table.

TABLE SIMPLIFIES SELECTION OF PROPER DRILL BIT

A copy of this table, showing the nearest, numbered drill bit for the lead diameter of a component, when posted at the workbench, speeds the drilling of holes in printed-circuit boards. — *Charles E. Terry, W4FZX*

BONDING ALUMINUM WITH SOLDER AND FLUX

Several times in the past there has probably been a need to bond something made of aluminum to some other metal used in a home-built project. Alpha Metals offers a solder and flux package called "Depend-A-Bond" that does the job quite well. Several repair jobs have been done using the Alpha Metals product with favorable results. A 100-inch coil and 0.35-fluidounce package are available as a combination from most hardware stores for approximately $2. — *WA6GVC/1*

WIRE-WRAPPING TOOL

A dried-out ball-point pen refill may be converted into a wire-wrap tool by cutting off the tip just above the ball, and filing or sawing a small notch in the metal. Be sure the refill is dry before cutting the tip! — *Chas. C. Whysall, K4WZ*

TOROIDAL COIL FORMS FROM PLASTIC TUBING

In situations where a low-Q toroidal inductor is desired, it is practical to cut a section of plastic tubing for use as a coil form. Acrylic and polystyrene tubing are better than nylon or vinyl, due to the high rf losses of the latter two. I found that 3/4-inch (19 mm) diameter tubing, cut to a height of 1/4-inch (6 mm) and wound with No. 20 wire, yielded coils with a Q of 40 to 50 for a 2- to 5-μH inductor. Some plastic supply houses may give away small scraps of tubing. — *Don Lawson, WB9CYY*

SPAGHETTI

Your local hospital is an excellent source of spaghetti tubing. For medical applications, the tubing can only be used once. A request to a doctor or nurse will usually bring you enough plastic tubing of various sizes to provide a lifetime supply for ham purposes. — *W1KLK*

STRAIGHTENING AND REALIGNING DIP IC PINS

Here is a four-step procedure using only fingers and a 16-pin dual-in-line socket to bend the pins of the IC into correct alignment: (1) Use the tip of a finger on the *end* of each bent pin to put the pins approximately in line with each other. Only the ends need be in alignment since the next step should straighten the shanks of the pins. (2) Insert *one* row of pins fully into the socket as shown in the drawing. Very little force should be required for the insertion of the pins. Remove the IC from the socket and insert the second row of pins as described above. (3) Place the IC on the socket and visually check the pin alignment. If the two rows of pins are too far apart, or otherwise misaligned, reinsert one row of pins in the socket as in step two. (4) Hold the IC by its body and use the socket to bend the pins until the row spacing is correct, and insert the IC all the way into the socket in the normal manner. The socket will be easier to handle if it is mounted on a three or four-cm square base made of pc board. — *D. F. Zawada, W9MJG*

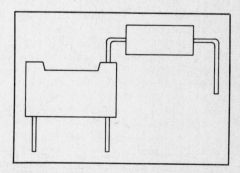

The second of four steps in straightening and realigning DIP IC pins. See text.

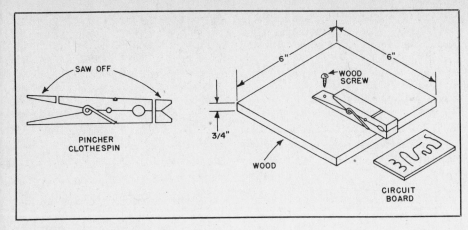

A clothespin pc board and cable holder.

CIRCUIT-BOARD HOLDER

The holder for small-pc boards, as shown in the Heath HD-1250 manual, is also excellent for holding small cables while soldering. — *Dr. J. H. Grant, K4HHR*

ANOTHER SOURCE OF EQUIPMENT FEET

A handy source of supply for equipment feet is the local automobile tire shop. It is general practice when mounting or changing tires, to replace the rubber valve stem. This is usually done by tearing the old valve out of the rim. The nub which held the valve in the rim is dropped on the floor. The limit to the number of feet that may be obtained is only how busy the tire shop is. — *W1CW*

DETERMINING THE VALUES OF JAPANESE COMPONENTS

Some months ago we had fun trying to figure out the coding on Japanese components. A copy of the code was found in

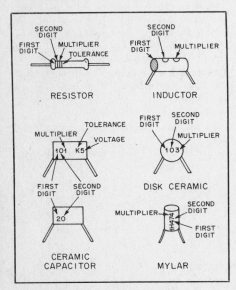

Markings on Japanese components are interpreted according to this chart.

the modification kit for my FT-101. The color code is the same as the one for resistors and capacitors as tabulated in *The Radio Amateur's Handbook.* The drawing indicates how to interpret the markings on the Japanese components. The values are in ohms, microhenries and picofarads.

For example, an inductor marked brown, red and black would be 12×10^0, or 12-μH. A ceramic capacitor marked 301K5 would be 300 pF, 10-percent tolerance, and 500 volts. In general, the working voltage for ceramic capacitors is 500 unless otherwise noted. — *Noel B. Eaton, VE3CJ*

HOMEMADE VHF TOROIDAL INDUCTORS

The self-shielding property of a toroidal-wound inductor, whether it's air-wound or contained on a toroid core of some variety, can be beneficial in circuits where unwanted interstage coupling is to be avoided. Some amateurs believe that in order to qualify as a toroidal-wound inductor the coil must be wrapped around a doughnut-shaped object made of ferrite, powdered iron, or some other material than has an mu factor. Not so, for by bringing the ends of any solenoid-type coil together (by bending the coil into a circular configuration) the ends of the inductor, each being of opposite polarity, are now in close proximity. Thus the magnetic

Homemade toroidal inductors for vhf.

fields are converted to closed loops within the toroidal geometry, and a self-shielding characteristic results.

By employing core materials which have specific permeability factors, the number of turns for a given value of inductance can be reduced, as can the mass of the assembly. However, one can use a variety of materials for constructing a toroid core, provided the dielectric property of the substance used is suitable for the frequency of operation.

The photo shows three homemade toroidal inductors for vhf use. Each unit is wound for operation at 144 MHz (0.12 μH), to resonate in the band with a shunt capacitance of 10 pF. The toroid on the left is made from a slice of 1/2-inch diameter plexiglas rod with a hole drilled in the center. The unloaded Q measured 150. The center toroid is wound on a polystyrene washer, and is measure Q checked out at 160. The smallest toroid (far right) was fashioned from a piece of 1/4-inch (6 mm) diameter Teflon rod. The Q measured 130.

Proof of the self-shielding properties of the inductors came when a dip meter was used to check the resonant frequencies of the coils (10-pF capacitor across the windings). No dip could be obtained, and this is characteristic of any toroidal inductor.

Test inductors were made using vhf toroid cores (ferrite) of commercial origin. Using the same L-C ratio, unloaded Qs between 70 and 90 resulted. Still pretty good, but fewer turns were needed to provide a like amount of inductance to that of the homemade units. The fewer the turns, the more difficult it is to find the precise tap point on a coil when matching impedances. Therefore, the nonferramic cores may be preferred at vhf.

Those wishing to lessen the need for shielding in vhf solid-state transmitters and receivers, or to cut down on the size of the tuned circuits, may be interested in this information. — *W1FB*

INSULATING ALLIGATOR CLIPS

Here is a simple method to add insulation (sleeving) to alligator clips that already have wires attached to them. Use a length of shrinkable tubing about 1-1/2 times longer than the clip being used and large enough to slip over the closed clip. Most tubing will shrink to about one-half its diameter, so when heat is applied to the *far end only*, it will usually shrink far enough to keep it from sliding off the front end. If you like a loose sleeve, the job is done.

My preference is for a sleeve that does not slip back, and that is done easily by tying a knot in the wire behind the tubing or by building up the wire with tape. The experimenter will doubtlessly discover many variations to suit his particular needs. — *James A. Herb, W3SHP*

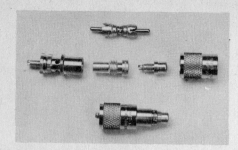

Handy homemade adapters.

HANDY HOMEMADE ADAPTERS

The two adapters shown in the accompanying photograph are simple to assemble and useful for hams using their 2-meter rigs for both base and mobile operation. The adapter at the top is for connecting one chassis jack to another. Two male phono plugs (RCA type) and a 2-inch piece of No. 16 wire are all that are necessary. Place the plugs back to back. Run the piece of wire through both male plugs, and solder the wire to plug tips. Be sure the backs are touching one another, then solder them together.

For the other adapter, drill out the hole in the reducing adapter (UG-175) to a 0.242-inch diameter, using a letter "C" size drill. Remove the nut and washers from the chassis jack. Solder one end of a 3-inch long, No. 16 wire to the center terminal of the chassis jack and the reducing adapter with a pair of pliers and thread the jack all the way into the 0.242-inch diameter hole.

Some resistance will be encountered because the steel chassis jack is cutting its own threads into the brass adapter. The reason for assembling these two pieces in this manner is that the chassis jack has a 1/4-32 thread and a tap for this thread is not readily available to the average ham. Solder the other end of the No. 16 wire to the center terminal of the PL-259 and trim off the excess wire. — *Wayne L. Jung, WB9IQC*

ANOTHER SOURCE FOR COIL FORMS

For those fellows who like to wind their own coils, another source for form material may be your local coin dealer. Clear plastic tubes are used by collectors for storing their coins. There are six sizes of "coin tubes" ranging from the one-cent to the silver-dollar diameter. To use the coin tubes, cut off the top and bottom sections with a fine-bladed hacksaw, or

just cut off the top section and leave the bottom section for use in mounting with a small screw. — *Stan J. Zuchora, W8QKU*

CHEAP-AND-EASY PANEL TRIM

Adding a stripe of color to the panel of a piece of homemade radio equipment will often impart a professional appearance that might otherwise be lacking. Those ubiquitous gray Hammertone rack panels certainly need something to dress them up, and the technique described here does the job rather well.

Select a roll of masking tape that is made to the width you prefer for a stripe of panel trim. (The writer has rolls of tape in various widths to meet various design requirements.) Remove from the roll a length of tape somewhat in excess of what will be needed. Next, affix one end of the tape to a solid object. Hold the free end in one hand, and spray paint the nonadhesive side of the strip your favorite color. White, black, or red contrasts nicely with gray panels. After the paint has dried, the strip can be applied to the panel, and the free ends of excess material sliced off with a razor blade.

White decals do not stand out well against a gray panel. A strip of painted masking tape can be attached to the panel, full length, above and below the row of controls. White press-on decals placed on the trim strip will be easy to read. Alternatively, black decals can be installed on a white or yellow strip.

Though the writer has not tried to use Mystic Tape (available at most hardware stores and supermarts), it should serve nicely as trim. — *W1FB*

ANOTHER HOMEMADE ADAPTER

Many times the need arises to connect the output of a transmitter to a low-pass filter or coaxial relay. An adapter will enable you to connect two SO-239 female connectors together as shown in the accompanying photograph. All that is needed is two PL-259 connectors, a UG-175 reducing adapter and a short length of insulated wire.

Saw off the "shoulder" on the UG-175 reducing adapter. Thread the wire through the UG-175 and then through the outer shell of the PL-259 into the center pin. Solder the wire to the center pin.

Another homemade adapter.

Screw a few threads of the adapter into the PL-259. Next, place the outer shell of the second PL-259 over the wire and insert the free end of the wire into the center pin of second connector. Screw the second PL-259 onto the adapter snug against the first PL-259. Solder the two connectors together; then solder the remaining center pin. Snip off any excess wire protruding from the center pin. — *Mac Bruington, W4NJE*

TOWARD BETTER-LOOKING PANEL LABELS

Few of us have access to engraving tools and silk-screen equipment for making professional-looking labels on our equipment panels. Yet, most of us feel that a piece of homemade gear that works well deserves to look nice if it is to become a permanent part of the ham station.

Having grown weary of battling with water-transfer and press-on decals over the years (to say little of trying to keep a fresh supply on hand at all times), I turned to the more common practice of using Dymo tape labels. I recalled the rather tired and "hammy" look that I had obtained when using them in the past, and then decided to try a better approach than before: I painted the panel a color that would match the available label-tape colors. The results were considerably more impressive than when I had put, say, black labels on a red panel, blue labels on a black panel, etc. By selecting paint and label colors that were matched closely, the lettering on the labels predominated so that the main body of the labels did not stand out as grotesque rectangles on the panel.

A further improvement came when I trimmed the ends of the labels to an arc by means of scissors. Getting rid of the right-angle corners imparted a more professional look. A pair of fingernail clippers turned out to be a useful tool for that job. — *Doug DeMaw, 8P6EU*

Chapter 2

Test Gear Ideas

ECONOMICAL FET VOLTMETER

Many amateurs may consider building this simple voltmeter which uses one active device — a JFET. It will provide two dc-voltage ranges, 0 to 2 and 0 to 20 volts. For most amateur solid-state experimentation, it will not be necessary to measure dc levels greater than 20. The accuracy of the instrument is sufficient for all but the most exacting applications.

M1 is a 100-μA meter. Some current will flow in Q1 even when no dc voltage is applied to the gate. Therefore, control R7 is adjusted to provide a zero reading on M1. R8 is tweaked to provide a full-scale reading when two volts of dc are applied through R4. It may be necessary to readjust R7 and R8 a few times to achieve final calibration. It is best to calibrate the voltmeter after it has been on for one minute. Later, when the meter is to be used for voltage measurements, a one-minute warm-up period will assure proper zeroing of the meter.

Isolated pads were formed on the circuit board by means of a Moto Tool and cutting bit. It may be convenient to mount R7 and R8 on the front panel of the voltmeter case. This will permit easy recalibration. For greatest accuracy, R1 through R4, inclusive, should be 1-percent units. However, 5-percent resistors will suffice for most amateur work.

Readout on M1 will be linear. Full-scale deflection will represent 2 or 20 volts, depending on the range in use. Midscale readings will equal 1 and 10 volts, respectively. It may be helpful to draw a new meter scale having two ranges represented — 0 to 2, and 0 to 20 volts. — *8P6EU*

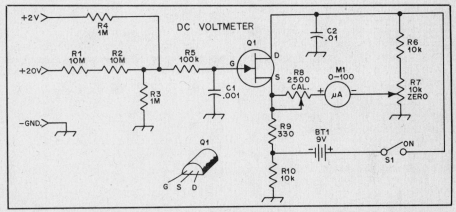

Circuit for the FET voltmeter. Fixed-value resistors are 1/4- or 1/2-W composition. C1 and C2 are disk ceramic. M1 is a 100-μA dc meter. Q1 is a Motorola MPF102 or HEP102 or HEP802. R7 and R8 are pc-board-mount composition controls.

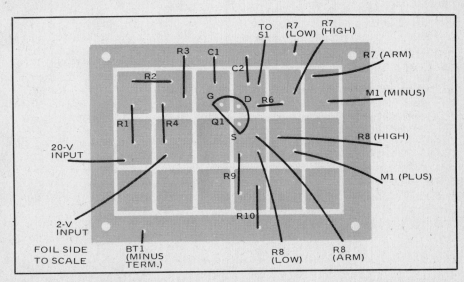

Circuit-board pattern for the FET voltmeter. The metal between the copper pads can be removed by means of a hobby tool and cutting bit.

An rf power meter/SWR indicator designed for use with QRP equipment.

A QRP MAN'S RF POWER METER

There are a lot of pint-size hf-band signals being transmitted nowadays, and this up-surge in QRP enthusiasm suggests a need for some specialized test equipment. An rf power meter/SWR indicator is certainly one piece of apparatus that all operators have frequent need for, but most instruments that have been described in amateur journals are keyed to the QRO (high) power level. Rigs with less than five watts of output barely move the needles on medium- or high-power wattmeters or SWR indicators. Some kinds of indicators — the Monimatch for one — are frequency sensitive, making it impractical for the user to establish meaningful rf power calibration for so-called all-band use (3 through 30 MHz).

Because of the writer's interest in QRP work, it was decided to fill a personal need with respect to owning a low-power measuring device. The circuit described here satisfies the requirement, and can be calibrated for 0 to 5 watts, and is suitable for operation from 80 through 10 meters. It is not "frequency conscious," so it will provide the same meter deflection per watt on all of the bands mentioned.

With the sensitivity control set at maximum, only one watt of rf energy is required to provide a full-scale meter reading. The user may wish to calibrate the instrument for some range other than five watts full scale. If so, he need only follow the calibration procedure discussed later, but set the sensitivity control at the appropriate point to provide the desired range.

Circuit Information

The circuit for the instrument is based on the classic Bruene design[1] and was mentioned in an earlier *QST* article.[2] It is

[1] Bruene, "An Inside Picture of Directional Wattmeters," *QST*, April, 1959.
[2] DeMaw, "In-Line RF Power Metering," *QST*, December, 1969.

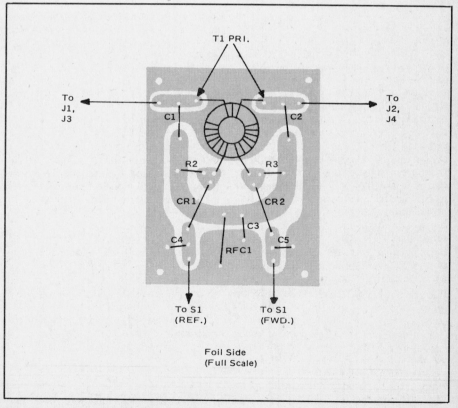

Schematic diagram of the QRP power meter.
C1, C2 — 0.5- to 5-pF trimmer (see text).
C3 — 330-pF silver mica.
C4, C5 — Disk ceramic.
D1, D2 — Germanium diode, 1N34A or equiv.
J1, J2 — Phono jack.
J3, J4 — SO-239 type connector, or coax fitting of builder's choice.
M1 — 50-μA panel meter (see text).
R1 — Linear-taper 1/4- or 1/2-watt, 25,000-ohm control.
R2, R3 — 33-ohm, 1/2-W composition resistor

(matched pair recommended).
RFC1 — 1-mH rf choke (Millen J300-1000 or equiv.).
S1 — Spdt toggle.
T1 — 60 turns no. 28 enam. wire, close wound on Amidon T-68-2 toroid core (secondary). Primary is 2 turns of small-diameter hookup wire over T1 secondary.*
*Amidon Associates, 12033 Otsego St., N. Hollywood, CA 91607.

Scale template of QRP power meter pc board.

This is an interior view of the QRP power meter. Visible at the lower left are the piston trimmers used for nulling the bridge. Toroidal transformer, T1, is located between the trimmers. The pc board is mounted on the bottom plate of the utility box by means of two 1-inch-high metal standoff posts which are attached to the ground foil of the board.

not arranged (physically) for operation above, say, 25 watts. At the higher levels of rf power there is not enough isolation between the various parts of the circuit to ensure a complete null when setting up the bridge circuit. The null will, however, be complete at 25 watts or less. Those desiring to build a small power meter that will work well from 25 to 1000 watts should consider constructing one of the units described in the article referenced by footnote 2.

A toroidal transformer, T1, is used in the rf-sampling circuit. A two-turn link assures sufficient pickup to provide full-scale meter deflection (T1 primary). The two trimmer capacitors, C1 and C2, in combination with C3 constitute the network for nulling the bridge. A pair of surplus 5-pF glass piston trimmers was used in the author's model. Subminiature air-dielectric variable capacitors can be substituted, provided the minimum capacitance is 1.5 pF or less. Alternatively, one can substitute a piece of double-clad pc board, 1/4 × 3/4 inch in size, for each of the trimmer capacitors. Each side of the board then becomes a plate for the homemade capacitor. A bus-wire lead is soldered to each plate near one end. The capacitor is adjusted by snipping off a bit of the board, continuing the process until a null is obtained (a piece of glass-epoxy pc board of the foregoing dimensions exhibits approximately 6 pF of capacitance).

Construction

The QRP power meter is housed in a 4 × 4 × 2-inch utility box. Other types of enclosures can be used if desired. Phono jacks are connected in parallel with SO-239 type jacks on each side of the instrument. This was a convenience feature

desired by the writer and need not be employed if just one type of fitting is perferred.

Most of the small components of the circuit are contained on a pc board. It is important that all of the components in the rf portion of the circuit be mounted with the least amount of lead length. This will assure minimum inductive and capacitive reactance, thereby making the job of nulling the bridge much easier.

A 1-1/2-inch square Simpson meter is shown in the photograph of the completed instrument. Any meter with a 0- to 50-μA movement will suffice. For power levels in excess of 2 watts a 0- to 100-μA meter will be suitable. Those wishing to avoid the expenditure connected with purchasing a meter can use an existing VOM or VTVM for visual indication. Simply install a pair of test jacks to permit connection of an external indicator to the existing metering circuit. Use one of the low-voltage ranges on the VTVM for your measurements.

Adjustment

It will be necessary to have a nonreactive 50-ohm dummy load for initial adjustment of the power meter. A Heath Cantenna was used by the author, but a 2-watt 51-ohm composition resistor (5 percenter) will work fine if the leads are kept short, and if no more than 5 watts of rf power are applied during any 10-second period.

Connect the dummy load to one port of the instrument and apply rf power to the remaining port. S1 should now be thrown back and forth to determine which position gives the highest meter reading. This will be the FORWARD position. Adjust the sensitivity control for full-scale reading of the meter. Now, move the switch to the opposite (REFLECTED) position and adjust the trimmer nearest the transmitter input port for a null in the meter reading. The needle should drop to zero. It is recommended that these adjustments be made in the 10- or 15-meter band. Next, reverse the transmitter and load cables and repeat the nulling procedure while adjusting the trimmer on the opposite side of the pc board. Repeat these steps until a perfect null is obtained in both directions. The switch and the coax connectors can now be labeled, TRANSMITTER, LOAD, FORWARD and REFLECTED, as appropriate.

Meter calibration can be effected at any frequency from 80 through 10 meters. It will be necessary to measure rms voltage across the 50-ohm load by means of an rf probe and a VTVM.[3] Those having access to a wide-band scope can do the calibrating by reading pk-pk rf voltage

across the 50-ohm load, then converting the value to rms volts

$$E_{rms} = \frac{E_{pk-pk} \times 0.707}{2}$$

Rf wattage can then be found by

$$W = \frac{E_{rms}^2}{R}$$

$$W = \frac{10^2}{50} = \frac{100}{50} = 2 \text{ W}$$

It will be necessary to vary the transmitter output power by means of the drive control, or by detuning the tank circuit of one of the early stages, to obtain the rms voltage across the load that corresponds to the desired full-scale reading versus rf watts. Calibration points on the meter scale can be selected by adjusting the rf voltage across the load to a known value versus power, then noting the meter reading and preparing a chart. The required voltage can be determined by

$$E_{rms} = \sqrt{W \times R}$$

Example: To find the rms voltage across 50 ohms for 1 watt,

$$E_{rms} = \sqrt{1 \times 50} = 7.07 \text{ V}$$

If the builder has an rf ammeter or milliammeter he can do the calibration by using the formula $W = I^2R$. Thus, if 0.2 A of rf current is flowing through the 50-ohm load, the power equals 2 watts (.04 × 50 = 2). Be sure the rf ammeter is rated for reasonable accuracy at the operating frequency.

Some Final Remarks

The power meter can be used for adjusting an antenna for minimum SWR, or in tuning a Transmatch.[4] Place S1 in the REFLECTED position and make the required adjustments to provide a meter reading of zero.

If a zero reading can't be obtained while adjusting a Transmatch or antenna, it is likely that the transmitter has an abnormal amount of harmonic energy in its output. A resonant load will not accept the harmonic current, causing it to register on the SWR indicator as reflected power, even though the SWR at the desired frequency may actually be 1. A harmonic filter can be installed between the transmitter and the power meter to reduce the harmonic output, thereby making measurements more accurate.[5] — *W1FB*

[3]Construction information on rf probes is given in the chapter on measurements, *ARRL Radio Amateur's Handbook,* all recent editions.

[4]DeMaw, "A Transmatch for QRP Rigs," *QST,* February, 1973.
[5]McCoy, "Getting Rid of Low-Frequency Harmonics," *QST,* April, 1968.

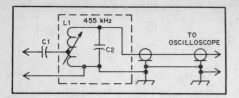

A high-impedance test probe can be assembled from an old i-f transformer, or from a shielded inductor and capacitor. C2 should be less than the normal value for resonance with L1, to compensate for the capacitance of the cable and input circuitry of the oscilloscope. See text for a discussion of obtaining a value for C1 and C2.

A LOW I-F TEST PROBE

A high-impedance test probe may be assembled from an old i-f transformer, or from a shielded inductor and capacitor. Used with an oscilloscope, this probe enables one to look at the i-f signal amplitude without appreciably affecting or loading an rf circuit. When alignment and repair work are completed, the probe may be removed without detuning the circuit.

The probe is built from an i-f transformer and RG58/U coaxial cable. C1 should be 10 pF or less if the oscilloscope to be used is sensitive. Ten pF at 455 kHz represents a capacitive reactance of 35 kΩ. This high impedance, together with the high impedance of the tuned circuit, provides a probe with very little loading. C2 should be less than the normal value for resonance with L1 to compensate for the capacitance of the cable and input circuitry of the oscilloscope. The value of C2 may be calculated by adding 30 pF/ft. of RG58/U and the input capacitance of the oscilloscope, then subtracting this from the value that is needed for resonance at 455 kHz. For example three feet of RG58/U is 90 pF, plus 30 pF. A 700-μH inductor for L1 requires 180 pF; thus 180 — 120 gives a value of 60 pF for C2.

Tune the probe by feeding a 455-kHz signal at C1 and peaking L1 for maximum signal as observed on the oscilloscope. — *Carlos H. Daniels, WB4FIR*

EMERGENCY CONTINUITY TESTER

A simple continuity test can be constructed with a receiver and two test leads. One test lead is connected to the receiver antenna terminal and the other is connected to the antenna. With such connections, continuity can be easily detected by the increase in gain in the receiver. — *Ronald J. Finger, WN9VCH*

A FIVE-CENT TRANSISTOR TESTER

Do you own a collection of unmarked, untested diodes and transistors? Plenty of semiconductor assortments are bought for bargain prices on today's market, but finding out which are the good or bad devices can be perplexing!

A conventional transistor tester can be used to grade out the defective units or to identify the leads of diodes and transistors, but the same process is possible by using a simple ohmmeter and a single resistor. Interested? Read on.

One five-cent resistor and an ohmmeter are all that's needed to determine the base connections of unmarked transistors, tell npn from pnp types, distinguish between silicon and germanium devices, and even measure the current gain of junction transistors. For an additional 10 cents you also can measure the transconductance of FETs.

The ohmmeter function in either a VOM or VTVM involves an internal battery and a current-indicating meter. Almost any ohmmeter type is satisfactory if it has a range with a center scale reading of 500 or 1000 ohms. First, determine which test prod is positive when the VOM or VTVM is used as an ohmmeter. Measure the voltage between prods with another voltmeter or open the case and trace the circuit. Also, it's helpful to know the voltage of the internal battery, which is often either 1.5 or 3.0 volts.

Identifying Diode and Transistor Types

A semiconductor pn junction such as a diode rectifier or the emitter-base junction and base-collector junction in a transistor have a low resistance in the forward direction when the p-type side is positive with respect to the n-type side. Therefore, when you connect the positive test prod of the ohmmeter to the p-type side and the negative prod to the n-type side, the ohmmeter indicates a low resistance. Reversing the test prods should result in a very high resistance reading. Thus, you can distinguish the anode and cathode terminals of unmarked semiconductor diodes and rectifiers. A convenient way to relate the anode and cathode terminals with n-type and p-type regions and with the polarity for forward bias is illustrated.

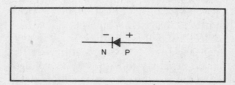

Diagram of a junction diode indicating n and p regions. If the ohmmeter probes are connected with the polarity shown, the diode will be forward biased and a low resistance reading will occur.

In this way you can identify the leads of an unmarked junction transistor and tell whether it is a pnp type or an npn type.

Find the common lead which shows low-resistance forward conduction with both other leads, and you have discovered the base terminal. The polarity of the test prod touching the base lead is negative for a pnp transistor and positive for an npn type. It is easiest to find this by connecting one ohmmeter test prod to any transistor lead and touching the other prod to each of the remaining two leads in turn. Repeat for the other leads, each time watching the ohmmeter reading. If none results in a low resistance between both of the other two leads, reverse the test prods and start over. There is only one successful combination (since there is only one base lead), unless the transistor is open or shorted.

In the process of identifying the base lead, an indication of whether or not the transistor is made of germanium or of silicon can be obtained also. This is often useful information in connection with transistor-bias design, particularly in direct-coupled circuits, and for operating-temperature considerations.

The properties of semiconductors are such that pn junctions of germanium usually have a lower forward resistance than the silicon type at the same forward voltage. The exact resistance reading noted on an ohmmeter depends somewhat upon the range scale and the internal battery voltage. Typical ohmmeter readings are about 200 ohms for germanium devices compared with 800 ohms for silicon units when using a 1000-ohm center scale (VTVM ohmmeter) with a 1.5-volt internal battery. The same units indicate about 100 ohms and 200 ohms respectively (VOM type of ohmmeter) with a 500-ohm center scale and a 3-volt internal battery. These differences in readings using the two meters are expected because of the nonlinear properties of pn junctions. Also, there is some variation between different devices of the same general type, such as would result from their internal design for maximum current-carrying capacity and other factors.

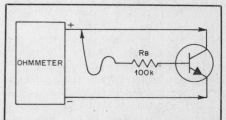

Testing a bipolar transistor with the ohmmeter. For npn transistors highest gain occurs when connected in this fashion. Conversely, the negative prod is at the collector terminal for pnp units.

Measuring the Current Gain

The next step is to determine the collector and emitter leads of the transistor and to get a general idea of its current gain. Excluding the base lead, clip one ohmmeter test prod to one transistor lead and the other test prod to the remaining lead of the unknown transistor. The ohmmeter will indicate a very large resistance since one of the junctions is under reverse bias. Now connect a resistor (an inexpensive 100-kΩ carbon type is quite satisfactory) from the base lead to the positive test prod if the transistor is an npn type. Connect the base lead to the negative test prod in the case of a pnp type. This biases the emitter junction in the forward direction, which results in collector current and a deflection on the ohmmeter. In effect, the transistor is now operating as a dc amplifier.

The transistor base-collector current gain is approximately the ratio of the base-bias resistor to the ohmmeter reading R or

$$\beta = \frac{R_b}{R} = \frac{100,000}{R}$$

The reading is now repeated after the ohmmeter test prods are reversed. The arrangement producing the greatest current gain determines which of the leads is the emitter lead and which is the collector lead.

The exact value of current gain determined by this simple circuit depends somewhat on properties of the ohmmeter used. Consequently, the results should be viewed as indicative of transistor parameters. Actually, measurements of a selection of transistors in a typical assortment showed gains ranging from 20 to 400. All units that looked alike had approximately the same current gain, although there were occasional exceptions which produced significantly lower values. Good correlation between gains measured with the tester and tabulated values for several known transistors was observed also.

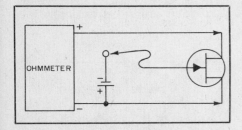

An ohmmeter and a battery can be used to test a junction FET.

The scheme works best for small-signal transistors, although most power transistors can be tested as well. Power units do not seem to yield particularly reliable values for gain. However, the test does indicate clearly whether or not a device is operational. Incidentally, for convenience in testing different kinds of transistors with a variety of base and lead arrangements, it proves convenient to attach an alligator clip to each end of the resistor. Thus the ohmmeter prods and the resistor are simply clipped to the transistor leads and interchanging connections is easy.

Testing FETs

A technique similar to that used for bipolar transistors is applicable to junction FETs as well. First, identify the drain and source leads of the FET by finding the pair of leads that indicates the same resistance when the test prod connections are interchanged. The resistance between drain and source in an FET arises simply from the channel resistance, so it is the same for either direction of current flow. A typical value is 200 ohms. You can tell whether the FET is an n-channel or a p-channel type by noting the polarity of the test prods for forward conduction between the gate lead (the third lead) and either the drain or source lead. An n-channel FET shows a low resistance reading when the positive test prod is connected to the gate in conformity with previous tests.

The gain of an FET is measured by its transconductance, which is the change in drain current resulting from a change in gate voltage. Notice that an FET is a voltage-controlled amplifier in contrast to a junction transistor which is current controlled. Therefore, in order to test FETs, you need a small battery to use as a bias source.

Connect the ohmmeter between the source and drain leads as determined previously. Short the gate to the negative ohmmeter prod in the case of an n-channel unit, or to the positive prod for a p-channel FET. The reciprocal of the ohmmeter reading is the zero-bias channel conductance, G_o. Now connect the gate as shown for an n-channel FET to the negative terminal of the penlight battery (the gate is connected to the positive battery terminal for a p-channel FET). The reverse bias at the gate in either case causes the channel resistance reading to increase, which shows that the FET is operating. The reciprocal of this reading is called G_b, and the transconductance, g_m, is proportional, to the difference: $G_o - G_b$. Here, again, the actual value depends somewhat upon the ohmmeter properties, but the test is indicative enough for most experimental purposes. — *James Brophy*

METER CASES FROM COCOA BOXES

A neat looking serviceable meter box or case may be made from a discarded cocoa box. (See photo.) First the ancestry of the box is hidden by application of a coat of paint. Then the meter hole is cut with a small knife in the pasteboard side of the box. Rubber grommets may be used to protect wires passing into the metal case. Removal of the cocoa-box lid provides access to the meter terminals. — *Arthus S. Gillespie, Jr., K4TP*

A meter enclosure made from a cocoa box.

BATTERY REPLACEMENT CIRCUIT NOTES

The "Battery-Replacement Circuit for the VTVM," described by K5LZT/9 ("Hints and Kinks," *QST* for January, 1976) is a fine addition to most VTVMs. However, those contemplating making the change should be aware of some (usually minor) shortcomings observed while bench testing similar circuits prior to installing one in my Heath VTVM:

1) The regulator draws about 145 mA from the transformer which also supplies 450 mA to the pilot lamp and tube filaments. The added load will decrease the heater voltage approximately 0.5 V. Replacing the 6-V pilot lamp with a lamp across the 117-V ac line will keep the transformer output voltage at its former level.

2) When the ohmmeter probes are used to measure the small resistance, the regulator output will drop by a few tenths of a volt. This causes a measurement error of about 20 percent at 10 ohms and about 3 percent at 20 ohms.

3) Even with a 1000-μF capacitor in the supply, there is an appreciable amount of ripple in the output of the regulator. Ordinarily it will have no effect on a measurement, but it is well to know it is there.

I recommend two additional changes which have proven useful over the years: Bring out the (nominal) 1.5 V to a terminal on the front of the meter so that dc-volts calibration can be readily checked at any time, and drill two holes in the side or back of the cabinet so that ac and dc volts can be recalibrated without taking the VTVM apart. The latter change may require relocating the calibration controls in some models. — *Donald F. Zawada, W9MJG*

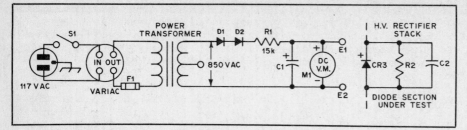

A circuit for testing power diodes. Because of the voltages used, precautions mentioned below must be observed carefully. D1 and D2 are silicon rectifiers, type 1N4007 or equivalent.

TESTING "DYE-ODES"

Power diodes are not always what they appear to be — that is, although failure seldom results from excessive current, not all "new" diodes will "hold-off" their rated reverse voltage when placed in the circuit.

This startling fact was revealed after my linear amplifier final high-voltage diode-rectifier stack partially blew itself several times in an erratic fashion. Indication was that there should be some dynamic method (other than the usual cold resistance check on a VOM) of evaluating these components before they give up the ghost during a QSO.

Most diodes used in amateur and commercial power circuits are rated in several amperes forward current with a reverse voltage rating of 1000 volts. With this statement in mind, I decided to design a circuit which would permit each diode section to be tested to the full voltage. The circuit is shown above.

With S1 in the ON position and test leads E1 and E2 clipped across the diode section under test, the Variac setting is increased from zero until C1 is charged to exactly 1000 volts through R1 as indicated by the dc voltmeter.

Assuming CR3 and C2 are good components, the discharge path of C1 is only through the meter and R2. If any additional resistance appears in parallel with these resistances (such as a defective diode or capacitor in the section under test), the voltage indication on the meter will read lower because of the extra voltage loss across R1.

After the initial setup has been made on a "good" section, just flip S1 to the OFF position. Watch the meter reading decrease from 1000 volts to zero (as C1 discharges through the meter and R2), move E1 and E2 to the next diode section, turn S1 on, and watch for the meter to return to the "good" reading of exactly 1000 volts. If the meter reads anything except 1000 volts, you have a bad component (usually a diode) in that section.

When using this procedure, please remember that you are working with *lethal* voltages. Be certain the transmitter power supply is disconnected from the mains and the rectifier stack is lifted from the load; also, be certain the dc voltmeter falls to zero before moving the test clips to another diode section. With a little practice, you will find that this system works extremely well in locating those strange electronic devices known as *"dye-odes"* — *R. K. Dye, W8YLN*

DC VOLTAGE MEASUREMENTS

Ordinary VOMs (volt-ohm-milliammeter) are suitable for much of the routine work done in the amateur lab. Some of the small imported instruments can be purchased for less money than one would spend to build a comparable tester from scratch. The primary limitation of most VOMs is, however, that of loading the circuit under test. A typical VOM will exhibit a characteristic of 1000 to perhaps 5000 ohms per volt when applied to a circuit test point. Loading of this variety will sometimes cause incorrect readings (lower than normal). A more practical voltmeter is one which has a high input resistance, such as a VTVM (vacuum-tube voltmeter) or a solid-state equivalent. The latter can often be built at a cost lower than that of a factory-assembled unit or commercial kit. The complexity of a homemade instrument will depend upon the accuracy desired. — *Staff*

AN ACCURATE STANDARD FOR CALIBRATING FREQUENCY METERS

Digital frequency meters are gradually becoming more common pieces of test equipment for the radio amateur and experimenters. Precise calibration of frequency meters, especially those in kit form, can be a problem since an accurate and stable frequency source is usually not available to the average experimenter. The crystal-controlled secondary frequency standard available to the amateur is not stable enough for precise calibration purposes because they tend to drift slightly with temperature changes.

If a color television receiver is available the crystal reference oscillator in the frequency meter can be calibrated by comparing its frequency to that of the color-reference signal broadcast by the major television networks. A TV set tuned to a network color program is a highly accurate and stable reference since the four major television networks all use rubidium reference oscillators to generate the 3.58-MHz color reference signals. Every color TV receiver phase locks to those references.

The calibration process is carried out by coupling the input of the counter, through a low-capacitance probe, to the plate of the tube or the collector of the transistor used to regenerate the color subcarrier signal in the TV receiver.

While the TV set is tuned to a station broadcasting a color program, set the calibration adjustment in the counter so that the frequency indicated is exactly 3.579545 MHz. When the counter probe is connected to the color oscillator in the TV set, be sure to view the screen to verify that the picture is still in color sync. A rainbow of color bars floating through the picture indicates a loss of color sync. If this should happen decrease the loading of the probe with a series resistor until the screen has a normal color picture. — *Stephen Pawlowicz, WA3SDV*

ETC ETCETERA

Easy Transistor Checker Evaluating Transistors for Every Radio Amateur

Now, with that out of the way, here are the "specs" . . . ETC can not compete with a Tektronix 576 Curve Tracer but it will do the following

1) Indicate the type of transistor (pnp or npn).

2) Show whether the transistor is open or shorted.

3) Indicate the approximate gain.

S1 is positioned to pnp or npn, both positions to be tried if the transistor type is unknown. Actuating S2 (Ref) checks the battery supply and lights DS1, giving a visual degree of illumination for comparison with DS2. S3 (X1), S4 (X10) and S5 (X100) are actuated sequentially — the gain of the transistor overcoming the bias-

The ETC transistor checker. The two penlight batteries can be seen through the plastic enclosure. At the right of the npn/pnp switch are the test switch and two indicating lights.

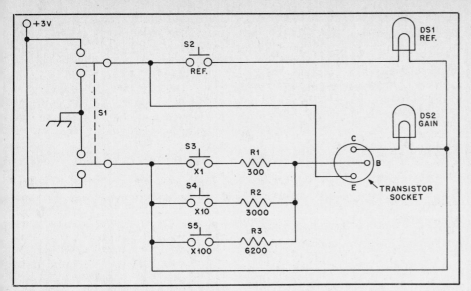

DS1, DS2 — Panel lamp, type GE 338 or equiv.
S1 — DP3T (center off) miniature toggle switch Raytheon type MST205P or equiv.
S2-S5, incl. — Momentary contact microswitch, any type suitable for this application.

Delco 137-8864-9-512 lamp holder and Keystone battery holder, type for holding two penlight cells, and a suitable chassis are recommended.

During this measurement a two-tone audio signal is supplied to the speech amplifier of the transmitter. The primary limitation in using a scope is that the display-tube face is too small to provide a well-defined voltage reading (resolution). As an example, 2-kW PEP signal is applied to a 50-ohm load, resulting in a pk-pk voltage reading on the CR-tube face of 632.45. The accuracy of such a measurement would be rather absurd, thereby leading to possible unlawful operation. Furthermore, most scopes aren't set up to measure voltages of that magnitude. The lower drawing shows the methods for voltage-resistance power measurement. — W1FB

ing of R1, R2 and R3 to illuminate DS2. Depending on the characteristics of the transistor, if DS2 lights to one-half the brilliance of DS1 when S4 (X10) is pressed, it is a good transistor. If DS2 lights above a dim glow when S5 (X100) is pressed, the transistor is exceptionally good. If DS2 lights *without* actuating S3, S4 or S5, the transistor is shorted. If DS2 does not light when pressing S3 (X1), the transistor is open.

R3 was selected to give a dim glow with an average good transistor, when S5 is actuated. S2 through S5 should be pressed with the tip of your fingernail.

I claim no originality for the circuit, as a variety of these have appeared from time to time. I just wanted something compact, reliable, and quick, *etc.* — *Howard L. Findlay, KØBYC*

MEASURING POWER OUTPUT

A method which can be used to measure output power is to determine the rf voltage across a dummy load of known resistance. An rf probe can be used in combination with a VTVM to measure the rms voltage present across the load resistance. In this instance $W = E^2R$. Accuracy will be within ± 10 percent if the rf probe described in the measurements chapter of the *Handbook* is used with a VTVM which has a 10-megohm input characteristic. The waveform of the rf energy being measured must be pure if accuracy is to be expected. Cw power output can be measured by applying a steady carrier to the dummy load. For ssb power-output measurements, apply a 1000-Hz single audio tone to the modulator and

measure the rf voltage across the load. Multiply the computed power (in watts) by 2 to obtain PEP.

An oscilloscope can be used to read pk-pk (peak-to-peak) rf voltage across the load. However, the instrument must be capable of full response at the operating frequency of the transmitter (vertical amplifier bandwidth) and the instrument must be capable of being calibrated to read the displayed waveform in pk-pk voltage. A scope is able to respond to instantaneous voltage peaks (unlike a dc current or voltmeter), so PEP can be determined by the scope reading if the resistance of the dummy load is known. To obtain PEP in watts see the drawing.

CALIBRATING A DC VTVM OR FET VOM

A VTVM or FET VOM can measure voltages quite accurately primarily because their input impedance is very high, which allows only a small amount of current to flow through them. In most cases they present such a light load to the circuit being measured that the voltage they indicate is almost the same as the actual voltage which would be present in the circuit without the added load of the meter. To take advantage of this accuracy the meter calibration should be checked periodically.

The usual methods for checking the calibration of these instruments are by comparison with another meter of known accuracy or by comparison with a source of emf whose potential is known. The standard of comparison should have an error which is appreciably less than that of the instrument to be calibrated. For example, the dc ranges of a VTVM with an inherent accuracy of ± 2 percent should be

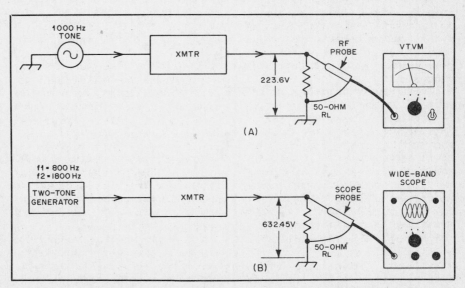

Rf power output can be measured by means of an rf probe, known-value resistive load and VTVM (A). A scope, as shown at B, will provide a pk-pk voltage reading but suffers the limitations discussed in the text.

calibrated with a cell whose potential is known to within ±1 percent, if not closer. Errors may accumulate, so the overall accuracy of the instrument would then be ±3 percent. It would be within ±2.25 percent if the cell voltage was known to be within 0.25 percent.

Few batteries, however, can be trusted to be within 1 percent of their nominal voltage, and most hams do not have access to another meter much less one they know to be accurate to within one or two percent! The calibration instructions for Heathkit's popular VTVMs call for setting the meter to a point on the scale corresponding to 1.55 volts while measuring a fresh, size-C flashlight battery. But the ubiquitous flashlight or transistor battery is one of the least stable sources of emf. These types of batteries may present an open-circuit voltage between 1.5 and 1.68 volts. This is a possible variation of −3.4 percent or +8.4 percent from the nominal 1.55 volts of a fresh battery. Of course high accuracy laboratory standards are available, but they are prohibitively expensive sources for some amateurs.

Probably the best readily available voltage source for calibrating the dc ranges on a VTVM or FET VOM is the popular PX-13. These batteries are commonly used in photographic exposure meters and cameras. Most photographic stores stock them and ought to have a reasonably fresh supply since they are so widely used. The open-circuit voltage of an unused PX-13 is nominally 1.35 volts, and in fact about 85 percent of the batteries tested in one manufacturer's laboratories had a potential of 1.35 volts. The rest of the units ranged from 1.34 volts to 1.36 volts. But even this variation (exhibited by only 15 percent of the batteries tested) is only ±0.74 percent. The tests included batteries just off the production line as well as ones which had been stored up to a year.

To calibrate the dc ranges of your VTVM or FET VOM — use only a new battery — one which has never been subjected to any appreciable load. Check the meter to make sure the mechanical zero is adjusted correctly, then turn the instrument on and allow it to warm up until stabilized. If there is a front-panel "zero adjust," set it so that the meter reads zero. Hold the probe tips to the PX-13 and adjust the dc-calibration potentiometer so the meter needle reads 1.35 volts on the range which gives the greatest needle deflection at that potential (usually the 1.5-volt scale). Remove the probes and zero the meter if necessary, and then repeat the calibration procedure. — *Daniel A. Gomez-Ibanez, WB9ICI*

BATTERY TEST AID

Here is a simple device for use in measuring a battery current drain. It is a piece of double-sided pc board tapered at one end, allowing the board to slide in between two batteries (or a battery and its terminal) easily, for measuring current being drawn by the equipment in which the battery is employed. Insert the probe, connect a milliammeter to the terminals on the pc board, turn the device on and measure the current being drawn. Plug a battery charger into the equipment and if current indication reverses, read the net charge. — *Ralph H. Janowsky, W2RPO*

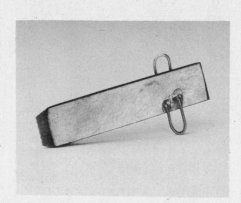

A milliameter connected to this probe indicates battery drain when load is applied.

A UNIVERSAL TRANSISTOR TESTER

Most hams who do solid-state construction quickly learn one thing about transistors — the devices are easy to destroy and may give no warning when they fail. The result: They must be tested for quality often, in and out of a circuit. However, many transistor testers on the market are expensive and somewhat cumbersome to use.

This article describes a simple low-cost transistor tester that was designed to solve these problems. It will test all kinds of devices in or out of their circuits, and it will give a good relative indication of noise figure and/or gain (beta). A ham accustomed to fishing cw signals out of QRM can probably tell more about the relative gain or noise figure of several random production units of the same type device with this gadget than he could using a tester with an expensive meter movement or curve tracer.

For someone building anything from uhf preamplifiers to a regulated dc power supply, these test functions are extremely useful. Most hams should be able to duplicate this tester in one evening with a low-cost collection of parts, even if everything is purchased new.

This tester produces an audible tone when connected to any conventional transistor, JFET, MOSFET, Darlington-pair IC and so on, if the transistor is capable of amplifying a signal. Among similar JFETs or MOSFETs, those producing the lowest pitch of audible tone have the lowest noise figure. And among similar devices of any type, those producing the loudest audio tone have the highest gain. For a ham who has ten 2N5245 JFETs in his junk box and wants to install the best one in his 144-MHz preamp, this is valuable information.

Circuit Description

The transistor tester inductively feeds back an audio signal through two transformers to create sustained oscillation when any device capable of amplifying is attached to the proper terminals. S1 is used to apply either positive or negative voltage through an audio-output transformer, T2, to the device under test. T2 feeds a signal to the 8-ohm speaker and to T1, another similar audio transformer. Positive feedback from T1 is applied to the device under test through C1 or C2, sustaining oscillation only if the device has gain. C3 and C4 must be nonpolarized electrolytics because the current-limiting resistors R1 and R2 may produce either a positive or negative voltage in relation to ground, depending on the type device under test.

Construction Details

Mount T1 and T2 on a 3 × 4-1/2-inch (7.5 × 11.5 cm) copper-clad circuit board. Then install three terminal strips for component wiring. All components are placed on the upper side and interconnected with flexible insulated wire. Since there is so little circuitry, etching a circuit board is not necessary.

The pc board, speaker and battery are mounted in the 6-1/4 × 3-3/4 × 2-inch (15.9 × 9.5 × 5 cm) plastic case, as shown in the photograph. The simplest way to proceed from here is to mount the seven post terminals shown in the diagram

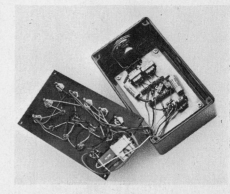

The wiring of the top panel and circuit board is shown here. A variety of sockets is wired to conform to various pin configurations in common use. To simplify the circuit wiring, all components are attached to a series of terminal strips soldered to a one-sided, copper-clad board. All of the sockets could be eliminated and clip leads could be used for all testing, if the builder wishes.

Almost all devices can be tested without removing them from their circuits, as shown here. A set of small clip leads is needed to test a device installed in a pc board.

(collector, base, emitter, drain, gate two, gate one and source/substrate) on the top plate and wire them to the circuit board as shown.

If the builder wishes to include a series of transistor sockets to match the more popular lead configurations as the author did, this can be done. Simply wire all socket terminals to their corresponding post terminals. Alternatively, slip leads can be used eliminating the need for socket wiring.

Testing the Tester

Once all wiring is completed and carefully checked, attach a bipolar transistor of known quality to the collector, base and emitter terminals. Switch the polarity selector to the proper position (an incorrect setting will *not* damage the device). A tone should be heard in the speaker, indicating sustained feedback. If there is no tone, double check the polarity switch and circuit wiring. If there is still no oscillation, T1 may be feeding back out of phase. To change its phase relationship to T2, reverse the

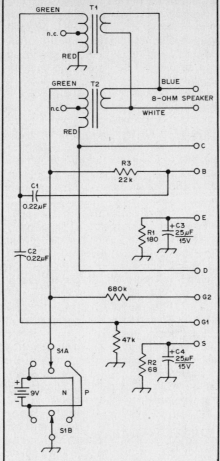

Circuit diagram and parts information for the Transistor Tester. Not shown is the wiring of the various transistor sockets, which is described in the text.
C3, C4 — Nonpolarized electrolytic.
S1 — Two-pole switch, on-off-on, (Radio Shack no. 757-0247 or 757-0301).
T1, T2 — Audio-output transformer, pri. imp: 1200 Ω red and green, sec. imp: 8 Ω white and blue (Calectro transformer no. D1-724.

primary or secondary leads of either transformer (but not both).

Here an rf power transistor capable of delivering 10 watts of output at 1296 MHz is being tested. The tester will reveal the sad news quickly to a uhf enthusiast if he has just blown up his prized device.

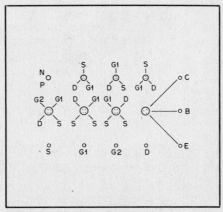

Bottom view of the socket panel. All sockets are wired to the terminals corresponding to their pin configurations (collector, base and emitter for bipolar transistors, source, substrate, gate one, gate two, and drain).

How to Use the Tester

When testing various devices, an audio note between 1000 and 5000 Hz should be heard. A note above 10,000 Hz indicates that the device has some gain but will not meet its specifications or may have been connected to the tester incorrectly. If there is no audible tone, the device is defective and should be discarded.

JFETs are tested in the same manner as bipolar transistors with the exception that the drain and source are interchangeable in the tester, and may be connected either way as long as the gate is attached to its designated terminal (gate one). When testing MOSFETs, the source and substrate are both connected to the source terminal post. However, gate one and gate two on dual-gate MOSFETs must be attached properly (note the manufacturer's lead configuration).

As pointed out earlier, the relative noise figure of similar JFETs or MOSFETs can be compared, with those producing the lowest pitch being best. Among production units of most types, there are significant variations in both gain and noise figure, so this type of test is essential for anyone seeking high performance in a uhf preamplifier, for instance.

Of course, the tester will also identify whether an unknown device is of the pnp or npn type. It will only oscillate with the polarity switch in the proper position, and an incorrect setting of this switch will not damage any device except possibly a nondiode-protected MOSFET. Thus, MOSFETs should not be tested unless their polarity and lead configuration is known.

Certain "programmable" transistors (unijunctions, for example) will produce an audio note of varying frequency. This is normal and does not indicate a defect in the device.

Devices with a current-carrying capability above 10 amperes usually will not oscillate in this circuit and therefore cannot be tested. A builder who wishes to test such devices should add a double-pole double-throw switch so R3 (the forward-bias resistor in the base lead) can be varied from the designated value of 22,000 ohms to about 5000 ohms. However, low-current devices may be damaged if tested with this switch in the 5000-ohm position.

Almost every amateur owns something that uses some of the solid-state devices this unit is designed to test. The tester's ability to indicate quickly and simply whether a transistor is working — usually without removing it from its circuit — makes it one of the most basic pieces of test

equipment needed in any ham shack.
— *Wilson E. Anderson, WB6RIV*

[Editor's Note: We queried the author about the term *noise* figure as used in this article. Here is his reply: "As used in this article, the term does indeed refer to that characteristic of FETs that is commonly known as *noise figure* or *noise factor*, i.e., the amount of internally generated noise in the device.

You wondered whether the tester will discern the relative noise figure of 10 FETs of the same type and make, when all 10 are between 1.5- and 2.0-dB noise factor at 450 MHz. In our experience, the answer is yes. . . .

Obviously, this tester provides only an indirect indication of noise figure. But because a number of devices can be tested quickly and easily with this unit, its audible indication of noise figure is an excellent preliminary test. . .".]

HARMONIC GENERATOR FOR CALIBRATION WORK

It is often difficult to hear the high-order harmonics of a signal generator when doing calibration work in a frequency range that is far removed from the fundamental frequency of the oscillator. In such cases a simple harmonic generator, such as that shown, can be used to provide a stronger "signal" in the desired range. An 1N34 crystal diode is used to rectify some of the output of the signal generator. The rectification generates harmonics throughout the spectrum. — *Russell O. Deck, Jr., DL4OM, W9JVI*

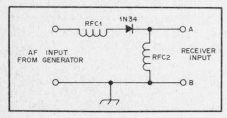

A diode harmonic generator.

TEST AIDS

Here are a couple of test aids for use around the shop. Both are constructed of standard 1/2-inch copper plumbing fittings. The modified coaxial plug, which slips on or off the popular SO-239 uhf chassis connector, is just a standard PL-259 cable plug with the threaded shell removed. The shell is replaced with a

Test cable equipped slip-on connectors.

1/2-inch copper pipe coupling.

Construction requires minor modification of the pipe coupling. As the inside diameter is slightly larger than the threaded portion of the PL-259, the end of the coupling should be "rolled" in by lightly tapping the edge of the fitting with a hammer while rotating the coupling until a proper fit is achieved. Then the coupling should be slotted as shown in the photograph. After cleaning, assemble the plug and position it, with the cable extending vertically at the top. It is soldered easily with the aid of a propane torch and rosin-core solder. Finally, fit the working end of the quick connector to an SO-239 connector by slightly squeezing the copper adjacent to the slots with a pair of pliers.

The cable attachment is conventional, with the only difference being that the cable is soldered to the reducing bushing only; then, the bushing is screwed into the plug and snugged down tightly.

The 6-dB hf-band attenuator pad, shown in the photograph, is constructed from a short length of 1/2-inch copper pipe and two end caps. BNC connectors are used for convenience; however, any coaxial type of connector of small size would work. Construction requires the appropriate resistor values be used. In this case a T pad was used. First, the resistors are soldered together and then to the end of one of the BNC connectors. Then the assembly is slid into the pipe and soldered to the other BNC connector. It is important to allow just enough lead length at the second end to facilitate soldering, because a necessary amount of slack is introduced when telescoping the unit together. This slack should be as small as possible. Secure the caps to the body by drilling a small hole and installing small sheet-metal screws. — *John Bipes, KØYQX.*

A 6-dB hf-band attenuator pad, useful as a test aid.

HEATH IM-104 VOM MODIFICATION PREVENTS METER PEGGING

The critical spacing between contacts 11 and 12 on the front of range switch wafer 3 may result in a momentary open circuit resulting in meter needle pegging when the instrument is switched between ohmmeter ranges. The pegging may be eliminated by

installing another switch contact at any unused position on the front of wafer 3. An insulated jumper wire should be connected between the new contact and either contact 11 or 12. If no new contact is available, remove either contact 11 or 12 by carefully drilling out the rivet and replacing the contact in any unused position on wafer 3. A similar problem resulting from contact spacing on the rear of wafer 3 may be corrected by moving either contact 1 or 2 to any unused position. — *David Kraeuter*

A SIMPLE FIELD-STRENGTH METER

Few amateur stations, fixed state or mobile, are without need of a field-strength meter. An instrument of that type serves many useful purposes during antenna experiments and adjustments. Extreme meter sensitivity is not always a requisite, and for hf-band near-field checks this circuit should be fine. Amateurs desiring to make far-field checks (several wavelengths from the antenna under test) may wish to build the instrument described in an earlier issue of *QST*.

The unit described here has ample sensitivity for most amateur work. The larger the pickup antenna, the greater the sensitivity. Far-field measurements can be made by using the alternative input circuit shown in the diagram. In that application a reference dipole, cut for the frequency of interest, is connected to the input link. Alternatively, a one-quarter wavelength wire can be used as a far-field pickup antenna. The polarization of the two antennas involved in a test should be the same if meaningful results are to be obtained.

Most of the simple field-strength meters used by amateurs are capable of recording only *relative* signal levels, and such readings are useful in a number of tests. However, knowing the approximate dB increase resulting from antenna adjustments can be helpful in evaluation work with matching networks, loading inductors, and the like. Reasonable accuracy can be had with the circuit as shown.

Circuit Highlights

In this model the tuned circuit, L1, C1, C2 and C3, was selected for the 160-meter operation. The constants can be changed for the amateur bands from 80 through 10 meters. Table 1 lists the inductance and capacitance values needed.

The capacitive divider (C2 and C3) is

[1] McCoy, "A Linear Field-Strength Meter," *QST* for January, 1973, p. 18.

Table 1

Band	160 M	80 M	40 M	20 M	15 M	10 M
L1 (µH)	100 (Nom.)	25 (Nom.)	10 (Nom.)	2.2 (Nom.)	1.3 (Nom.)	0.5 (Nom.)
C2 (pF)	25	25	15	15	10	10
C3 (pF)	100	100	68	68	47	47
Miller Coil	4409	4407	4406	4404	4403	4303

Component values for the various amateur bands in which the field-strength meter will be used. Miller coils can be ordered by mail from J. W. Miller Co., 19070 Reyes Ave., P. O. Box 5825, Compton, CA 90224.

Rear view of the meter cabinet showing the calibration chart in dB. Ranges 1, 2 and 3 are discussed in the text.

used to provide a low-impedance connection point for the voltage doubler, CR1/CR2. Since the rectifier diodes would otherwise load down the tuned circuit and spoil the Q — assuming they were connected at the high-impedance end of L1 — the capacitive divider is employed. Because CR1 and CR2 provide a square-law response as rectifiers, the meter deflection (respective to changes in signal-input level) will be nonlinear. Addition of the 10,000-ohm resistor between CR2 and R1 helps to linearize the meter response, but it also reduces the sensitivity of the instrument somewhat. This design trade-off is acceptable for most amateur work.

Construction

It makes little difference what the size or shape of the enclosure is. It should be made of metal to prevent rf energy from entering the tuned circuit by any path than that of the pickup antenna. A 4-1/2-inch meter was used in the model shown here, primarily because it was at hand in the writer's "goodie cache." Physically smaller meters are quite acceptable, but the builder should use a 50-µA instrument if good sensitivity is desired. Large-format meters are more suitable for viewing from a distance, and with advancing age it is not uncommon for some of us to suffer the "tired-eyes syndrome," which can be offset considerably through the use of large meters! For far-field observations one can use a telescope or field glasses to read the meter scale.

Component wiring inside the instrument box can be of the builder's choosing, provided all rf leads are kept as short and direct as practical. Although metal knobs are shown in the photographs, they aren't necessarily the most ideal kind to use. Touching them will affect the meter readings markedly if the meter case is not connected to an earth ground. Plastic knobs are, therefore, recommended.

Calibration

A simple technique for obtaining calibration of M1 in dB is shown in the second diagram. D1 and D2 are used as rectifiers, but the tuned circuit of the first diagram is disconnected from them. T1, R2 and C4 are used temporarily to provide low-level 60-Hz voltage for calibrating the instrument. It is necessary to install C4 and C5 (electrolytic capacitors) for 60-Hz work. The capacitance values shown are suitable for low reactance at this frequency.

T1 and R2 are used in combination with a VOM or VTVM to supply and monitor 60-Hz energy between 0.1 and 1 volt. Midscale (25) on M1 represents zero dB. All readings below 25 are *minus* dB, and the readings above 25 are *plus* dB. Thus, midscale, or 25, is the reference point for all measurements. Meter calibration is effected at three settings of the sensitivity control, R1. This is done because the meter readings versus field strength in dB will vary somewhat as the ohmic value of R1 is changed. The greater the amount of resistance, the more linear the meter response.

During calibration, R2 is adjusted for midscale response of M1 at each of the settings of R1. Maximum sensitivity will occur when R1 is set at maximum resistance (position 1). Position 2 (moderate sensitivity) is established by using an ohmmeter to locate a position of the R1 arm that places 8000 ohms of resistance between the high end of R1 and M1. Position 3 (low sensitivity) is established when the arm of R1 is positioned to provide 16,000 ohms of resistance between the high end of R1 and M1.

Decibel reference points are found for the three preselected settings of the sensitivity control by varying the voltage to CR1 and CR2 by means of R2. In each in-

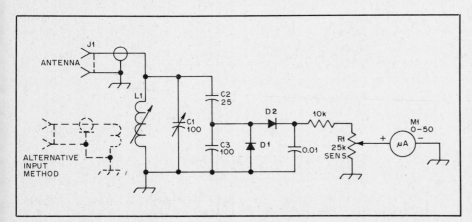

Schematic diagram of the simple field-strength meter. Fixed-value capacitors are disk ceramic unless otherwise noted. Fixed-value resistors are 1/2-W composition. C1 is a small 100-pF variable. D1 and D2 are 1N34A germanium diodes, or equivalents. J1 is an antenna connector of the builder's choice. L1, C2 and C3 are selected values (see Table 1). M1 is a 50-µA meter, and R1 is a 25,000-ohm, linear-taper composition control.

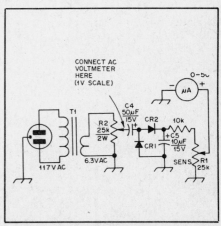

Schematic illustration of a suitable circuit for calibrating the instrument in dB (see text). T1 is a small 6.3-V filament transformer. C4 and C5 are electrolytic capacitors.

stance the value of ac voltage at *zero reference* is recorded. Then the setting of R2 is changed until the meter reading drops or increases to the next numbered point — 30, 35, 40 and so on, or 20, 15, 10 and downward. The change in dB for each change in meter reading can be computed by

$$dB = 20 \log \frac{E1}{E2}$$

where E2 = ac voltage at zero reference (25 on the meter scale), and E1 = the voltage above or below zero reference. Thus, if E1 was 0.9 volt, and E2 was 0.2 volt, the increase in dB would equal 13. Example

$$dB = \frac{0.9}{0.2} = 20 \times \log 4.5$$

$$= 20 \times 0.6532 = 13$$

which tells us that working in the opposite direction our answer would be in *minus* dB.

A rear-panel view of the author's instrument is shown photographically. If the first circuit is used, the calibration points visible in the picture will be valid for 50-μA meters. — *Doug DeMaw, W1FB*

A WHEATSTONE BRIDGE FOR ACCURACY

The Wheatstone bridge named for Sir Charles Wheatstone, a noted physicist of the mid-1800s, is a nearly indispensable instrument in most electrical and chemistry labs. In its most familiar form it is a simple bridge used for measuring resistance. Because of its accuracy and almost infinitesimal resolution, it can facilitate measurements far beyond the ability of most other resistance-measuring devices.

Shown in the illustration is the basic bridge circuit. In operation, when R1/R2 = R3/R4, the bridge is said to be balanced and no current will flow through the galvanometer. R1 represents the unknown resistance, R2 the known resistance, and R3 and R4 are variable resistances of predetermined and known values. These resistors are changed to vary

the range of the instrument. In the bridge circuit to be described, R4 remains constant at 10,000 ohms and R3 is varied in decade steps. R4 could be varied in decade steps if better resolution were desired at the high and low extremes, or if ranges above and below those given here were desired.

There are at least two disadvantages associated with most commercial bridges as far as the amateur is concerned. The low-resistance galvanometers normally employed require considerable loop current. Second is the expense. The commercial units are very costly considering the relatively low use they would get around the ham shack. In the inexpensive bridges that the author has used, R2 and R4 are replaced with a potentiometer, the wiper serving as the junction. This results in a wildly nonlinear scale. Dial calibration on a pseudo-log scale can compensate for this; however, with the tolerance normally available, the erratic linearity, and the poor reset accuracy of carbon potentiometers, the accuracy is no better than that of a good VOM. The application of ac to these instruments may render them useless for some measurements.

The Circuit

The bridge described here can be constructed for about $50 when employing

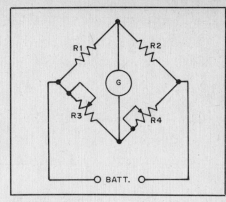

Basic Wheatstone bridge circuit.
R1/R2 = R3/4.
R1 — Unknown R.
R2 — Unknown R.
R3 — Variable R (known value).
R4 — Variable R (known value).

new parts. Accuracy should be better than 0.5 percent. By taking advantage of the surplus market, a comparable unit could be built for less than $20. Accuracy of better than 0.01 percent should be obtainable if a calibrated laboratory bridge is available for tailoring resistors. Multiturn potentiometers could be substituted for resistors R2, R3, R4, R5 and R6. Rule of thumb suggests that the standard should have an accuracy four

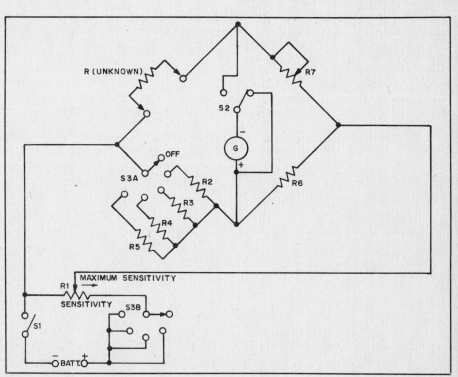

Shown here is the schematic diagram of the Wheatstone bridge. Battery information is given in the text.
M1 — See text.
R1 — Sensitivity potentiometer, 5000 ohms.
R2 — Precision resistor, 100 ohms, 1 percent or better.
R3 — Precision resistor, 1000 ohms, 1 percent or better.
R4 — Precision resistor, 10-k ohm, 1 percent or better.
R5 — Precision resistor, 1000-k ohm, 1 percent

or better.
R6 — Precision resistor, 10-k ohm, 1 percent or better.
R7 — Precision 10-turn potentiometer, 100-k ohm (see text).
S1 — Spst push-button switch, normally open.
S2 — Spdt push-button switch.
S3 — Rotary switch, 2 pole, 5 position, ceramic.

The Wheatstone bridge as assembled by the author. The large object mounted on the aluminum bracket is the precision potentiometer.

times that of the desired measurement. Thus, if the standard bridge has an accuracy of 0.001 percent, the measurement can be considered accurate at 0.004 percent. In this unit, the absolute accuracy of the 10- turn potentiometer (known element) is of less importance than the linearity. This potentiometer and the dial will probably be the most expensive components in the instrument.

In this bridge the known element (R7) is a Borg Model 205, which has a linearity accuracy of 0.1 percent. The battery is a nine-volt transistor-radio type. A 22-1/4-volt battery could be substituted to improve resolution at the high end of the R × 1000 scale. However, this bridge was designed primarily with a range of 10 ohms up to about half a megohm in mind. As stated previously, better resolution may also be obtained by switching in other decade resistors at R6. Do *not* substitute a supply with high current capability (more than a few mA). Current *must* be limited, as the known element is easily destroyed. One of the best ways to limit the current is through the internal resistance of the supply.

Construction

It is vitally necessary to avoid erratic contacts or resistances. Special attention must be paid to all soldered connections. The rotary switch should have silver- or gold-plated contacts and the push-button switches should be the snap-action type to avoid possible changes in contact resistance. On S-2 the normally closed contacts are used to short out the galvanometer and damp the meter movement when transporting. It is not necessary to run the conductors exactly as shown in the pictures. This does not represent the only way, or possibly even the best way, to wire the unit. The dial is an Amphenol Type 1350 which boasts an indexing accuracy of 1000:1. As the ultimate accuracy is a function of the dial and potentiometer combination, don't skimp.

The meter is a surplus 0- to 100-μA unit which was modified for zero-center use. This is a fairly simple operation and results in an excellent and inexpensive

galvanometer. In as nearly a dust-free environment as possible, remove the movement from the housing. Three screws around the case are usually all that hold it in. Sealed meters are not normally usable. Remove the meter face carefully, clean the back with solvent and spray paint it flat white. Apply suitable dial markings, spray with clear enamel, and replace the face on the movement. Displace the front and back spring levers an equal amount to bring the needle to center zero. Do this carefully as the meter adjustment screw is not normally usable after this operation. Linearity of the meter may not be exact, but this is not important as a center reading is all that is required. Commercially available meters may be used but are quite expensive especially for the better quality units. A flexible drive from the dial assembly to the potentiometer is a necessity. A dual flexible coupling was used in this meter. Calibration of the instrument is best performed with a laboratory bridge. However, quite accurate results may be obtained by using a number of 1 percent or better resistors and setting the dial to the mean readings on the various ranges. Keep in mind that even a 1-percent, 100-kΩ resistor may vary 1000 ohms either side of its 100-kΩ value. With off-the-shelf parts used in construction, and assuming a 0.5 percent accuracy, this could be as much as 1500 ohms each way. This looks good since most VOMs and VTVMs operate at approximately 5-percent accuracy.

The cabinet was constructed from 1/4-inch thick Masonite panels using epoxy resin and glue strips at the corners. This method worked well; however, a metal cabinet would be better.

Using the Instrument

A few uses for the bridge include measurement of meter-movement resistance (meters as sensitive as 25 μA have been measured with no damage to the movement), matching resistors, determining cable length, locating shorts, or tailoring resistors for meter repair or construction. In fact, it is useful anytime that it is necessary to measure resistance with a

high degree of accuracy.

In use, always start with the sensitivity control at minimum. With both buttons depressed, advance the sensitivity control until a meter reading is obtained. If polarities have been observed in constructing the instrument, turning the dial to the right will result in galvanometer deflection to the right and vice versa. Zero the needle and advance the sensitivity toward maximum and re-zero the galvanometer. The final reading should be found by alternately pressing PB-2 with PB-1 depressed and re-zeroing with the dial until no change is noted on the meter. Measure meter movements in the same manner, being careful not to "pin" either the meter under test or the galvanometer. This bridge, incidentally, is best used in a horizontal position to minimize any tendency of the meter to stick near zero. Carefully constructed, this instrument should be a valuable asset to any ham shack. — *Sidney Gilstrap*

READING CAPACITANCE WITH A VOM

Got a lot of mica and ceramic capacitors in your junkbox that you don't know what to do with? Wish you could read them so that you could complete that project that has been sitting on the shelf for the past year? Well, this is your lucky day — here is a simple circuit that will allow you to convert your VOM so that it reads capacitance, for only around $22 (probably less with a healthy junkbox!).

Circuit Theory

Everyone knows (even the Novice — right?) the relationship that says: capacitance times voltage = charge. If we keep this relationship in mind and use the basic measurement circuit shown, we see that our unknown capacitor C_x is charged through R1 and CR1 when the switch is open. When the switch is closed, the unknown capacitor is discharged through the switch, CR2, and the meter.

Now replace the switch, static-power supply, and R1 with a TTL-derived, square-wave generator. When the waveform is high, the capacitor C_x is charged to a value of approximately 3.5 volts and when low it discharges as before.

The frequency at which the generator

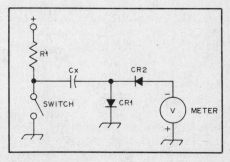

Basic capacitance-measuring circuit.

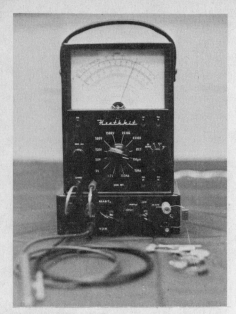

The capacitance checker is shown beneath the Heath VOM.

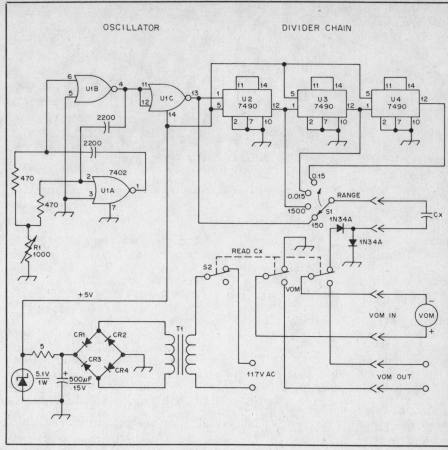

Schematic diagram of capacitance checker. Unless otherwise specified, resistors are 1/4-watt composition and capacitors are disk ceramic.
CR1-CR4, incl. — Mallory PTC 401 silicon-diode bridge rectifier.
R1 — Control, Mallory MLC13L.

T1 — Filament transformer, 6.3 V ac —Stancor P-6465 or equiv.).

runs determines the discharge current through the meter.

since $Q = C_x V$
$nQ = nC_x V$

but nQ = charge stored per second
$nQ = dQ/dt = i$ (average current)
$\therefore = i = nC_x V$

where: Q = charge supplied to C_x per pulse.
C_x = unknown capacitance
n = number of pulses per second (frequency of generator)

The most sensitive scale of my VOM is 150 μA (Heath MM-1) so the following calculation was made to determine the free-running frequency of the generator for 150 pF at full scale.

$n = i/C_x V$
$= 150 \times 10^{-6}/(150 \times 10^{-12})(3.5)$
$= 285$ kHz

Larger values of capacitance can be read by decreasing the frequency which is obtained digitally through decade division (7490s). The power supply is straightforward and many different types may be employed (batteries, LM335, μA723). The simple Zener circuit shown was used by the author with a total current drain of 90 mA.

Construction and Calibration

The instrument was built on a 1-3/4 × 3-1/2-inch single-sided, printed-circuit board and mounted into a 6 × 3-1/2 × 1-7/8-inch black plastic case. The physical layout is left to the builder since nothing is critical to actual circuit operation. The

Bottom view of the tester.

unit could use a higher frequency oscillator to extend its range down to lower capacitances and employ a self-contained meter. Example: A 50μA meter and a 571-kHz oscillator should give a 25-pF full-scale reading. Dream up your own variation!

The author calibrated his instrument by setting S1 to the 150-pF full-scale position and placing a 100-pF 1-percent silver-mica capacitor across the C_x terminals. The calibrate control was then adjusted for the capacitance value indicated. If no forward reading is obtainable, then check the 7402 oscillator for output either at pin 4, 11 or 13. The other scales are checked with cor-

responding larger capacitors. The function of S2 is to disable the power supply when using the VOM in normal operations. — *Kenneth H. Carcey, WØYOR*

USING BC RECEIVERS AS MAKESHIFT TEST GEAR

Not all of us are fortunate enough to own an rf signal generator for use in aligning and calibrating homebuilt receiving gear, but almost anyone can scare up a spare broadcast set. Here are several methods for using the bc receiver as a substitute.

To align the i-f section of a receiver which has a BFO for 456 kHz or 465 kHz, attach a couple of feet of antenna wire to the BFO and run it near the broadcast receiver. Tune the bc set to the second harmonic of the BFO (912 kHz or 930 kHz) and adjust the BFO until a beat note is heard. Finding frequencies in the broadcast band is simplified by the fact that the carriers are spaced at 10-kHz intervals through the band. The frequency of your local station is usually published with the daily program schedules, and other publications are available with listings of all stations. For a 456-kHz i-f, try to find a station on 910 kHz. The 2-kHz dif-

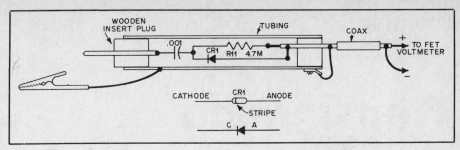
Details of the rf test probe.

ference beat note can be estimated, but make sure that the BFO harmonic is *higher* in frequency that the bc station. A slight tuning of the bc receiver dial will determine this. Then, without disturbing the ''antenna'' on the BFO, align the i-f amplifier by peaking it on noise, not on the signal. This method is accurate enough for any receiver except one which uses a crystal filter. The third harmonics of the 456 kHz and 465 kHz also fall within the broadcast band, and can be used, but they will not fall directly on any bc station frequency.

The spare bc set can also be used for band-edge calibration of another receiver. The hf oscillator in most bc sets can be tuned to 1000 kHz. In some instances it may be necessary to add a very small amount of tuning capacity to the oscillator circuit, but in most cases this can be done merely by screwing down the padding capacitor a couple of turns. Attach a couple of feet of wire to the oscillator tuning capacitor in the bc set and place one end of it near the receiver being calibrated. Tune the bc set to the low-frequency end of the tuning range so that the harmonic of the oscillator beats with WWV. Then, without disturbing the bc receiver or the temporary antenna, the communications receiver can be tuned to pick up harmonics of the bc set oscillator at 1000-kHz intervals through a large part of the spectrum. It should be possible to pick up this signal at 4 MHz, 7 MHz, 14 MHz and perhaps at higher frequencies.

If the exact i-f of the bc set is known, the hf oscillator may be used for approximate calibration of a receiver between the 1000-kHz points mentioned above. The oscillator frequency will usually be higher than the dial frequency by the i-f. Thus, if the bc set is tuned to a station at 700 kHz and the i-f is 465 kHz, the oscillator will be tuned to 1165 kHz. Harmonics of this frequency can be used to obtain addi-

tional calibration points. It should be remembered, however, that only when the ''generator'' can be tuned to beat the WWV or some other frequency standard, can the calibration points be considered as exact.

To determine the i-f of a receiver which has a broadcast band, tune the receiver to a bc station of known frequency near the low-frequency limit of the band. With a second bc set, tune higher in frequency until a beat note is heard. In my area we have bc stations at 850 kHz and 1300 kHz, just 6 kHz less than 456 kHz apart. The required 6-kHz beat note can be estimated, and a slight retuning of the second receiver will tell whether the i-f is 6 kHz higher or lower than 450 kHz. If the hf oscillator of the receiver being checked is *lower* in frequency than the mixer, the set being checked will have to be tuned to a station at the high-frequency end of the bc band while the auxiliary set will have to be tuned lower.

To determine an unknown i-f in sets which do not have broadcast band coverage, the same principles described above are used, with the receiver being checked tuned to any station of known frequency. Tune an auxiliary receiver with a calibrated dial until the oscillator of the first receiver is heard. The difference between the frequency of the known station and the dial reading of the second receiver is the approximate i-f of the first receiver. — *James B. Bamberg, W8OPX*

A USEFUL RF PROBE

An rf probe can be built for use with a voltmeter. It will be useful when determining relative rms values of rf voltage from 50 kHz to at least 148 MHz. It can be used with numerous commercial VTVMs to provide *accurate* rms voltage measurements, provided the voltmeter with which it is used has a 10-megohm input characteristic. The internal 4.7 megohm is chosen to change the peak rf voltage response of the probe to an rms value compatible with voltmeters which have the 10-megohm characteristic.

Signal tracing and relative rf voltage readings can be taken during circuit development or trouble-shooting. When used with a 10-megohm instrument, best accuracy will result when the waveform under test is a pure sine wave. Distorted waveforms will change the voltage readings significantly.

The probe is made from a short length of copper tubing (3/8 or 1/2 inch in diameter). Wooden end plugs are installed to fit snugly inside the tubing. The probe tip can be made from a small nail or a piece of brazing rod which has been sharpened to a point on one end. CR1 is an IN34A. An IN914A silicon diode is suitable also. — *Doug DeMaw, W1FB*

Chapter 3

Transmitting and Receiving Kinks

PLUS OR MINUS 600 KHz FOR THE HW-2021

To make my Heathkit HW-2021 2-meter hand-held transceiver more versatile I decided to modify the unit for either a plus or minus 600 kHz offset. The transceiver is supplied with a 600-kHz offset crystal (Y8 —10.1 MHz). There is no internal provision for a + 600-kHz crystal, other than removing Y8 and inserting a 11.3-MHz crystal,[1] which is not supplied as original equipment. The modification was accomplished for under $10 and within 90 minutes.

SW3 (offset switch) was removed and replaced by a double-pole, three-position, subminiature slide switch.[2] I cut 1/8 inch from each mounting ear on the new switch. In order for the switch to be inserted, 1/8 inch of plastic had to be removed from the inside flange of the mounting slot. Plastic also had to be removed from the external slot to allow for the extra position on the new SW3.

Locating a ground point on the printed-circuit board was the next step. The chosen point was the printed-circuit board mounting screw located behind the squelch control. A two-inch piece of wire was connected from this screw to one of the two pin sockets.[3] The schematic diagram illustrates the remaining connections to be made.

The 11.3-MHz crystal was then inserted in the two-pin sockets and the crystal and sockets were wrapped in electrical tape and laid over the grounding screw. Because there was insufficient room available to mount the crystal on the pc board, it had to be positioned in this manner.

When SW3 is wired properly, the lower position is for the —600-kHz offset, the center position for simplex and the upper position for + 600 kHz offset. Amateurs who plan to make a similar modification should remember to order local-oscillator crystals cut for the receive frequency, whether for 146- or 147-MHz repeater operation. — *William C. Boyer, WA3YOX*

[1]The 11.3 MHz crystal may be ordered from the International Crystal Manufacturing Co., Inc., 10 North Lee, Oklahoma City, OK 73102.
[2]SW3 is a double-pole, three-position, subminiature slide switch available from Circuit Specialists Co., Box 3047, Scottsdale, AZ 85257. Catalog no. 1239.

[3]The two pin sockets for the crystal are available from the Heath Company, Benton Harbor, MI 49022. Part no. 432-878.

CHANGES FOR THE WILSON 1402SM

A useful improvement for the Wilson 1402SM hand-held transceiver is to replace the type F antenna connector with a BNC connector, which may be installed very easily. Only three connections need to be lifted; the inner conductor, the outer conductor and a ground strap. Be careful not to melt the dielectric of the coaxial cable!

Another change I made was to move the internal microphone from the bottom of the case to the upper right-hand corner of the speaker grille. A convenient hole is provided as well as a little insulating block. A square of black tape covered the hole at the bottom.

Because the Wilson manual did not describe the pin configuration for the new round microphone connector, I turned to WA9FRC for assistance. He explained that looking from the top, the pin connections are identified as: no. 1, microphone; no. 2, speaker; no. 3, PTT lead; no. 4, ground; no. 5, + 12 V and no. 6, n.c. — *Peter Wang, WB9PLI*

HERRINGBONE PATTERN FROM SB-303

In performing TVI checks while using my Heathkit SB-303/SB-401 combination, it was observed that a herringbone pattern would appear on the channel 8 picture whenever the equipment was set for 20 meters. Further checking indicated that the SB-401 was not the source of the interference but rather the problem originated in the SB-303. Evidence of the harmonic would disappear when the HFO cable was removed from the '303.

I presumed that the undesired harmonic signal was the eighth multiple of the 22.895-MHz crystal oscillator, although

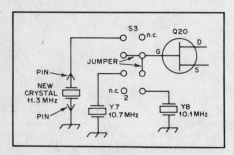

An additional crystal provides + or — 600 kHz offset for the HW-2021 transceiver.

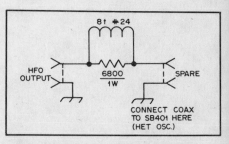

A harmonic suppressor for SB-303/SB-401 eliminates TVI.

the second harmonic would fall squarely on the 45.790-MHz i-f of the TV set.

An effective attenuation of the harmonic signal was achieved by connecting a 6800-ohm, 1-watt resistor wrapped with eight turns of No. 24 wire from the SB-303 HFO connector to a nearby spare connector. Also, enclosing this trap in a small Minibox inserted between the HFO connector and the coaxial line to the SB-401 is helpful. Although it would be expected that the HFO output would be somewhat reduced, there is still adequate excitation for the SB-401 to reach full output on all bands. — *John W. Hartung, W7THY*

IMPROVED RECOVERY FOR HEATH TRANSCEIVER AND A MODIFICATION FOR THE SB-200 LINEAR AMPLIFIER

The popular Heathkit transceivers (HW-100, HW-101, SB-100, SB-101 or SB-102) and the SB-200 kW linear-amplifier combination are used by many amateurs on phone and cw. Some have found that recovery in the receiving section of the transceivers is slow after a long transmission. This seems more prevalent when operating on cw and on the higher frequency bands where the MIC/CW control must be advanced for adequate drive. The transceiver S-meter in some instances shows extremely "Scotch" readings, particularly on 10 and 15 meters where an S5 signal may not move the S-meter. The SB-200 linear amplifier tends to overheat

on cw because of the greater duty cycle as compared with ssb operation. This causes the 572Bs to go soft, which require frequent replacement.

My solution for each of these problems is relatively simple. The receiver recovery problem is caused by V2, the 6AU6 isolation amplifier. When transmitting, this amplifier couples the output of the balanced modulator to the crystal filter input. In the receive mode it is still coupled to the filter, but no input is fed to the tube while the grid is at a high impedance with respect to ground.

The modified circuit shows the grid-bias lead of V2 connected to V3 permanently instead of only during the transmitting periods. This places a negative avc grid bias on V2 when the transceiver is in the receive mode. The effect of this is to cut off V2 immediately upon returning to the receive mode, thereby eliminating the slow receiver recovery phenomenon. V2 is not used in the receive mode. Therefore, there is no disadvantage in having it cut off.

To implement the change, the alc line is disconnected from R22 (1 megohm) on the circuit board near V2. The lead is taped and stowed. A new wire is then soldered to R22. This new lead is routed through the chassis-wall grommets, past the crystal filter, and is connected to R102 (100 kilohms). There, the alc line connects to the circuit board near V3. The wire need not be shielded.

The S-meter problem is quickly solved by removing the S-meter shunt, R115. No replacement seemed necessary in the case

of the HW-100, with signal readings increasing approximately three S units on the high bands after removing the shunt. If, however, the meter seems too generous for some individuals, various shunt values can be tried until a satisfactory level is reached. This modification will also cause alc readings to increase during the transmit mode, giving a better indication of modulation peaks.

Improved cw operation of the SB-200 linear can be obtained by reducing the "key-up" plate current to zero (Class B operation instead of Class AB). The modification will substantially increase tube life, increase the amplifier output somewhat and reduce "key-up" idling power from about 200 watts to zero. It can be accomplished by inserting a 250-ohm, 10-watt resistor in series with the antenna-relay lead. The resistor may be mounted externally or internally. A switch to short out the 250-ohm resistor for ssb work will facilitate moving from phone to cw and vice versa.

By adding the 250-ohm resistor, the grid-bias voltage is increased. It normally is taken across a 33-ohm resistor. Fortunately, the resulting reduced current is still adequate for operating the antenna relay that is in series with the negative grid-bias supply output.

Owners of the HW-100 are referred to past issues of *CQ* magazine[1,2] for additional modifications on that particular transceiver. In addition, Heath has provided a kit which compensates for Miller-effect detuning of their transceivers.[3] Heath also recommends retuning transformer T1 for maximum output obtainable. The slug should be adjusted at the top of the coil instead of the bottom, providing a more balanced modulator output on all bands. — *John Abbott, K6YB*

[1] Kirsch, "The 2 & 2 Dial for the HW-100," *CQ*, March, 1969.
[2] Abbott, "Variable A.F. Bandwidth for the HW-100," *CQ*, June, 1970.
[3] Modification Kit Model SBM-102-1, The Heath Company, Benton Harbor, MI 49022.

ONE FOR THE HALLICRAFTERS SR-400A

My Hallicrafters SR-400A transceiver developed a malady that was disconcerting. After 30 to 45 minutes of operation, the rf output would drop to about 30 watts PEP (depending upon the band and frequency). Efforts to retune the final amplifier produced no improvement. Could there by an alignment problem? Fortunately, the solution was simple. I discovered that the heterodyne oscillator, V12, was not firmly seated in the tube socket. Removing and reinserting it in the socket cleared the problem. Power output was restored to normal. — *John F. Marthens, WA7YRQ*

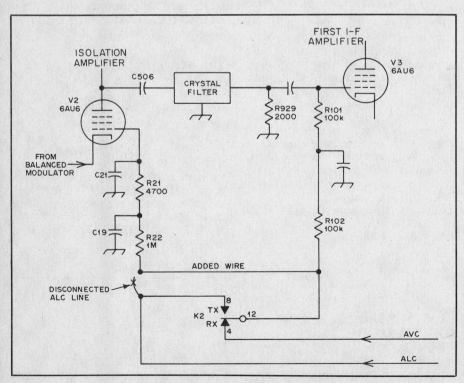

A circuit modification for improving receiver recovery in Heath transceivers.

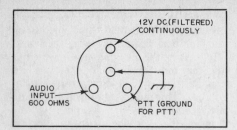

The Kenwood TR-7400A Touch-Tone-pad socket connections as seen from the transceiver exterior.

AN UPDATE ON THE KENWOOD TR-7400A TRANSCEIVER

The latest modification to the Kenwood TR-7400A 2-meter fm transceiver is a replacement of the Touch-Tone-pad input jack. The old miniature phone jack provided for audio input and ground only. The new jack is a DIN type wired for audio input, 9-V dc on transmit only, and ground. While this is an improvement, there are still two main drawbacks. The 9-V dc is supplied only on transmit. Touch-Tone-pads with built-in PTT line keying circuits do not work with this set because no power is applied. The other problem is that there is no PTT line connection at the jack (apparently an oversight in manufacturing).

These problems may be resolved by making the following changes. Locate the gray wire from the TT pad socket to the tie bar near C64. This gray wire is the B+ lead. Remove the wire from the tie bar, feed it through the chassis and connect it to pin 6 of RL1. This provides 12-V dc continuously at the TT pad socket. Complete the change by connecting a wire from the unused pin on the TT pad socket to pin 8 of RL1. This is the PTT line which functions when grounded. — *Murray Lampert, VE3FXA*

MARKING THE NOVICE BANDS

As a holder of a Technician-class license, I'm a newcomer to the low bands. Since I'm restricted to the Novice subbands, I have found that I was constantly referring back and forth between my VFO dial, receiver dial, and frequency chart to make sure my operation was legal. The solution to this inconvenience was to mark the Novice subbands right on the dials. Doing that neatly was difficult.

I then discovered a transparent graphics tape, manufactured by Chart Pak and others, in an art supply store. The tape is available in many colors and widths at a cost of about $1.30 for 24 feet. It enabled me to mark the Novice ranges on the dials with 1/8-inch wide tape of suitable length. Amateurs with more privileges could use other colors to identify their band segments such as cw, phone and Extra.

With backlit translucent dials, the Novice subbands show up quite easily with original frequency numbering still

readable. The tape can be removed without harm to the set whenever my license is upgraded or I decide to sell the equipment. Builders might like to know that glossy, matt and metallic tapes are also available: They may be used to give that final professional trim to homemade equipment. — *Gary Wilson, WB2BOO*

REDUCING HUM IN THE HW-7

The hum problem encountered by many amateurs using the Heathkit HW-7 powered by an ac-operated supply can in some instances be eliminated by simply bypassing the primary leads of the power transformer to chassis ground with two 0.001-μF capacitors. This may avoid the need for an external ground* which some operators say is a "must." After this simple modification my HW-7 sounded as though it were running on battery power. — *Lee M. Clark, WB4SYC*

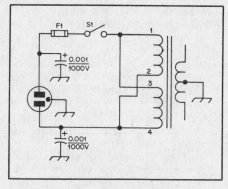

Connecting 0.001-μF capacitors across the 117-V ac line eliminates hum in the HW-7.

After trying every possible way I could think of, I still was unable to rid my HW-7 of a terrible hum, particularly when operating on the 40-meter band. Considered were such ideas as adding more filter capacitors to the power supply or using batteries permanently!

While moving the equipment around in the shack, a different ac outlet was used. The hum disappeared. After checking the old outlet, I found that the ground lead was broken inside the wall! In summary, be sure the ac outlet to be used for the HW-7 power supply has a three-conductor receptacle on which the ground terminal is effectively grounded.* — *Bruce Ault, WA4UVG*

*[Editor's Note: It is a matter of good practice to have an earth ground connected to the chassis of the HW-7.]

USING THE SB-650 FREQUENCY COUNTER ON THE DRAKE R-4A/B/C

To use the Heath SB-650 frequency counter with a Drake R-4A, R-4B or R-4C, simply apply the injection frequen-

cy from the Drake receiver directly into the HFO input of the SB-650. Also apply a 5645-kHz signal to the LMO input of the SB-650. This signal can be derived from an rf signal generator or an oscillator constructed for that purpose. The 5645-kHz signal must be very accurate.

Such an arrangement may be used with many receivers. If, for instance, the local oscillator is 455 kHz above the incoming frequency, build a 455-kHz oscillator. I used such an approach to update an SX-101. If one remembers that the counter will display the difference between the HFO, LMO and BFO inputs, other systems can be designed. — *Nenad Downing, WB4SLO*

FREQUENCY STANDARD FOR 2-METER FM

A simple synthesized frequency standard for 2-meter fm (and possibly ssb use) is available to those amateurs who have a GLB model 400-B Channelizer, or have access to this unit. I have found that the Channelizer is rich in harmonics well into the 2-meter region. In my application, the GLB and discriminator meter are tied into an IC-22A through a single socket in the back of the rig. I disconnect the PTT line between the Channelizer and the IC22A. 12-V dc is then applied to the transceiver and Channelizer, followed by dialing the desired frequency. The PTT line must not be connected to the transceiver during this operation: By doing so, the transmitter will be activated when grounded at the synthesizer. The GLB 400-B provides a full-quieting signal when placed near the transceiver. This makes a handy means for frequency checking and spotting. — *Daniel L. Steinhoff, WA7UPP*

THE WATTSIT

Almost every amateur is interested in knowing the line voltage in his shack. The "Wattsit" will tell the story. The diagram shows the simple series circuit consisting of a diode, resistor and a recording level meter. The resistor value should be such that the indicator of the meter rests on a red mark on the meter face when the applied voltage is 120 V. A VTVM is required to measure the line voltage while choosing the proper resistor value. — *Wade Rogers, W4EN and Bill Richards, WB4WYG*

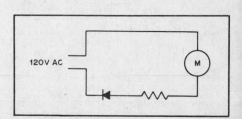

A simple line-voltage indicator circuit.

REPLACEMENT FOR TRANSCEIVER CONTROL BELTS

After much use the plastic or rubber belts in many transceivers may become brittle and come apart. I found an ordinary piece of insulating spaghetti threaded around the pulleys and then tied into a knot makes a satisfactory replacement in many cases. The spaghetti should be pulled tight when making the knot. Trim any loose ends. There will be some give as the spaghetti warms but for most plate and loading controls the backlash is not troublesome. In six months of use the replacement has served the purpose well. — *Joseph Gregor, WA3WRN*

A SIMPLE MODULATOR FOR THE ARRL 10-WATT TRANSMITTER

A young man in my neighborhood has visited my station many times and apparently was bitten by the "ham bug." He passed his Novice examination and then the General. On another visit he asked if I had a circuit for a low-power transmitter. Knowing that I had an over-flowing junk box, we decided to build the small 10-watt cw transmitter described in a recent edition of *The Radio Amateur's Handbook*. I thought it would be fun to add a modulator to this little transmitter.

In my collection of miscellany was this circuit, but I must admit that I do not know to whom I should give credit for the design. Scrounging again in the parts box brought forth a Stancor A-2871 modulation transformer, well suited for this purpose. A small chassis would serve for mounting the rf section and the modulator. We wound plug-in coils and even found an illuminated milliammeter . . . talk about class! The power supply used an old Elmac M-1070, which provided the 250- to 300-V dc needed. Since the power unit was designed for a 12-V filament circuit, we simply connected the two 6T9 tubes in series.

We finished the project with enthusiasm, delighted with the beautiful, crispy clear audio produced by this two-tube modulator. In our opinion, this would make a dandy beginning project for any club helping people just starting in our wonderful hobby. — *Harry E. Stewart, W8PSV*

A CONNECTOR FOR THE KW-1000

Amateurs who have the KW Electronics KW-1000 linear amplifier may have experienced difficulty with the two female pins which connect the T-R relay to the transceiver VOX relay. A solution to this annoying situation is to use a five-pin plug such as the ones found on eight-track tape players. Drill out three pins, leaving the two wide-spaced pins, nos. 3 and 4. The modified plug fits the receptacle perfectly. — *Ron Pierce, WB0EFG*

GETTING YOUR FOOT INTO THE ACT

There is no need to fret over someone asking you to send next with your left foot when using this idea! This one is for cw operators and comes from an old-timer. Send-receive switching is facilitated by using a foot switch.

For receiving, the foot switch is open. This releases a relay which controls the screen voltage of the buffer amplifier. With differential keying the oscillator is off when the key is open. To spot a frequency, simply operate the key and tune the VFO to zero beat by means of the receiver BFO. Use appropriate bypassing of the screen leads to reduce rf leakage.

To transmit, the foot switch is actuated, closing the screen relay. The rig is ready to be keyed normally. The operation is so simple and useful that I am surprised transmitter manufacturers have never incorporated this idea in their equipment. — *George Seyffert, K4IG, ex-4CA, ex-W3CD*

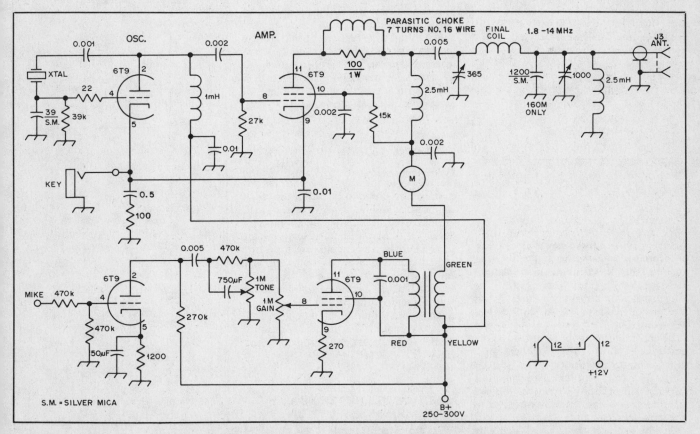

Circuit for a modulator to be added to the 6T9 transmitter described in *The Radio Amateur's Handbook* for 1972. Coil information for the separate coils used in the final amplifier: 160 meters — 48 turns No. 24, 32 turns-per-inch, 1 inch dia. (B&W Miniductor 3016). 80 meters — 43 turns No. 20, 16 turns-per-inch, 3/4 inch dia. (B&W Miniductor 3011). 40 meters — 30 turns No. 20, 16 turns-per-inch, 3/4 inch dia. (B&W Miniductor 3011). 20 meters — 19 turns No. 18, 8 turns-per-inch, 3/4 inch dia. (B&W Miniductor 3010).

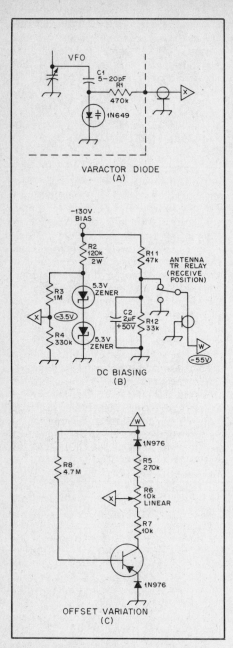

Offset tuning is provided for the HW-101 with these circuit modifications.

SOLUTION TO KEY CLICKS

My HW-101 produced key clicks 15 kHz up from the transmitting frequency after making the offset-tuning modifications described in *QST* for March, 1975. The offset-switching transistor apparently was turning on momentarily as the key was released. The fact that I used a pnp HEP-52 from the junk box instead of the prescribed 2N2907A may have had some bearing on the problem.

I solved the matter by keying the offset tuning through the T-R relay, and instead of using the cw-keying line to supply dc to the varactor, I used the —130 V bias circuit. This provided the required —55 V by means of a voltage divider.

To obtain more or less offset tuning range, C1 may be varied as needed. C2

was added to eliminate the ripple that affected the VFO. Increasing the values of R11 and R12 from those shown would reduce the current drain on the —130 V supply. Except for these changes, all other components are the same as those specified in the original article by W6KVD. For ssb operation, the new circuit has the added benefit of providing offset tuning — desirable for use at a net control station. — *Jim Themig, WA0MSI*

WWV ON THE DRAKE R-4C

An extra crystal is not needed to receive the 5-MHz signals from WWV on the Drake R-4C. Tune to 3632.5 kHz. Detune the preselector to the 40-meter band. Reception is adequate for most purposes. By placing the function switch in the calibrate position, the calibration oscillator may be accurately set to zero-beat with WWV. The mode switch should be in the a-m position. — *Lou Phillips, K9SPD*

ERRATIC EQUIPMENT PERFORMANCE

All of the tubes in tube-type or hybrid equipment should be removed from tube sockets periodically to clean any possible corrosion build-up that may occur on tube pins or socket contacts. This should be of particular interest to radio amateurs or any user of tube-type electronic devices located in areas of high humidity, such as seacoasts or islands. This corrosion build-up acts as a partial insulator and may cause erratic functioning or failure of equipment. — *John Marthens, WA7YRQ*

REDUCING MUFFIN-FAN NOISE

While an extra 24-watt muffin fan mounted on the back of transmitting equipment is useful in extending the life of components and reducing VFO heat drift, the air turbulence created by the fan produces noise. My method of lowering the noise factor defies engineering principles of limits for synchronous-motor slippage and starting torque, but it works. A 40-watt bulb connected in series with the muffin fan does the trick. The series bulb arrangement should be used only on added fans — not on fans originally installed in the equipment. — *A. H. "Ted" Heavens, VE7CHE*

MORE ON THE DRAKE TR-4 OUTBOARD MODIFICATION

When I decided to try the TR-4 outboard receiver modification described by Dr. J.R. Sheller, WA8ZDF, in the February, 1977, issue of *QST*, I found, unhappily,

that my TR-4 had only one set of contacts on the antenna-changeover relay, K1. In Dr. Sheller's modification the extra set of contacts operate the receiver mute function by breaking the dc path to ground via RFC7.

An alternative to the approach used by Dr. Sheller may be easily accomplished in 15 minutes by following this two-step conversion. First, the coaxial cable that is connected to T9 should be removed from S4 (TCVR-RCVR). Insert a 0.001-µF ceramic capacitor in series with the switch and cable. This provides dc isolation from ground for the RCVR muting jack via T9.

Next, solder a jumper across all three contacts of the spdt switch, S4, rendering it nonfunctional. This parallels the TR-4 receiver and the outboard receiver inputs. At the same time the receiver mute feature is allowed to function normally. Neither of these steps require any harmful drilling or physical changes that could spoil the appearance of the TR-4. Restoration of the circuit requires another 15 minutes at resale time. — *William P. Winter, Jr., WB8JCQ/LU1AKO*

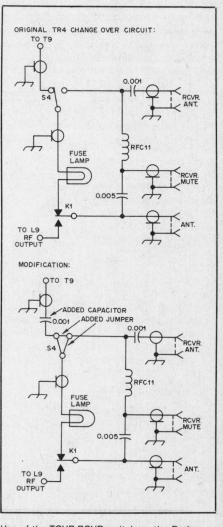

Use of the TCVR-RCVR switch on the Drake TR-4C is eliminated by means of the modification shown here, a helpful change when operating with an outboard receiver.

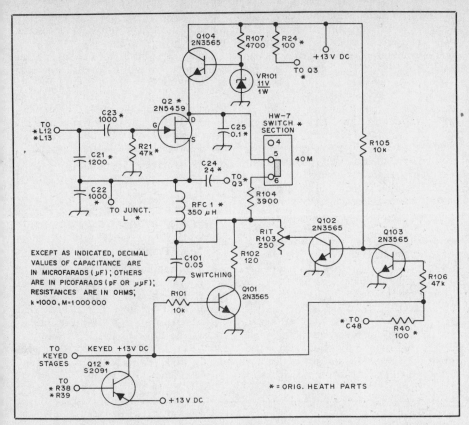

Schematic diagram of the modified section of the HW-7 where incremental tuning has been added. Numbered components not appearing in this caption are so identified for text discussion purposes only. New fixed-value resistors are 1/4-W composition or larger. R103 is a 250-ohm, linear-taper, miniature control, Allen Bradley no. WA2G056S251UA used by author. C101 is a disk ceramic. Components not bearing an asterisk are new parts required for the modification.

RIT FOR THE HW-7

This article describes a receiver incremental-tuning (RIT) that can be incorporated in the HW-7 for only a few dollars. It will allow the receiver to be tuned independently several kHz either side of the transmitter frequency.

The original design of the HW-7 included no circuit to offset the transmitting and receiving frequencies from each other. Instead, Heath depended on the change in loading of the subsequent stages to pull the VFO frequency between key-up and key-down conditions. In the author's transceiver, which uses a regulated power supply, the offsets were measured as 20 Hz on 40 meters, 600 Hz on 20, and 400 Hz on 15. An offset of 400 to 1000 Hz provides suitable copy with the HW-7.

The Circuit

The HW-7 VFO uses a JFET (Q2) in a Colpitts oscillator circuit. The frequency of the oscillator can be shifted by varying the bias voltage across the gate junction of the JFET. As the bias is decreased, the capacitance of the junction increases, thereby lowering the frequency of the oscillator. A bias change of 1 volt will produce a frequency shift of 1.5 kHz on 40 meters, and more on the higher bands. To obtain the bias, a resistor is inserted in the source lead of the JFET oscillator, Q2.

During key-down periods a fixed-value 120-ohm resistor is used, and during the key-up condition a 250-ohm potentiometer serves the purpose. These resistors are switched in and out by means of transistors Q101 and Q102. Both transistors are saturated and have a voltage drop across them of less than 0.1 volt. Transistor switch Q101 is driven directly from the keyed 13-volt line. Q103 inverts the signal of the keyed line to drive switch Q102. As a consequence, either Q101 or Q102 is always conducting. (An earlier version of this circuit used a second relay in parallel with the transmit/receive one to do the switching, but it was discarded because of its higher current drain.)

On 40 meters the potentiometer cannot provide a sufficiently wide frequency swing. To increase the bias available on this band, additional current is fed through the potentiometer by connecting a 3900-ohm resistor from the positive supply to the cold side of RFC1. Since these modifications make the VFO more sensitive to supply voltage changes, the drain of the oscillator, Q2, is regulated at 10 volts by using Q104 and VR101 in an emitter-follower voltage regulator. This circuit was chosen because its current drain is lower than when using a Zener diode alone. The regulated voltage at the emitter of Q104 will be 0.6 volt less than the Zener-diode voltage because of the base-emitter voltage drop.

The switching circuit is built on a small piece of Vectorbord and mounted on the side of the chassis. The transistors used are not critical of specifications, but they should be npn silicon types with beta greater than 100, and a breakdown voltage greater than 15. When lifting the ground end of RFC1, drill a small hole in the circuit board just beyond the ground pad and run the wire from RFC1 through it. Connect bypass capacitor C101 directly to ground at this point. The rest of the circuit operates at dc and can be wired in whatever neat manner the user desires. The 250-ohm potentiometer is mounted in the screw hole that originally held the left side of the front panel in place. The emitter-follower voltage regulator is constructed on the main circuit board in the space formerly occupied by R25.

Operation

By listening to the HW-7 VFO output with an additional receiver, the RIT control can be adjusted so that zero beat is obtained under both key-up and key-down conditions. This position can be marked on the front panel for each band. When receiving a signal, adjust the HW-7 main tuning for a zero beat while the RIT control is set at its marked position for that band. Then, turn the RIT control for best copy. Answering a CQ on the same frequency can do wonders for increasing the number of stations responding to you, especially while operating QRP!

This circuit provides a maximum frequency shift of 1.4 kHz on 40 meters, 2.4 kHz on 20, and 3.4 kHz on 15. Tuning with the RIT is easier than with the main tuning dial. On-the-air tests indicate that this circuit doesn't cause any chirp on the HW-7 signal.

The modification described here, along with some of those of previous articles, make the HW-7 into a more versatile performer. The author's unit has operated admirably under extreme conditions, from the top of 14,000-foot peaks in the Sierra Nevadas, and in the depths of the Grand Canyon. If anyone can modify the HW-7 for operation on 80 meters, I'd sure like to hear about it. — *John Grebenkemper, WA6BVA*

1-WATT MODIFICATION FOR THE CLEGG FM-27B

Here is a $3 modification for the Clegg FM-27B that avoids wasted rf or excessive TVI when the unit is operated in the 1-watt position. Furthermore, there is still plenty of power in the 25-watt position.

Remove the RG174/U coaxial cable between the pc board and the power amplifier assembly. Drill a hole for a miniature dpdt toggle switch on the back plate beside the SO-239 receptacle. Solder a 1000-ohm, five-percent, 1/2-watt resistor across one end of the switch. Short the terminals on the other end of the switch. Install a new length of RG174/U to the center terminals of the dpdt switch from the pc board drive stage. Then use a new length of RG174/U to connect the switch terminals (shunted by the resistor) with the power amplifier. This replaces the RG174/U which was removed. The coaxial line braid should be grounded to the chassis at both ends. — *Ted Lucas, K3TNH*

THE GTX-200 AND INTERMODULATION

When I tried to make a few contacts in a June VHF QSO party using the GTX-200, I found that the front end was being rattled by the strong local signals to the point where we were losing contacts. The installation of a 22-element beam at 50 feet didn't help this problem. Obviously, something had to be done to relieve the problem.

In looking at the circuit, I noted that Genave built the rig with no rf stage. The bandpass filter and bipolar first mixer were not quite enough for the average ham operator, so Genave added a preamp using an MPF102. This does reduce the noise figure, but it adds enough gain that the first mixer overloads with carriers away from the tuned frequency. I have a great respect for the higher inherent dynamic range of FETs so I decided it would take very little effort to try one in the Genave. I did not want to have to perform major surgery, however.

What resulted is shown in the accompanying diagram. The only thing that requires a little care is the correct CBE to DGS placement in going from the transistor to the FET; they are not always arranged in the same sequence. The manual has a rather complicated procedure for aligning the bandpass filter between the preamp and the mixer. I found that it was much easier to peak C101 at 146.0, C102 at 146.94 and C103 at 147.9. This has to be repeated several times, but most people don't have access to the equipment called for in the manual. I did not notice any change when I tried moving the oscillator coupling capacitor, C107, to the top of the receiver oscillator tank. No L designation was given for this coil.

I am pleased with the change. I can detect no difference on overall sensitivity and have not been able to hear any of the intermodulation which was so prevalent before the change was made. The simplicity and the benefits derived from this change should make it good reading for fellow owners of the Genave GTX-200. — *Richard Frey, W1FCC/3*

IMPROVING VOX RELAY RESPONSE DURING CW OPERATION OF THE HEATH HW-101 TRANSCEIVER

When attempting to key the HW-101 at speeds over 20 wpm, the VOX relay will not actuate quickly enough, causing the loss of the first dit sent. Replacing R328, a 470-kΩ resistor, with a 330-kΩ resistor increases the drive to the VOX amplifier tube, V17A. V17A is turned on sooner, and the VOX relay is actuated more rapidly. — *Ed Solov, WA2DIW*

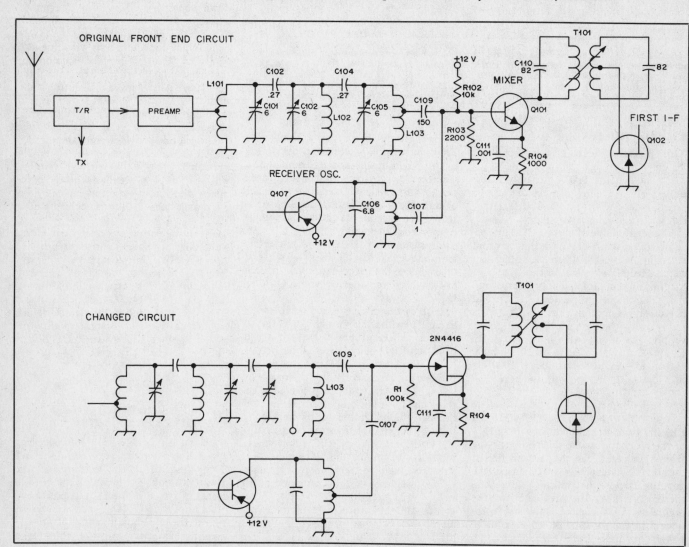

No major surgery is required for this simple modification of the Genave GTX-200. It effectively reduces intermodulation.

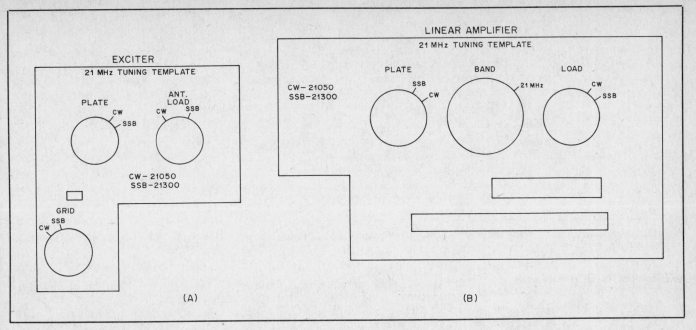

These templates make frequency changes quick and easy. An exciter template is at the left and at the right is a template for a linear amplifier.

TEMPLATES FOR QUICK TUNING

The problem of changing transmitting frequencies from high- to low-frequency portions of a band, or from phone to cw, has been a chore to me because I have a separate receiver and transmitter. Both are transceivers and tune quite sharply. To simplify frequency changes without the need to consult a table of dial settings, I devised a set of tuning templates for my transmitter and linear amplifier.

I made templates for each amateur band, using manila file folders for material. Two or more settings are indicated for each band, the markings being made after careful and precise tune-up. It is then an easy matter of placing the templates against the front panels and in seconds setting the transmitter and linear-amplifier dials.

This system for quick retuning can be used with almost any make of transmitter, amplifier or transceiver. The time and effort expended in making a set of templates will pay off in the satisfaction experienced in rapid band changes. — *David J. Gaeda, Sr., W8RI*

HW-101 MODIFICATION UPDATE

Several hams have reported to me after making the offset tuning and keying modifications described in March, 1975 *QST*, that their transmitters had key clicks when operated in the offset mode. Although I was not aware of the problem, a close inspection of my transmitted signal revealed that I had key clicks also. The following changes were made to correct this problem. Connect a one-megohm resistor from the base of Q1 to ground. Prepare two silicon diodes by connecting them in parallel, with the anode of one

diode connected to the cathode of the other. The back-to-back diodes should be connected between the wiper arm of R6 and the offset switch, S1. — *Glen Carlson, W6KVD*

SIMPLIFIED OUTPUT METERING PROTECTS QRP TRANSMITTERS

After destroying a few transistors while tuning QRP transistors into a mismatched load, I decided I needed some way to indicate proper transmitter adjustment, and then protect the rig while the antenna tuner was adjusted. An adaptation of the simple resistive SWR bridge described in the ARRL *Handbook* provides me with a dummy load, relative power-output indicator and a safe method of tuning the transmitter.

As shown in the schematic diagram, the input divider (R1-R4) has a total

resistance of 50 ohms. Four 1/2-watt composition resistors safely dissipate the output of my transmitter when S1 is in the TUNE position. Meter M1 indicates relative power applied to this load. The antenna is connected (through a Transmatch) and the antenna tuner is adjusted for minimum deflection on S1, or lowest SWR. R5 acts as an attenuator and effectively isolates the transmitter from the antenna, preventing possible damage to the output transistor of the rig. When the SWR has been reduced to its minimum, S1 is placed in the OPERATE position. M1 now indicates relative power output into the antenna. CR1 may be any germanium signal diode; C1 is either a ceramic-disc or silver-mica capacitor. S1 should be a ceramic rotary switch (dpdt), although a phenolic rotary switch or a slide switch is adequate for use on the 80-meter band — *Albert S. Woodhull, W1GSJ*

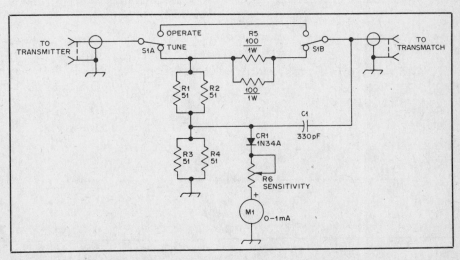

Protective circuit for QRP transmitters.

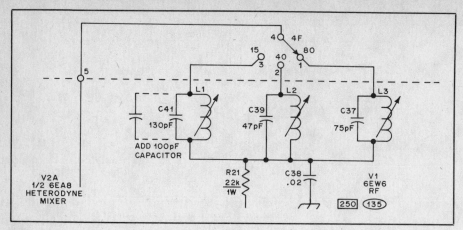

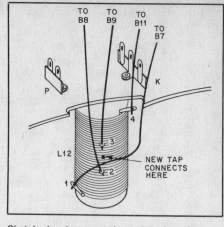

Partial schematic diagram of the HW-16 showing the addition of a 100-pF capacitor across the rf-stage plate-tuning coil.

Sketch showing approximate location of the 20-meter tap on L12.

MODIFYING THE HW-16 FOR 20 METERS

The HW-16 transceiver performed admirably on the 40- and 80-meter bands despite the European broadcast interference. There never seemed to be much activity on the 15-meter band at times when I could operate. As a result, the instruction manual was inspected to see how difficult it would be to convert the transceiver for 20-meter operation. Surprisingly, it was a simple operation, requiring one new crystal and two capacitors along with an easy alignment procedure. The following steps explain the conversion.

Simple arithmetic and reference to the circuit description (pages 54-56 in the HW-16 manual) show that substitution of a 19.545-MHz crystal for the 26.545-MHz crystal will put the 6EA8 heterodyne oscillator on the correct frequency for 20-meter receiver coverage. Remove the chassis bottom plate and the top cover. Unsolder the ground wire from the top of the 26.545-MHz crystal and push the wire aside temporarily. From underneath the

chassis, carefully unsolder the crystal pin connections while pulling on the crystal from the top side of the board. Replace the old crystal with the 19.545-MHz unit. Resolder the pins and the ground wire on top of the crystal.

Power was applied to the HW-16, and weak 20-meter signals were received. A check of the L1 and C41 resonant frequency showed that the circuit tuned from 17 to 25 MHz. A 100-pF mica capacitor was soldered across L1. The circuit now tunes from 12 to 19 MHz. Refer to the receiver alignment instructions on pages 42 and 43 in the instruction manual. Perform the 21-MHz alignment procedure, bearing in mind that you are actually aligning the receiver for 20-meter operation. Remember that the transceiver now tunes from 14.0 to 14.250 when the band switch is placed in the 15-meter position. At this point the received signals will be somewhat weak. This is because the transmitter pi-network output circuit serves also as the receiver antenna circuit, which has not been adjusted for 20-meter operation thus far.

Transmitter modification involves changing the tap on L12. Unsolder the four wires which connect to L12, remembering where each of them was connected. Unscrew the two 6-32 hex nuts which secure the coil to the chassis, set the nuts and lock washers aside, and remove the coil. The 15-meter tap is located 7 turns from the bottom of the coil (chassis end). Use a pair of pliers to remove the loop that forms this tap. From the bottom of the coil, count up 11 turns (half way between the 15- and 40-meter taps) and grip the wire at this new position with a pair of pliers. Twist the wire to form a new loop. This will retighten the turns on the coil form. Scrape away the insulation on the loop and solder a one-inch piece of bare wire to the new tap. This wire is necessary to reach from the new tap to the wire coming from the band switch. Replace L12 and resolder the four wires which were previously removed. Solder a 20-pF mica capacitor across the two terminals of L9, the driver-plate coil. This completes the transmitter modifications. Refer to the transmitter alignment section of the instruction manual and perform the 15-meter alignment procedure. Use 40-meter crystals or 40-meter VFO output for 20-meter operation.

Replace the bottom plate and top cover and the job is finished. It might be well to make a small label, "14.0" and tape it over the "21.0" lettering on the front panel. The HW-16 can be returned to 15-meter service by reversing the foregoing procedure. — *Llewellyn P. Rose, G5BGA*

AN IN AND AN OUT FOR A CW FILTER WITH THE TS-520

After installing a cw filter in my TS-520 transceiver, I found (to my dismay) that I was tuning right past several weak (and not so weak) DX stations because of the sharp characteristics of the filter. Placing the mode switch in usb and lsb provided

Partial schematic diagram of the HW-16 driver plate circuit. A 20-pF capacitor must be connected in parallel with L9.

ease in tuning, but when returning to cw the station would be lost because of the slight offset between modes.

Problem: How to switch between cw *without* the filter and cw *with* the filter, using a convenient, accessible switch. The switch would have to be mounted in such a fashion that the front panel would not be marred.

Solution: Since I operate strictly VFO and have no need for the fixed-channel capability offered with the CH. SELECT switch, I decided to press this switch into "filter-in, filter-out" service. I believe that most users of the TS-520 do not use this switch, so this suggestion is offered.

Procedure: Remove the top cover of the transceiver. Locate the Fixed Channel-AVR Board. Disconnect the wires from terminal C, 1 and 2. Now locate the i-f board and the ssb and cw filters. Disconnect the brown wire which is connected to the i-f board cw terminal. Connect this lead to the wire disconnected from terminal C of the fixed channel board. This is the wire moved during the installation of the cw filter in sets where the filter was not installed at the factory). Connect the wire disconnected from terminal 1 of the fixed channel board to the ssb terminal of the i-f board and connect the wire disconnected from terminal 2 of the fixed channel board to the cw terminal of the i-f board. Insulate all wiring splices and put the top cover back on the transceiver.

Final results will be worth the 15 minutes of work necessary to make this mini-modification. With the CH. SELECT switch in position 1, the unit works just as it did before the cw filter was installed, with nice broadband-width to tune in the weak ones. When a station is tuned in properly, switch to position 2. This cuts the filter in (simplicity itself!). If you decide to return your unit to the factory configuration it will take another 15 minutes: You will have not even scratched the front panel! — *Patrick Bailey, K7KBN*

REPLACE WITH CARE OR SPURIOUS YOU MIGHT AIR

With many transmitters or transceivers it is possible to transmit on spurious frequencies because of improper adjustment of the final-amplifier tuning or preselector controls. This past weekend the PA tuning knob fell off my FPM-300 transmitter. I replaced it while the rig was properly tuned for operation on the 40-meter band. However, the capacitor rotates a full 360 degrees, and I just happened to replace the knob 180 degrees from its proper position! Therefore, although giving a correct indication for 40 meters, the reference numbers on the panel were reversed for the other bands. Setting the control to the "10" position actually resulted in its being set correctly for 80 meters, and vice-versa.

After much frustration from being unable to obtain a match to my 80-meter antenna and two attempts to raise W1AW on 3580 kHz, it dawned on me — I wasn't transmitting anywhere near 3580 kHz. The signal was probably outside the amateur bands entirely.

If a plate-tuning capacitor rotates 360 degrees it is very easy to replace a knob the wrong way. Also, one should make sure that the dip in plate current occurs when this control is set for the correct band. The results of little mistakes like these could be disastrous. — *Stan Gibilisco, WA0OKV*

ELECTRONIC BIAS SWITCHING REVISITED

I wanted to incorporate electronic bias switching in my home build 4-250 linear amplifier.[1] It occurred to me that the protective measures and high-power transistors used in the original *QST* article were not needed if the bias were applied to the grid instead of the cathode. I lifted the control grid from ground and applied 80 volts of bias from a voltage divider across a small power supply. The two 0.01-μF mica capacitors keep the grid at rf ground potential. I opted to use a slower-acting system like that described by W6VFR.[2] If the bias circuit fails, either the high bias remains on the tube and the amplifier won't operate, or the grid will be at dc ground potential, resulting in very high plate current with no drive. In either case, there is no danger of high voltage appearing anywhere in the bias circuit as is the situation when the bias is applied to the cathode. The SENSITIVITY control is set just above the point where ambient noise and hum in the exciter activate the bias switch. — *Barry Boothe, W9UCW*

[1]Bryant, "Electronics Bias Switching for RF Power Amplifiers," *QST*, May, 1974.
[2]Gonsior, "Electronic Bias Switching for Linear Amplifiers," *Ham Radio*, March, 1975.

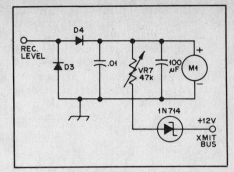

Zener diode improves battery charger.

IMPROVED BATTERY-CHARGE INDICATOR FOR THE WILSON 1402 TRANSCEIVER

The addition of a Zener diode, as shown in the schematic diagram, provides a better indication of battery charge in the Wilson unit. A 9- or 10-volt Zener diode will drop the supply voltage sufficiently that VR7 may be readjusted to provide full-scale meter deflection when the battery is fully charged. There will be no deflection when the battery is depleted. — *Steve Hope, WA5YCG*

TONE PAD CONNECTION FOR THE HW-202

A quick glance at the inside of the Heath HW-202 might give the impression that there just isn't enough room to connect the rig up for Touch-Tone use, particularly is a tone-burst encoder has already been installed. It is not as hard as it might appear; just follow these steps. On the transmitter board, locate connector pins AB, U and AD. These are the same pins used to connect the HWA-202-2 encoder. Take a length of RG174/U cable, solder the inner conductor to pin AB and the shield to pin U. Take a length of stranded insulated wire and solder to pin AD. Run these wires along the edge of the power amplifier board and pass them through

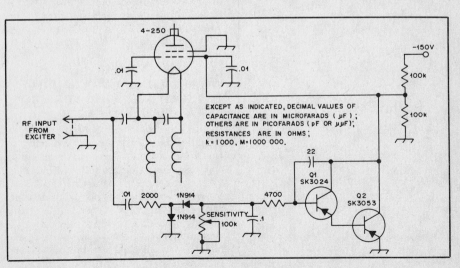

An electronic bias switching circuit.

the slot provided for the dc voltage line. Secure them with a cable clamp fastened to one of the rear-apron machine screws.

You will find the 11-volts dc provided by pin AD superior to a 9-volt battery and always "fresh." Should the tone pad load the microphone input circuit, you should provide a means for switching the tone pad out of the circuit when not in use. — *J. P. Taylor, W4CWB*

PROTECTING TRANSISTORS IN THE HW-202

Two-meter fm operators using the Heath HW-202 transceiver should be mindful that while the rf output transistor is rather tolerant of operator mistakes, the *audio* output stages are not as forgiving. Keep the audio output properly loaded into a speaker or earphones. You will save more transistors that way. — *Hilary McDonald, W5UNF/6*

A CW MONITOR FOR THE SWAN 270

The ability to hear what one is sending on cw transmissions is usually a great aid. If you are one of the many owners of the Swan 260, 270, 270B, or for that matter, any transceiver that doesn't have a built-in sidetone, here is a simple, inexpensive audio oscillator, built on a homemade pc board that has more than ample power to drive my headphones and sufficient power to drive my built-in speaker when the room is quiet.

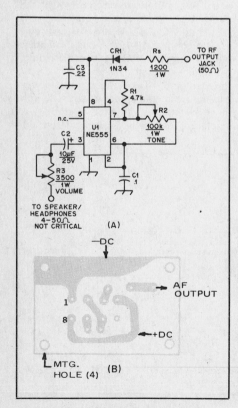

A sidetone circuit for the Swan 270.

The circuit is an adaptation of one found in the 1973 *Handbook*, p. 12. It uses an NE555 IC timer chip. But instead of a battery, I made a simple rf voltage supply. The output is very clean, and can be varied in both tone and volume to suit your personal preferences.

Because I didn't want to, or was not able to, key the ground side of the speaker, as is shown in the *Handbook*, I resorted to keying the voltage on and off. I had reservations about this, wondering if I might not get a chirpy note, but to my surprise the output is nice and crisp.

The printed-circuit board shown was homemade from a scrap of copper-clad board, about 1 × 1-1/2 inches (25.4 mm × 38.1 mm). I have found that one of the best etch-resistant lacquers available is ordinary fingernail polish. It is cheap, readily available, has a built-in applicator, and is easily removed.

The other components on the board were all from the junk box, but even if purchased new they shouldn't be over $3. The NE555 cost 99 cents. R1, C1 and R2 determine the pitch, and R3 the volume. I used a miniature slide switch (mounted on the back panel) to break the voltage lead to the monitor, so it wouldn't "talk" while I was using ssb.

The value of R_s will have to be determined experimentally if a rig of a different power level is used. The 1200-ohm resistor used here sampled enough power that, after rectification by D1, gave about 25 volts with no load. When the IC starts oscillating, the voltage drops rapidly. However, it is still in the vicinity of 6 volts, more than enough to power the monitor.

The board is small enough to be placed in any convenient spot. I ran leads to the switch on the rear panel and to the tone and volume controls which I mounted in the ventilation holes, so no other holes were necessary.

This monitor has certainly made cw operation more pleasant for me, and has improved my cw. It is very easy to construct, and gives one a small idea as to the wizardry contained in just one IC. — *Jerry Arnold, WA6MBP*

OVERCURRENT RELAY MODIFICATION FOR THE HENRY RADIO 2K-4 AMPLIFIER

In the present arrangement of the 2K-4 amplifier there exists a possible danger. If for some reason the overcurrent delay engages, causing the amplifier to shut off, there is a chance of damaging the tubes. When the amplifier has been shut off, the exciter can still feed power to the grids, making it possible to destroy the tubes. A simple change in the wiring of one terminal strip will eliminate the possibility. In the power supply upper deck, on terminal-barrier TB101, remove the

yellow wire from terminal no. 2 that goes to pin 4 of socket SK-1. Remove enough yellow wire from the cable harness so that it will reach the unused, normally closer terminal of relay RY101A. Connect a new wire from the unused common terminal of RY101A back to terminal no. 2 of TB101. This change provides automatic disabling of the antenna relay when the overcurrent relay is activated; thus the exciter rf bypasses the amplifier, going directly to the antenna when this overcurrent condition exists. — *Dave Porter, K2BPP*

OSCAR RECEPTION WITH THE SB-101

Owners of SB-101s or SB102s might experience some difficulty when trying to receive the OSCAR 10-meter output frequencies, 29.45 to 29.55 MHz, because of the band-switching arrangement in the Heath gear. By replacing the 38.395-MHz crystal (in the heterodyne oscillator circuit) with a 38.295-MHz crystal, the 29.5-to 30-MHz position becomes 29.4 to 29.9 MHz. The only retuning required is that of L608, the plate coil for V19. — *Randall Smith, VE2BYG*

THE SB-101 AND A SEPARATE RECEIVER

The wiring of the receive antenna jack of the SB-101 can be modified to accommodate an auxiliary receiver. This is done by bending contact 4 at the socket of relay 1 and soldering it to contact 3. To prevent rf from reaching the front end of the outboard receiver when the antenna switch is in the COMMON position, disconnect one side of the switch AK. Now the auxiliary receiver has the same antenna as the transceiver and can be used for separate receive and transmit operation. — *Timothy J. Brown, WB2ARG/6*

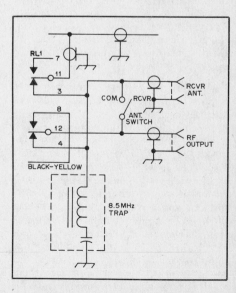

SB-101 separate receiver modification.

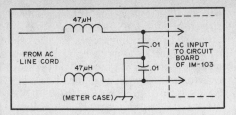

Filter connected to the ac input of the Heath IM-103 voltage monitor eliminates rf problem.

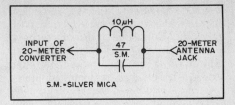

A trap to eliminate interband QRM in the Dream Receiver.

KEEPING RF OUT OF THE HEATH IM-103 LINE-VOLTAGE MONITOR

I noticed an apparent line-voltage increase whenever I keyed my transmitter and determined that rf was being rectified by D1 in the Heath monitor. A power-line filter was constructed and installed in the unit. As shown in the schematic, the inductors were Nytronics no. RFC-S-47, but any value of rf choke greater than 45 μH may be used, as long as the dc resistance of the coil is less than 5 ohms. My thanks to Tom Baustert, W2HEO, who assisted me in correcting the problem. — *Alan W. McCormick, WA2GTT*

ELIMINATING AC BUZZ IN THE HEATHKIT SB-102 TRANSCEIVER

My Heathkit SB-102 produced an annoying ac buzz at low volume settings. My homebrew power supply was suspected, but a check made with a Heath HP-23 power supply at a local Heath store gave the same problem. The problem was solved by connecting a nine-inch length of coaxial cable from point C on the audio circuit board, directly to the AF GAIN potentiometer, R930, and the cable shield was grounded at both ends. The original shielded wire (red band) was cut at the points where it emerged from the wiring harness. Apparently, its long, circuitous route through the harness, and poor shielding properties allowed the buzz to leak into the cable, because with the new RG58 cable installed, the buzz was almost completely eliminated. — *Joe Martorelli, WA6BUV/WA2TCE*

HUM IN THE SB-102

A slight but annoying ac hum in the receiver audio amplifier has been characteristic of some SB-102s, including my own. The hum is most noticeable with the af gain at minimum. Conventional methods, such as tightening circuit-board screws, adding capacitance across the B + line, and so forth, were tried unsuccessfully on my own receiver. A simple remedy was discovered however, which has worked for me and at least one other owner.

Disconnect the red harness cable from between C308 and the af gain control, and run either the same cable (out of the harness) or another well-shielded cable *directly* between the two points, grounding the shields at both ends. This completely eliminates that particular source of hum pickup, which is apparently from the adjacent filament lines in the harness. Before performing the alteration, this source can be confirmed by a simple test. Using a short screwdriver, alternately short to chassis ground each end of the cable (both ends are protected by dc blocking capacitors). The hum will remain when the audio-control side of the cable is grounded, but will disappear when the near side is grounded. — *John Sims, WB6NGF*

CURING SLIPPAGE AND BACKLASH OF HEATH VFO DIALS

Some Heath equipment owners complain of tuning-dial slippage and backlash on the transceivers, receivers and transmitters. The referenced dial-drive assembly is identified as their part no. 100-450. Here is a simple modification to the dial-drive pulley, part no. 100-444, which will solve this problem.

The drawing shows the details. Disassemble part no. 100-444, the dial-drive pulley assembly, noting the position of pulley wheels in relation to each other. Now replace the first pulley wheel in its original position on shaft. Hold it firmly against the shoulder and solder it to the shaft through 360 degrees. Be careful not to allow solder to flow back along shaft. Next, replace the spacer on shaft and then replace the second drive pulley. At this point a new part is added. Use a spring-tension washer, sometimes referred to as a dished washer, under the screw head which is now screwed into position. This completes the modification. When installing the dial-drive bushing in the keyhole slot, note whether the dial-drive pulley engages with the circular drive ring on the circular dial. It may not seat deep enough, in which case file out the keyhold slot to permit better grip. — *T. C. Galbreath, W2AXX*

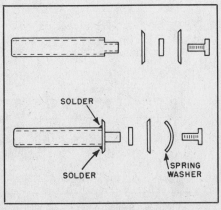

Anti-slippage modification of Heath dial drive.

ELIMINATING 40-METER SIGNAL LEAKAGE IN THE MINI-MISER'S DREAM RECEIVER

When using the Mini-Miser's Dream Receiver (DeMaw, "The Mini-Miser's Dream Receiver," *QST*, September, 1976, page 20) on 20 meters, I noticed that signals on the 40-meter band were leaking around the 20-meter converter. To correct this problem, a simple trap was constructed and installed as shown in the schematic diagram. The 10-μH inductor is available from Radio Shack stores (Radio Shack no. 273-101). — *John Lawson, K5IRK*

MORE OUTPUT FROM HG-10 SERIES VFO

Users of the Heath HG-10 and -10B VFO with other than Heath transmitters may have encountered problems with low output. The HG-10 is rated at 5 volts rms, and this just wasn't enough to provide adequate grid drive for my hundred-watter, using two 6CL6s as buffer and driver. No amount of work with tube operating conditions, tuned circuits, or improved coupling did any good. The problem was solved by changing the oscillator plate choke to one with a value of 1 millihenry. This change was all that was needed to yield ample drive on all bands. — *Jon G. Harder, W1GVN*

IMPROVED LOCAL-OSCILLATOR PERFORMANCE IN THE K9UIF 2-METER TRANSVERTER

The K9UIF transverter, which appears in *The Radio Amateur's VHF Manual,* is one of the most popular and effective designs in existence. One consistent difficulty has been the instability of the local oscillator. The oscillator may drift during warm-up, and its frequency will shift when the oscillator is tuned. The high drive levels required also may result in instability, as a result of the subsequent high crystal current. An OX oscillator module and EX crystal provide an excellent substitute for the oscillator. They are available from International Crystal Co., 10 N. Lee, Oklahoma City, OK 73102. The module is mounted in a small Minibox, and a 1000-pF ceramic feedthrough capacitor is used to bypass the 6-volt supply to the oscillator. The oscillator output is connected to a phono connector, and small diameter coaxial cable joins the output of the module to the grid of the tube formerly used as the oscillator. If the 100-kΩ grid resistor was connected across the crystal socket, it should now be connected directly from the grid pin of the tube to ground. Since the module requires a 6-volt supply, two 1000-ohm resistors are connected as a voltage divider across the 12-volt supply in the transverter. — *Dr. Ralph E. Taggart, WB8DQT*

QUICK CURE FOR AN R-4B VFO PROBLEM

After several years of use, some owners of the Drake R-4Bs may experience intermittently low VFO level, or find the equipment develops a vibrating, warbling quality. Before digging into the VFO, short the forward and center lugs of each pole of slide switch S-4, located on the left side of the receiver. This switch allows fixed frequency, crystal-controlled operation of the receiver. When the contacts of the switch become loose from wear, the problem mentioned occurs. — *Marty Woll, WB6VZI*

RECEIVING NOAA WEATHER REPORTS ON 2-METER FM RIGS

Most two-meter fm transceivers are sufficiently broadbanded to allow reception of NOAA weather reports on either 162.40 or 162.55 MHz by installing the proper receiver oscillator crystal. If the operator travels, it might be useful to have crystals for both frequencies installed in the rig, allowing one to receive current weather information while in transit. — *Bob Migliorino, K2YFE*

FASTER RELAY RESPONSE IN THE SB-401

I am a cw traffic handler, and was disturbed by the slow response of the VOX relay in my SB-401. I connected a 10-kΩ resistor in parallel with R135, the cathode resistor for V12B. VOX relay response is now much faster. — *Andrew Teetzel, WB8KVU*

UPDATING THE SWAN 350

The original Swan 350 transceivers use a pair of 6HF5 beam-power pentodes, designed for use as TV horizontal-deflection amplifiers in the rf output stage. It is a reasonably easy task to convert this final stage to use the General Electric type 8950 beam pentode which is actually designed for linear amplifier and rf power-output applications. We have

converted two Swan model 350 transceivers and found considerable improvement with both units. The 8950s not only run cooler, the plates show no color, than the 6HF5s, but also provide more output. It is possible to load the final amplifier to approximately 450 watts of input.

The same 12-pin Compactron socket is used for both types of tubes so socket changes are not necessary. The only connections that are common to both tube types, however, are the control grid leads; therefore *do not* remove anything that is connected to the socket pins no. 5 and no. 9 of either tube.

The "hot" heater lead on the rear socket should be moved from pin no. 1 and connected to pin no. 12; then ground pin no. 1. This change is all that is necessary to apply 12 volts to each tube. The 8950 tubes require 12 volts for heater operation, whereas the 6HF5 tubes required only six volts.

Carefully remove the ends of all resistors and capacitors that are connected to the remaining pins on both sockets, as these components can all be used in the conversion. In some cases the one-ohm one-watt cathode resistors will have to be replaced with a 2-watt resistor. In some model 350 transceivers, we have found 2-watt resistors already installed in the cathode circuit, in which case they can be reused.

Leave the two copper straps connected between both sockets in place: One is in the control-grid circuit; the other is left in place and both pins no. 4 and no. 10 on each socket grounded with the shortest possible leads. These are the beam-forming plate leads. Reposition the two 100-ohm screen-grid dropping resistors under the copper straps so that one connects to pin no. 11 of the rear socket and the other to pin no. 3 of the front socket. Wire pins no. 3 and no. 11 together on each socket. Wire pin no. 2 to pin. no. 6 on each socket; then connect the cathodes

of both tubes together by running a bare wire from pin no. 6 of one tube socket to pin no. 6 of the other socket.

Making all leads as short as possible, bypass pins no. 2, 6, 11 and 12 on the rear socket, and pins no. 2, 3 and 6 on the front socket to ground with the 0.01 NF disk-ceramic capacitors previously removed. Pin no. 3 of the rear socket and pin no. 11 on the front socket should be bypassed to ground using the two 0.002 NF disk-ceramic capacitors previously removed.

Resistors R405 and R406 in the cathode circuit should be connected to the center of the bare wiring running from pin no. 6 of one socket to pin no. 6 of the other socket. The 2-watt, 1-ohm cathode resistors should be connected from pin no. 2 of each socket to ground. It is imperative that all leads be kept as short as possible, particularly the ground leads. This completes rewiring of the tube sockets necessary for the conversion.

It will be necessary to touch up the driver tuning due to the change reflected from the amplifier tuning and loading. Neutralization will also have to be readjusted. See your Swan 350 manual for the details of tuning and neutralization procedures. I strongly suggest a thorough study of the manual, remembering the timely warning about the tune-up time limit of thirty seconds. Do not forget to make notes in the instruction manual regarding the changes you have made, correcting the PA stage of the diagram and the heater wiring circuit. The tube lineup on page two should be corrected, the voltage chart on page 14 and the trouble-shooting guide on the same page.

The type 8950 tubes, although not available everywhere, can be obtained in matched pairs from Slep Electronics Company at P.O. Box 100, Otto, NC 28763, on the East Coast, and from Swan Electronics, 305 Airport Road, Oceanside, CA 92054, on the West Coast. — *Carl Coleman, K4WJ*

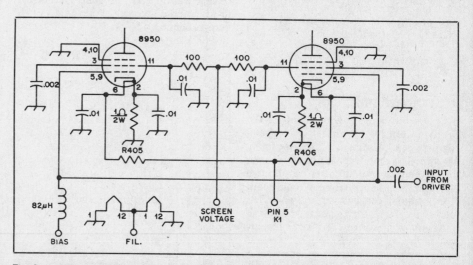

The Swan 350 may be converted for use of the type 8950 linear amplifier/rf output beam pentodes with this circuit modification.

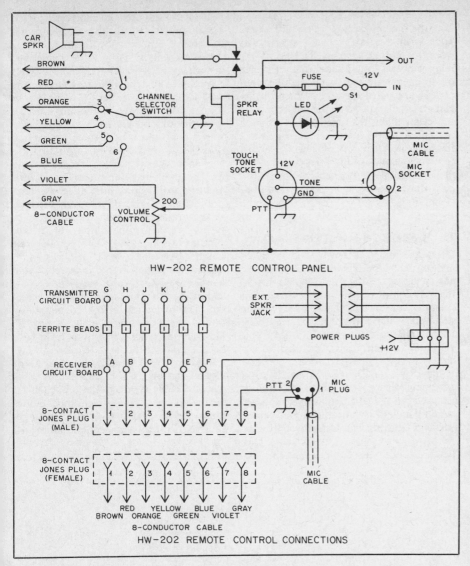

A remote control system for the Heath HW-202 transceiver is shown in this diagram.

REMOTE CONTROL FOR THE HEATH HW-202 TRANSCEIVER

My Heath HW-202 transceiver, installed under the right front seat, was stolen from the locked car while it was parked in front of the house. I had been considering the idea of a more convenient control load to be located in the dashboard, and placing the transceiver out of reach. Hence this project for trunk-mounting the new mobile rig.

Channel selection is accomplished in the HW-202 by grounding a diode through a resistor associated with a crystal oscillator, in each of the six transmit and receive channels. The transmit and receive channels can be switched independently on the front panel, but I found this feature more of a nuisance than advantage while operating mobile. The squelch control is another feature I found dispensable, once it is set to quiet an idle channel. A volume control is necessary but this function can be done remotely in the speaker circuit.

The essential items in the dashboard panel are: A six-position selector switch, speaker relay, fuse holder, sockets for Touch-Tone and microphone plugs, indicator light and volume control. The on/off switch could be included but I found a better spot which was reserved for a nonexistent "optional accessory" switch. The four-conductor Touch-Tone socket and plug, eight-conductor cable and LED pilot light were selected from the Lafayette catalog. The speaker relay was bought from Radio Shack and the microphone plug and socket are Heathkit parts. Others are junk-box items.

Except for the 12-volt power cable, for which I bought a small roll of No. 12 stranded automobile primary wire, the wires carry little current, and resistance is not significant. I found it necessary to run a separate shielded microphone cable. The parts are mounted in a 3-1/3 × 4-inch panel which fits in place of the ashtray.

Remote-control connections in the transceiver require no irreversible modification. The unit is assembled and checked out in accordance with the assembly manual. There are six harness wires from the transmitter board and six from the receiver board connected to the selector switches. They have pc-board connectors. These are lifted and carefully taped out of the way. New wires, terminated in pc-board connectors, are installed and brought out to the eight-contact Jones plug as shown in the diagram. Note the ferrite beads at the transmitter board. I do not have a tone burst encoder so I brought out a siz-wire cable through one of the four holes for that unit in the chassis. If the encoder were installed, another access hole would have to be made. A third pair of contacts is inserted in the power connector housings. These provide connection to a phono plug at the external speaker socket.

The transceiver is mounted in the supplied gimbal bracket. This is fastened sideways (by means of self-tapping screws) to the wall at the front of the trunk compartment near the top. I cut new slots in the bracket to limit motion of the case. With this installation the HW-202 is easily removable, although it is necessary to climb into the trunk to unplug it. For operation in the house I use a test lead to ground one of the Jones plug contacts for channel selection. For mobile operation the squelch is set to quiet an idle channel, and the volume is adjusted for a weak signal with the dashboard volume control wide open.

Incidentally, I found that the 5/8-wavelength whip makes an excellent antenna for the car broadcast receiver. The broadcast antenna cable was transferred to a relay box to share the whip. Turning on the HW-202 switches the antenna. This makes the broadcast antenna surplus. — *Erwin Aymar, W3SU*

ADJUSTABLE TEMPERATURE COMPENSATION FOR VFOs

While trying to stabilize a VFO with temperature compensating capacitors, I couldn't seem to find the correct value of capacitor. I connected a 100-pF air-variable capacitor in series with a 10-pF N750 temperature compensating capacitor. After a few tries, I found a setting of the variable capacitor that yielded the desired VFO stability. — *Philip J. Reich, W2HUG*

A BETTER-LOOKING DIAL FOR THE HW-101

After owning my HW-101 for awhile, I grew tired of looking at the plain, harsh black-and-white dial: I think it ruins the otherwise excellent appearance of the rig, subjectively speaking. I cut a 3-1/2 × 1-3/4-inch piece of heavy, green plastic sheet, such as that used on report covers and overhead projectors, and taped it in place between the circular dial and the dial window. Another piece of green plastic sheet, 4 × 2 inches in size, was fitted around the meter case and behind the panel: It may be necessary to loosen the meter case in order to facilitate slipping the plastic around it for a light-tight fit. When fastening the plastic behind the dial, be sure the plastic does not interfere with the operation of the dial drive.

These simple changes give a soft green glow to both the dial and the S-meter, and greatly enhance the appearance of the rig. When the HW-101 is turned off, the plastic sheet gives the dial a ''blacked out'' appearance. — *Jim Milburn, WB5BYK*

CORRECTING METER-POINTER STICKING IN THE DRAKE TR-4

Both meters in the TR-4 tend to stick at the far left position when the pointer becomes wedged in the corner of the dial face. To prevent this, the meters are removed and a small wire or wooden peg is inserted in a 0.030-inch hole drilled in the meter face. Mark the position for the hole before removing the face. The bottom cover of the PA meter and the top plate of the S meter are held in place by two screws. Locate the peg about 1/4 inch behind the dial, in order that the pointer will hit the peg when the pointer is within 1/16 to 1/8 inch of the corner of the dial. If the drilled hole provides a snug fit for the peg, it won't be necessary to cement the peg. — *Jerry Lieb, WA6GSA*

POOR SHIELDING IN AUDIO CABLE

I found that the wrap-around type of shield used on audio cable, though easy to work with, is a poor choice if used in the presence of rf fields, such as exist in an amateur station. I encountered the problem of rf feedback in my shack while using this cable and no amount of filtering of the transmitter would cure it. When the microphone cable was replaced with the standard woven-type of shielded cable the problem disappeared. This suggests that this wrap-around type audio cable would be no good for carrying rf. — *John Bipes, KØYQX*

PERKING UP SLUGGISH HEATHKIT SB-101 TRANSCEIVERS

After six or seven years of use, my SB-101 began to show signs of age. The S meter could not be zeroed, and the strongest signals barely moved the meter pointer. A check of the agc and alc diodes revealed no fault there, but a slight positive bias was detected on the grid of the first i-f

amplifier in the transmit mode, and on both the first and second i-f amplifier tube grids when receiving. This problem was traced to pin 12 of relay RL2. With the relay removed from its socket, a resistance of 30 megohms was measured between pins 11 and 12 of the relay. When the accumulated dust between the relay contacts was cleaned out, the positive bias problem was cured. The S meter was zeroed, and I found it necessary to replace the 6AU6 first and second i-f amplifier tubes. After the alignment was touched up, the SB-101 performed like new. — *Tom Monroe, W6GGR*

THE G3YMC 1.8-MHz CONVERTER

There are many currently used receivers and transceivers which do not incorporate any facilities for the 1.8-MHz band, and the question often arises of how to design a simple converter, capable of giving the standard of good performance needed by 1.8-MHz long-distance enthusiasts and yet compact and easy to build in a few hours.

David W. Sergeant, G3YMC, who is extremely keen on 1.8-MHz DX, recently acquired an FT-201 transceiver and so came up against this problem. He spent a weekend digging energetically into his

well-filled junk box and came up with the design shown (which by coincidence has something in common with the 144-MHz converter built by PA0GVK and described in the October *TT*). The use of a 5.5-MHz crystal makes it possible to translate the 1.8-MHz band to either 7.3-7.5 MHz or 3.7-3.5 MHz. G3YMC did not find i-f breakthrough on 7.3-7.5 MHz any problem, but should it be then of course it is possible to use 3.7-3.5 MHz, though this conversion has the disadvantages of having the main receiver tuning backwards and also transposing the sidebands.

T1 and T2 for the double-balanced mixer are wideband ferrite transformers or ferrite toroids using bifilar or trifilar winding techniques. G3YMC suggests that the secondaries can be 10 turns bifilar wound or as much in fact as can be wound on; connect the start of one section to the end of the other and use this as the center tap. The primaries or link couplings can be four or five turns. Details of how all these can be wound in trifilar form have been given previously (for example, *ART*). The FETs Q1, Q2 for the oscillator section can be UC734, 2N3819, etc., but not switching-type devices. The mixer diodes are preferably Schottky diodes such as the HP5082-2800 commonly advertised for this application, although I

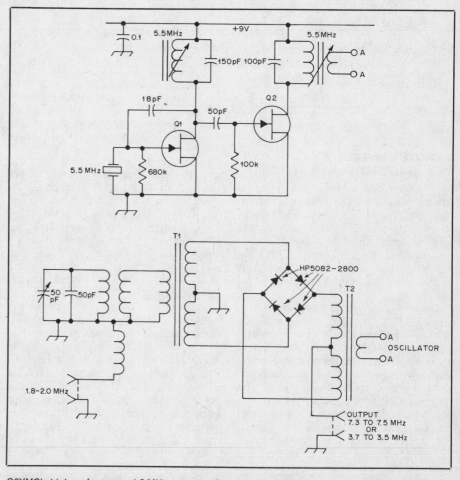

G3YMC's high-performance 1.8-MHz converter for use with receivers and transceivers covering amateur bands from 3.5 MHz upward. Q1, Q2 see text.

feel that at 1.8 MHz conventional germanium diodes, selected for matching, would probably prove quite satisfactory. The whole unit can be mounted in a small screened box, such as a tobacco tin, with screened coaxial connectors for input and output; it is important to ensure earth continuity since otherwise i-f breakthrough will be considerable.

With suitable crystal(s) and tuned circuits, of course, the same form of converter could be used for almost any required band in the mf or hf range.

Having so successfully solved the problem of receiving 1.8 MHz on his transceiver, G3YMC is now looking into the question of transmission. — *Pat Hawker, G3VA,* Radio Communication for December, 1975, RSGB

INSTALLATION AND SELECTION OF FILTERS FOR THE TS-520

The Kenwood manual suggests removing the i-f board to install the accessory cw filter. This job is difficult because of a cable harness obstructing the mounting screws and also the numerous connections to the board. The filter is installed easily by removing the mounting plate for the bias and VOX controls on the side of the TS-520. After removing the three screws that hold the plate, there is ample lead length to allow access to the foil side of the i-f board.

A separate spst switch, or the channel-select switch, can be used to choose filters in the cw position. This is done by switching the brown lead from the ssb terminal to the original ssb terminal or to the cw terminal on the i-f board. The ssb filter remains automatically selected in the upper or lower sideband position. — *B. J. Owens, WA5QAL*

A-M WITH THE ECHO II

Owners of the Echo II, 2-meter ssb transceiver may transmit a-m by closing the key and operating in the ssb mode. A-m is received by zero beating the carrier. — *Mark H. Wittmer, WA6FXM*

HEATH HW-7 SIDETONE LEVEL CONTROL

The HW-7 sidetone lacks a method of reducing the tone level, and it can be excessive to some people. I modified the circuit by replacing R35 with a 10-turn Trimpot. Two holes were drilled in the board to accommodate the two leads from the potentiometer. The trace between Q11 and C46 were severed and connected as shown. The desired sidetone level is easily achieved now, and operator fatigue is reduced considerably. — *David Palmer, W6PHF*

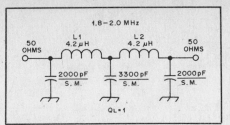

Filter section for adapting the Ten-Tec 405 amplifier to 160-meter operation.

160 METERS WITH THE TEN-TEC 405 AMPLIFIER

The writer needed an amplifier to go with his solid-state 160-meter exciter (*QST* for November, 1974), and it seemed likely that the Ten-Tec 405 amplifier could be modified for use on 1.8 MHz. The band switch in the 405 is used to select half-wave filters for the band of use. The filters are the only tuned circuits in the assembly and are inserted after the broadband transformer in the collector circuit of the 100-watt amplifier.

The first experiment called for external addition of a half-wave filter network, 50 ohms at each port, and with a loaded Q of 1. A filter was made from sections of Miniductor stock and surplus transmitting-style mica capacitors. The same constants as given in the accompanying schematic were used. Operation was tried with the band switch set for 80 meters. It seemed reasonable that 160-meter energy would pass through the 80-meter network since a half-wave filter is a low-pass filter. With the 160-meter outboard filter installed between the amplifier output and the coax feeder to the antenna, power from the exciter was fed to the 405. With approximately 5 watts of drive to the amplifier a power output of 50 watts was obtained. Apparently the input transformer and compensating network of the 405 was lossy at 1.8 MHz, thereby accounting for a higher required excitation level than for the hf bands. (The manufacturer rates the driving power at 1 watt for hf-band use.)

Some mismatch between the PA transistors and the outboard filter will result from having the 80-meter network con-

nected to the outboard one for 160 meters. Therefore, it is recommended that persons interested in making the amplifier usable on 160 meters give up the 80-meter band and rewind the two toroids in the 80-meter filter section. It will be necessary to install new capacitors in the network. This modification was done by the writer, and performance has been excellent. — *W1FB*

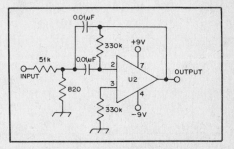

An active filter provides additional selectivity after the receiver audio circuit.
U2 — N5741V operational amplifier.

A SIMPLE AUDIO FILTER

The cw performance of many less-expensive receivers can be improved significantly by the addition of an audio filter. The circuit combines simplicity and some gain. The circuit is a bandpass active filter, using an integrated operational amplifier. It has a center frequency of 1 kHz, a bandwidth of 100 Hz, and a gain of 10. The filer is powered by two 9-volt transistor batteries. Headphones with an impedance of 600 ohms or higher can be used on the output of the audio filter. If it is desired to operate with a loudspeaker, an impedance-transformation stage is required along with some additional power gain.

The N5741V operational amplifier is made by Signetics and sells for $1. It is their short dual-in-line version of the popular 741 operational amplifier. The entire circuit can be built on a 1 × 2-inch circuit board and taped to the batteries. It can then be mounted in a Minibox or tucked into the receiver. A switch to remove power and bypass the filter is required. — *Robert R. Knibb, WA3LIO*

A sidetone level control for the HW-7.

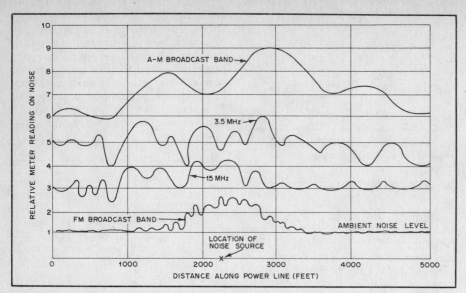

Graphs showing relative power-line noise strength according to specific radio frequency bands.

LOCATING SOURCES OF MAN-MADE NOISE

About six months after moving to my present location, relatively strong power-line noise began to appear. First it was intermittent, then it gradually became more continuous and stronger. Something had to be done! Cruising the area with an a-m automobile receiver proved useless in locating the source of the noise — it was just too general.

Recalling Nelson's article in *QST* for April and May, 1966, the writer studied it in detail. For anyone having noise problems, a review of Nelson's article is highly recommended. Without attempting to cover the ground outlined in the article, let it suffice to emphasize the importance of the use of some kind of vhf receiver with a signal-level meter.

Fortunately, the author had a combination portable a-m/fm receiver which had two earphone jacks. The audio-level meter shown in the schematic diagram was plugged into one of them. The first attempt, with the audio-level meter merely involved a diode in series with the 500-microampere meter, thus rectifying the audio signal and giving a dc reading on the meter. However, the particular meter used was not sufficiently damped for the application and in the presence of fluctuating noise, the meter pointer swung violently back and forth making it impossible to use it effectively. This difficulty was eliminated by the *RC* combination shown. It was arrived at by trial and error

using the receiver tuned to a broadcast station with voice modulation. These values also gave the proper amount of damping for noise sources also. However, different combinations may be required with another receiver/meter combination.

In the event that more meter sensitivity is required, a small output transformer having an impedance ratio in the order of 4 ohms to 2000 ohms (not critical) may be inserted between the diode and the plug. The low-impedance winding should be connected to the plug terminals and the high-impedance winding connected between the anode of the diode and the negative terminal of the electrolytic capacitor.

While not a problem with the author's receiver, the agc action with some models may suppress the variations in line noise. Whether or not this would affect measurements would have to be determined in a particular application.

Once a noise source becomes bothersome at the author's station, a homemade transistor receiver covering the range from 3.5 to 15 MHz is installed in an automobile equipped with a temporary 11-foot (3.4 m) surplus whip antenna attached to the car by means of insulated clamps. The portable a-m/fm receiver, equipped with its meter, is also taken along in the search. Those who have mobile hf equipment in their cars have half the battle already won.

The car is driven around until the area in which the noise is greatest is found. When the noise starts to give a meter indication up into the 15-MHz range, one may expect to be within a few blocks, or perhaps a mile, from the noise source. The objective is to find a localized area where the noise is greatest. Once this is accomplished, the fm receiver is turned on. If the noise cannot be heard, the localized area is searched until an indication on the meter is shown in the fm band.

The above technique was effective in locating the line noise mentioned at the beginning of this article. However, in this case, the culprit proved to be each and every insulator on a one-mile length of power line, newly constructed using the latest state-of-the-art techniques in power-line design.

In the past year, at least a dozen power line leaks have been first located without bothering the power company. Of this number, only three required the assistance of the company's noise experts. The rest of the cases were readily fixed by local linemen, once the source was located. The method has also been useful in locating other sources of noise.

It should be emphasized that on both hf and vhf measurements, widely fluctuating meter readings can be expected as one drives along a suspected power line. These variations may be caused by radiation from down leads, ground wires and other objects. It may be advisable to make a chart showing the various peak readings for different frequency ranges. A sample one is shown which illustrates the importance of the vhf receiver in locating the exact position of the offending source. — *William L. North, W4BX*

ADJUSTABLE AUDIO LIMITER

I found the "batteryless" audio limiter described by Lew McCoy, W1ICP, (*QST*, July, 1964) to be very effective. The one drawback was the 1-volt peak-to-peak output which proved to be a bit too low to drive my pair of headphones. A modification to the circuit is shown in the drawing. By adding diode pairs and a rotary switch, the output can be adjusted in 1-volt peak-to-peak steps. Silicon diodes are used because of the 0.6-volt drop across them when they are forward biased.

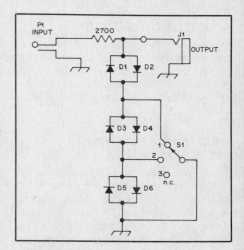

Adjustable audio limiter.
D1-D6, incl. — Silicon diodes, any voltage and current rating.
J1 — Headphone jack.
P1 — Headphone plug.
S1 — 3-position, single-pole, single-section phenolic rotary switch.

Damped audio-level meter for noise tracing.

Voltage and current ratings of the diodes are unimportant. I chose to use three diode pairs, but more can be added if desired. — *Stephen Pawlowicz*

FREQUENCY STABILIZING THE HEATH SB-300

The Heath SB-300 is considered to be a very stable receiver when in good condition. Heath specifies that for a 10-percent, line-voltage change, the receiver frequency change will be less than 100 Hz. After several years of operation my receiver failed to meet this specification. The main cause of trouble is the filament voltage change on the linear master oscillator (LMO). The LMO tube is a 6AU6A. A step change in line voltage produces an immediate change in the LMO frequency, followed by a drift to some new frequency. This effect could be reduced, but not completely eliminated by selecting a "good" 6AU6A. To remove this source of instability, a precision-regulated, 6.3-volt dc supply was employed. Fluctuations in line voltage still caused the LMO to shift frequency slightly. A voltage-regulator tube (VR-150) was used to stabilize the oscillator plate voltage. These changes effected a distinct improvement. Then, for a line voltage change of 10 percent, no change in LMO frequency could be detected. A frequency counter with 1-Hz resolution was used for this test.

Unfortunately, the receiver was still not completely stabilized. The crystal-controlled heterodyne oscillator was investigated next. It was somewhat surprising to find that the heterodyne oscillator was quite sensitive to changes in filament voltage as well as plate voltage. When these voltages were regulated, as in the LMO circuit, there was a marked improvement in receiver stability. The beat-frequency oscillator (BFO) appears to be quite stable without voltage regulation.

The power supply circuit is shown in the illustration. Any circuit capable of furnishing regulated voltages of 150 dc at 10 mA and 6.3 dc at 600 mA would be suitable. The value of Rsc (0.82 ohm) was chosen to limit the output current to approximately 700 mA. R1 should be adjusted to produce 6.3-V dc at the output with no load connected. Current limiting will occur when the supply is first turned on due to the low resistance of the cold tube heaters.

The regulated voltage sources are connected easily to the receiver without drilling holes or altering the printed circuit boards. Unsolder the two brown wires connected to the terminals marked C and D on the rf circuit board. Solder these two wires together and tape their ends to prevent unwanted contact with other circuits. Connect the regulated 6.3-V dc source to the terminal labeled C on the rf board. This feeds the regulated filament voltage to the LMO tube (V5) and the heterodyne-

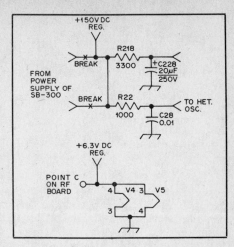

Connections to SB-300 receiver.

oscillator tube (V4). Next, disconnect and tape the wire coming from the power supply that is connected to R218, and do likewise for the wire coming from the power supply to R22. Connect the regulated +150-V dc source to these two resistors. The power supply cable can be passed through the rear hole that is in line with the band switch.

If the LMO, BFO and high-frequency oscillator are used to drive external devices such as a transmitter, they should be isolated by means of a buffer stage to prevent frequency changes due to variations in the load. — *Frederick H. Schmidt, W4VWS*

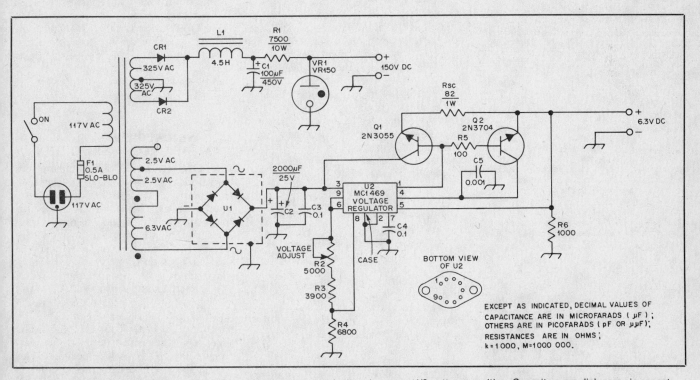

Circuit diagram for the regulated power supply. Unless otherwise noted, all resistors are 1/2-watt composition. Capacitors are disk ceramic except those with polarity marked, which are electrolytic.
C1 — 100-μF electrolytic, 450-V dc.
C2 — 2000-μF electrolytic, 25-V dc.
D1, D2 — Silicon diode, 1000-PRV, 500 mA.
F1 — 0.5 A, Slo-Blo type.
L1 — Choke, 4.5 H, 50 mA (Stancor C1706 or equiv.).
Q1 — 2N3055 transistor.
Q2 — 2N3704 transistor.
R2 — 5000-Ω linear-taper control.
T1 — 117-volt primary; secondary 650-V at 40 mA, center tapped; 5 V at 2 A; 6.3 V at 2 A (Stancor PC-8406 or equiv.).
U1 — Bridge rectifier assembly, 25 volt, 1 ampere.

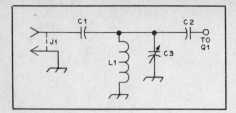

A tuned circuit for the solid-state preamplifier. Parts values are listed in Table 1.

Table 1

Band	C1	C2	C3	L1
80-40 Meters	47 pF	47 pF	356 pF	4 μH, 14T
20 Meters	27 pF	27 pF	100 pF	1 μH, 7T
15-10 Meters	12 pF	12 pF	50 pF	0.75 μH, 5T
6 Meters	6 pF	6 pF	50 pF	0.38 μH, 2-1/2T

Coil and capacitor data for the tuned-input circuit shown in the figure. The coil stock is 3/4-inch dia., 32 tpi (B&W 3012).

GENERAL PURPOSE SOLID-STATE PREAMPLIFIERS

Over the past few years there have been many articles describing various vhf/uhf amplifiers. There are few types, however, that are good for general-purpose hf amplification. How many amateurs have listened in vain for signals above 20 meters because of a poor receiver front end? How many transceivers have a "dead" sound when the band is out? Here is a preamp which provides usable gain up to 100 MHz. It can improve the noise figure of even a good tube-type receiver and should improve the image rejection of any receiver when used with the narrow-band modification. The noise figure of the unit described here is 2.5 dB at 30 MHz. This is sufficient to provide a 10 dB signal-to-noise-plus-noise ratio with 0.07 microvolt of signal at the input.

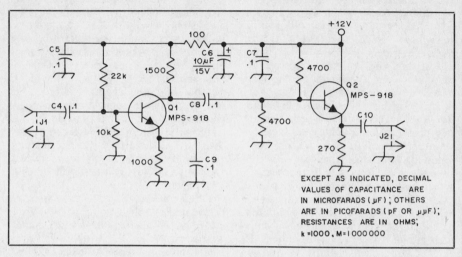

Circuit diagram for the broad-band amplifier. If the amplifier is to be used at 100 MHz, C4, C5, C8, C9 and C10 should be 10 μF in capacitance. C4 should be omitted if the tuned circuit at upper left is used.

C4, C5, C7, C8, C10 — 0.1 μF 100-V (Sprague Orange Drop or equiv.).
C6 — 10-μF 15-V tantalum.

J1, J2 — Phono jack.
Q1, Q2 — Silicon npn rf transistor (Motorola MPS-918).

Inside view of the preamp with the tuned-input circuit shown at the left. The switch is not included in the drawing at upper right. It is used by the author as an on-off power switch. The prospective builder might consider including a band switch with an "out" position if the amplifier will be used in front of a reasonably good receiver. Under some operating conditions, it might not be desirable to have the preamp in the line.

Preamp for HF receivers.

The amplifier consists of a common-emitter stage driving an emitter follower. Generally, emitter followers are not recommended at high frequencies because they tend to be unstable, but in this design there are no tuned elements following the amplifier and hence the amplifier is quite stable.

As with any high-frequency amplifier, good constructional practices should be followed. Short leads, in-line layout, and careful bypassing are all necessary. Since the unit has a gain of more than 40 dB at frequencies below 5 MHz, all of the bypass capacitors shown should be used.

If your application calls for wide-band gain, the device shown is what you need. But if you intend to use the amplifier as a receiver preamp, the circuit shown in the other diagram should be included. It can be mounted in the same box as the preamp.

The amplifier has a gain of 23 dB at 6 meters and a gain of 30 dB at 10 meters. It operates nicely with either a 50-ohm or 75-ohm receiver-input impedance and will serve as an inexpensive receiver accessory. The total cost, excluding the container and connectors, is about $10. — *Donald K. Belcher, WA4JVE and Alan Victor, WA4MGX*

HW-202 OWNERS, BEWARE!

Do not use an antenna connector with a long center pin to plug into the antenna socket on the rear apron of the HW-202. I found out the hard way. The pin was just long enough to touch the printed-circuit-board foil that carries the 13.8-V dc to the receiver, causing the foil to open at that point. I jumpered the open circuit and changed the antenna connector to one with a short center pin. — *Bruce Rattray, VE3FCH/W1*

LED INDICATORS FOR THE GLB TRANSMIT/RECEIVE SWITCHES

The GLB model 400B Channelizer has two front-panel switches for shifting each row of frequency selectors to either the receive or transmit mode. The operator must observe the position of the switches to determine which mode position they are in. This can be confusing and can result in operations on the wrong frequency, resulting in unintentional interference.

A simple and effective modification to provide a positive indication of switch position can be accomplished by the installation of LED (light-emitting diode) pilot lamps adjacent to each switch, corresponding to the switch position. This entails the careful drilling of four holes in the front panel of the GLB, the insertion of four LEDs, and the replacement of the original spdt switches with two miniature dpdt switches to handle the LED switching. LEDs of different color can be used if desired, making the indication of

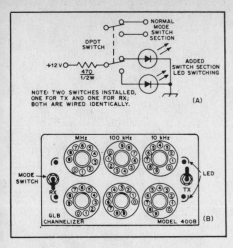

GLB 400B Channelizer modification. LEDs show switch positions.

mode selection easily determined. The modified switch circuitry is shown above. Both replacement circuits are wired identically; however, only one example is shown. The 470-ohm resistor is in series with the GLB 12-volt source in the common leg of the switch. Position of the LEDs on the front panel is a matter of choice, but they fit nicely within the quarter-circle panel markings shown in B. In addition to the mode-indication value of this system, the LEDs also provide a visible indication that the unit has power applied. — *Bill Vandermay, W7ZZ*

ADDING 1-MHz OFFSET TO THE KDK FM-144

Automatic plus or minus 1-MHz offset may be added to the KDK FM-144 simply and economically, using the circuit shown in the schematic diagram. No additional crystals are required. The only limitation is that the operator must place the rig in the SIMPLEX mode when the 1-MHz offset is to be selected. Normal operation of the transceiver is not affected by this modification.

K1 is a 12-volt miniature spdt reed relay. When transmitting, this relay is energized simultaneously with the existing T-R relay, whenever S1 is closed. The anode of D19 is separated from the 147 terminal on the MHz switch and connected to the arm of K1. While receiving, the anode of D19 is connected to the 147 terminal as in the original circuit, but when K1 is energized D1 is connected to the 146 terminal of the MHz switch.

If the operator is receiving in the 146- to 147-MHz segment of the band, selecting the 1-MHz offset will switch D19 to add a BCD "1" to the MHz counter while transmitting. When receiving in the 146-to 147-MHz segment, the modification causes a BCD "1" to be subtracted from the MHz counter. The frequency display of the transceiver will indicate the frequency the rig is transmitting and receiving on. Offset direction is determined by the selected receiving frequency. The proper offset is automatically chosen, and operation below 146 MHz or above 148 MHz is impossible. Placing S1 in the NORMAL or open position restores normal operation.

An additional circuit was added to the FM-144 which may be of interest to owners of other synthesized rigs as well. Lock-up time of the phase-locked loop may vary depending on ambient temperature. A transmit-inhibit circuit will prevent the rig from transmitting until the loop is locked. Voltage dropped across the UNLOCK lamp turns Q1 on, which holds the base voltage of regulator control transistor Q3 at ground. Turning off Q3, a 2SC1908, cuts off the regulator pass transistor which prevents the transmitter from operating. R1 prevents the base-emitter junction of Q1 from shorting the UNLOCK lamp. When the loop is locked, the UNLOCK lamp is extinguished, Q1 is turned off, and the rig will transmit. Lock-up time is generally very rapid.

K1 and Q1 may be mounted on a small perforated board installed between the S meter and the right-side chassis rail.

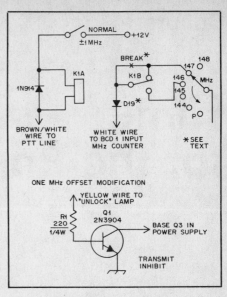

FM-144 modifications.

Color-coded leads from the board may be routed through the vinyl harness sleeves and result in a neat installation. S1 may be located in several places, depending on the needs of the operator. The author used a miniature toggle switch, mounted on the rear panel next to the dc power receptacle, toward the lower corner. An external switch may be connected to a plug compatible with the ACCESSORY jack. If the 1-MHz offset is used frequently, the operator may choose to mount S1 on the front panel.

Observation of the transmitter output on a spectrum analyzer confirmed that the modification had no effect on the excellent spectral purity of the FM-144. The modification does not require entry into any shielded enclosure, and no connection is made to any point where rf is present.

One last reminder: When 1-MHz offset is desired, the original OFFSET switch must be placed in the SIMPLEX position. Considering the simplicity of the modification, this is a small price to pay. — *Al Young, W2TMF*

Chapter 4

Hints
for the Power Supply

POWER SUPPLY FOR NEGATIVE AND POSITIVE VOLTAGES

Occasionally a negative voltage may be needed when only a positive supply is available. This may be necessary, for example, when using op amps. These are very useful devices, but suffer setbacks without a dual-polarity supply. Negative and positive voltages equal to and higher than the dc supply can be easily obtained without a transformer by using an RC oscillator and rectifying to the desired polarity. Such an oscillator is shown and operates at approximately 1200 Hz with added "totem pole" output transistors driven in complementary fashion. One output transistor is off when the other is on, and vice versa, which alternately connects the output load to the positive supply or ground. This gives much better efficiency than direct coupling to the oscillator. While a discrete-component oscillator is shown, it could be built with a digital-logic IC as discussed later.

Three rectifiers are shown in diagrams A, B and C. The one shown in A is a voltage doubler with positive output. The output voltage will not quite reach twice that of the supply, and will drop under load. The circuit shown in B is for a negative supply. Output voltage will be somewhat less than the positive supply voltage. However, many times an op amp will ignore such an imbalance.

The circuit shown in C is a negative doubler which requires some additional switching in conjunction to that provided by the oscillator. When the input is switched to the positive supply, C1 will be charged to the supply voltage with the polarity shown. The 2N3906 will be turned on by its base-bias resistors permitting C2 to charge to the supply voltage also. The 2N3904 will be slightly reverse biased by the forward-voltage drop across CR1, and therefore will be turned off. When the input is switched to ground, C1 makes the emitter of the 2N3904 negative which turns it on (but reverse biases CR1). The 2N3906 has no bias and is off. Therefore, C1 and C2 are connected in series across the output (CR2 also being reverse biased) and a negative voltage doubler is implemented. The advantage of these circuits, being driven by the oscillator against ground, is that they provide a common ground from supply to output. The actual output voltage of the negative doubler will be somewhat less than twice the positive supply voltage, of course. It could be used with a voltage regulator such as a Zener diode to obtain a negative voltage under load equal to the positive supply. Indeed, there are dual-tracking regulator ICs available such as the Silicon General SG3501, the Raytheon RC4194 and the Motorola MC1486 which will keep the positive and negative voltages identical.

The circuit values shown were for a very low current-drain supply for a low-power op amp. As an example of performance, the circuit in C yielded —23.5 volts no load from a + 12.6-volt supply with an input current drain of 0.57 mA. At an output current of 1 mA, the voltage dropped to —21.1 volts with an input current of 2.45 mA, and an efficiency of 68 percent.

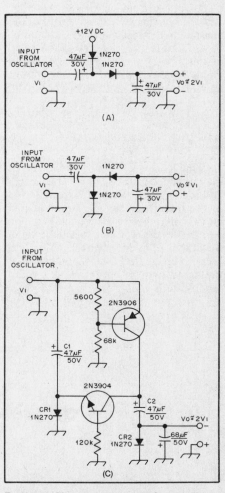

Typical rectifier circuits suitable for use with the oscillator. The circuit shown in A is a voltage doubler with positive output. The one in B will give a negative output equal to the supply voltage and the circuit in C is a voltage doubler with a negative output. Resistors are 1/2-watt composition.

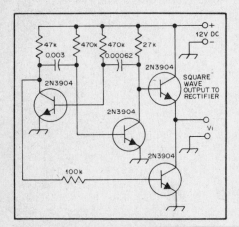

Schematic diagram of the discrete oscillator. Resistors are 1/2-watt composition. Capacitors are disk ceramic. Square wave output may be connected to the input of any rectifier circuit shown at right.

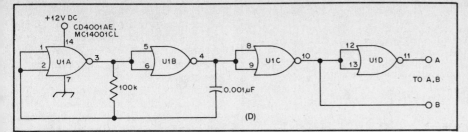

Schematic diagram of an IC oscillator. The outputs at A and B give equal amplitude voltages of opposite phase and may be fed to either the quadrupler or the octupler shown below.

Ripple was 15 mV pk-pk. The output dropped to the supply voltage at 1.6 mA drain, however.

IC-Oscillator Substitute

The circuit above shows a complementary MOS digital IC can be used as an oscillator in place of the circuit shown for the discrete oscillator, yielding the same efficiencies with fewer parts. Either output A or B can be used with the circuits of A, B and C; the arrangement will have common ground, and will be essentially identical to the discrete circuit since the IC has complementary MOS outputs. The RCA CD4001AE and Motorola MC14001CL as well as similar chips of other makers are a good choice here.

The IC circuit has greater capability than the discrete-component circuit since the two outputs A and B are exactly out of phase, or complementary, allowing us to implement higher multiplication. The quadrupler below is found in *The Radio Amateur's Handbook* and can be used by connecting to both outputs A and B of D. This arrangement yielded 40.5 volts at 0.5 mA with an efficiency of 62 percent with 12-V input. The circuit shown in F is an octupler and could, of course, be extended to many more multiplications. The disadvantages of these circuits are that they do not have a common ground between supply and output. Also, the power available is small since the IC should really not be called on for more than 3 to 4 mA per gate output. The supply voltage can vary from 3 or 5 volts at the low end to 15 or 18 volts at the high end depending on the manufacturer.

One can easily exchange pnp or npn transistors, reverse the diodes and electrolytic capacitors to obtain positive voltages from a negative supply. The IC oscillator can also be used in a positive ground arrangement. It is also possible to run the oscillator at much higher frequencies than those used in the previous circuits, thus reducing the necessary size of filter capacitor. Harmonic output at communications frequencies could be a problem, however.

All rectifier circuits are generally capable of quite high power levels if high-current rectifiers and switching transistors are used. The 1N270 has low forward voltage drop up to currents of approximately 60 mA. At higher currents, the new hot carrier rectifiers could be employed to keep the forward drop low and the efficiency high. High-current switching may best be done by using the oscillator as a wave-form source at low power, then switch with power transistors driven by it. The IC oscillator can produce base drive sufficient to switch respectable currents if high-gain output transistors are used. The complementary outputs A and B can be used to drive a totem-pole switch similar to the one used with the discrete-component oscillator, or complementary transistors (pnp and npn) could be used with a single driving waveform. Most likely, the simplest way to achieve high power would be with the very high-gain Darlington power transistors made by Motorola and others. Thus, there are many possibilities with regard to the voltages, polarities, and currents obtainable from a single dc supply without adding a transformer. — *Julian M. Pike, WAØTCU*

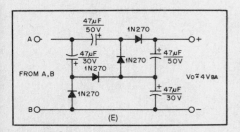

A quadrupler circuit suitable for use with the IC oscillator. The inputs A and B are connected to the outputs A and B of the IC oscillator above. A disadvantage — there is no common ground with respect to the initial voltage source.

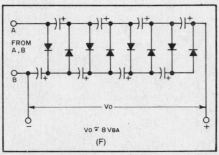

A voltage octupler circuit. Inputs A and B are to be connected to outputs A and B of the IC oscillator above.

RECTIFIER FOR DC RELAYS

Some of the best bargains in surplus relays are to be found in the low-voltage dc units. Their use where no battery is available, however, often means the construction of a separate power supply. This writer has used the circuit shown here to operate relays from a filament supply. To provide the normal operating voltage for the relay, the ac voltage should be about 2-1/2 times the rated dc voltage, since a half-wave rectifier is used. CR2 serves to carry the current generated by the decaying magnetic field of the relay coil, thereby protecting CR1 against high-voltage transients. If a high enough ac voltage is not available, a capacitor in parallel with CR2 will raise the dc voltage. This writer used a 50-μF capacitor in parallel with a relay coil rated at 12 volts, 200 mA, and operated it from a 12-volt filament circuit. The combination delivered only 10 volts, but this was' enough to close the relay reliably. — *The Rev. C. R. Clark, K4ZN*

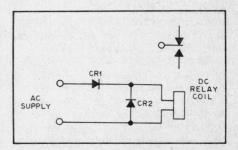

A simple method for operating a dc relay from an ac filament circuit. The PIV rectifier rating should be 2.8 times the ac supply voltage.

A HIGH-POWER SCR INVERTER

Desiring to operate portable from my trailer, I decided to build a high-power inverter. The unit described here will work off either a 24- or 32-volt storage battery. It can also be used with an alternator capable of delivering from 55 to 130 A. With a 55-A alternator, the maximum output is 1500 VA (volt-amperes). The 130-A alternator will give 3600 VA. A blower should be used if the output exceeds 1800 VA.

T1 is a modified Variac which allows operation from either 24/32- or 60-volt (dc) sources. If only 60-V operation is desired (some alternators are capable of producing 60 V) the 24/32-volt winding can be omitted. The movable arm on the Variac is removed and the center tap connected. The writer used a surplus Variac which was capable of handling 20 A. It had 205 turns of No. 12 wire for the original winding.

If 24- or 32-V operation is desired, the original 117-V winding of the Variac is used as a secondary and a bifilar primary

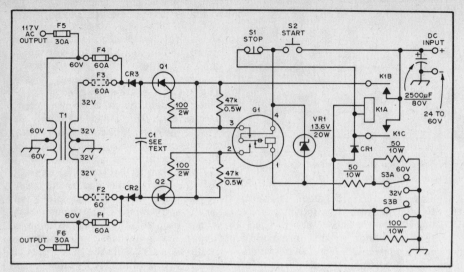

Schematic diagram of the inverter. The inverter is shown set up for 60-volt operation. For 24/32-volt operation, F1 and F4 are removed from their sockets and F2 and F3 are inserted at the dotted positions. S3 is switched to the 32-volt position.

C1 — 120 μF (see text for discussion).
CR1 — 2-A silicon diode, 400 PRV.
CR2,CR3 — 250-A silicon diode, 800 PRV (Poly Paks no. 87CU685).
G1 — 60-Hz vibrator, 12 volt (Cornell-Dubilier type 98600 or equivalent).
Q1, Q2 — 100-A SCR, 800 PRV (Poly Paks no. 92CU1167).
S1, S2 — Motor start/stop switch.
T1 — 20-A Variac, 117 V.

winding is added (observe the polarity shown on the drawing). For 24-V operation, the primary should consist of 38 turns (76 total) of No. 8 double-coated (glass) wire. It should also be possible to operate the inverter on 12 V (at approximately 720-W output), but the windings would be halved and heavier wire would be needed. For 32-V operation, the winding would consist of 48 turns (96 total). Since No. 8 wire is difficult to work with, 4 strands of No. 10 Formvar could be used. Two strands of No. 10 would be paralleled to give the equivalent of one strand of No. 8.

Operation

Operation of the inverter is as follows. Assume one SCR has just been turned on and the other one is in the nonconducting state. Current will flow in one half of the primary and the commutating capacitor (C1) will be charged through the other half. When the other SCR is turned on, it shuts off the one that was previously conducting. This is because the supply voltage plus the voltage in the charged com-

mutating capacitor appear as a reverse bias at the cathode of the previously conducting SCR.

The commutating capacitor (C1) consists of 10 120-μF oil-filled capacitors with 400-V (dc) rating each. *Do not use electrolytic capacitors for C1.* The SCRs are switched by means of vibrator G1. VR1 limits the voltage across the vibrator coil and consists of two 6.8-V, 10-W Zener diodes.

Using the Inverter

To use the inverter, the fuses F1 and F4 or F2 and F3 are inserted in either the 60- or 24/32-V sockets (but not both) and S3 is switched to the proper position. Always make sure the vibrator is in its socket — otherwise the fuses may blow if the unit is turned on. With 60-V battery operation, it is also advisable to use a 1-ohm, 200-W resistor in series with the inverter while starting. It should be shorted out while the inverter is running, however.

The START switch is depressed to energize the coil of K1. The contacts are closed and the inverter is connected to the line. When the STOP switch is depressed, the relay contacts open and the inverter is disconnected from the line. When the STOP switch is released, the line is still disconnected and remains so until the START switch is depressed again. The output voltage of the inverter varied from 150 V under no-load conditions to 110 V with a 1650-W resistive load. — *Russell Dunaja, W3BBF*

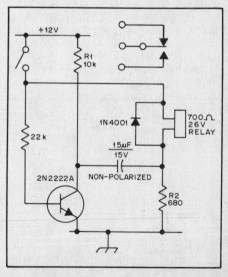

Schematic diagram of a voltage regulator suitable for use with the inverter and an alternator. In cases where this might be objectionable, this circuit would be useful, if the inverter is used with an alternator or generator only.
CR4, CR5 — 5-A silicon diode, 50 PRV.
T2 — 3-A filament transformer, 24-V ct.

REDUCING POWER DRAIN OF RELAYS

Two ideas for using 24- to 26-V surplus

relays on 12-V supplies were reported some time ago in *TT* (February 1973) and *ART5*. A modified version of one of these techniques turned up in *Electronics* (9 December 1976) but this time primarily as a means of substantially reducing the power drain of the relays. John R. Nelson points out that useful power saving can be achieved in this way with battery-operated equipment, taking advantage of the fact that a relay needs only about half of its nominal voltage during hold-in, provided that it can be given a boost during pull-in. By using a transistor to switch in voltage from a charged capacitor, the necessary extra voltage can be provided just when it is needed.

The system shown in the diagram is based on the non-polarized electrolytic capacitor which is initially charged to 12 V through R1 and R2. Closing the switch applies 12 V to the relay coil and, at the same time, turns on the transistor, thus dropping the positive side of the capacitor to earth. This effectively forces —12 V on the other side of the capacitor, putting some 24 V across the relay coil which then pulls in. Once the capacitor has discharged through R2 and the relay coil, approximately 7 V remains across the relay coil and this is sufficient to keep it energized.

The circuit as shown is intended for 26-V relays having coil resistances in the region of 1,000 Ω; to suit the requirements of different relays the value of R2 may have to be adjusted.

The capacitor should be a non-polarized type since there will be a reverse voltage across it whenever the relay is energized. Should power to the circuit be interrupted the switch must be opened and closed to reactivate the relay. A diode across the coil protects the transistor from transients. — Radio Communication, *February, 1977, published by the RSGB*

Operation of a 26-V relay from 12-V supply.

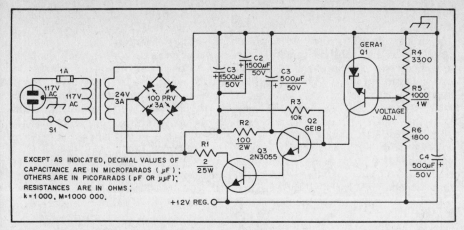

Inexpensive power supply for battery-operated transceivers.

BASE POWER SUPPLY FOR 2-METER TRANSCEIVERS

After getting my first 2-meter transceiver, it amazed me how many hams beside myself were running their rigs from batteries with chargers. Feeling there must be a need for an inexpensive 12-volt power supply, I dug through the junk box and found the parts to build this unit. If all parts for this supply are to be bought new, the cost will come close to $30.

The unit is compact, considering its capability to handle over 2 A of current, because of the series regulator doing away with the need for large filter capacitors. This regulating unit has the capability of handling up to 15 A through Q3, so that it could be used to power a mobile linear amplifier as well as a transceiver. The power supply shown here is capable of the 3 A required to run a Regency HR2A.

The supply is able to go from no load to full load with only a 0.2-volt drop. This works out to be 1.6-percent regulation. The ripple voltage for the unit is not measurable at the 200-mA level needed to run the receiver. When the unit is supplying 2.2 A, the ripple voltage increases to a level of 0.06 volt or 0.5 percent.

Output voltage for the unit shown in the drawing can be varied from 11.5 to 12.5 by use of R5 in the ripple-sensing network.

By varying the values of R4, R5 and R6 the builder can use the unit over a wider range of voltages. If the builder would like to increase the current capability of the supply, he need only increase the ratings of T1, CR1-CR4 and R1. Care should be taken not to make the wattage rating of R1 larger than actually needed, because R1 provides short-circuit protection for Q3.

If the builder has difficulty in finding Q1 (GE RA 1), a Zener diode in the range of 6.5 to 7.1 volts and a suitable npn transistor may be substituted. Component placement is not critical, and the only important requirement is the use of a large enough heat sink on Q3. Adjustment is accomplished by means of a dc voltmeter

while adjusting R5 to provide the proper output level. — *Dennis Sommers, WB4TTY*

ECONOMY POWER SUPPLY

In these days of transistorized equipment and digital logic, no workbench is complete without a power supply capable of delivering 12 and 5 volts dc with reasonably good regulation. The schematic diagram of a power supply that will answer this need was derived, with suitable modifications, from power supplies that have been featured in the ARRL *Handbook*. Many of the parts needed to construct the power supply can be found in the average junk box or may be purchased from Radio Shack or a similarly stocked parts emporium.

The output current from each supply is limited to approximately 500 mA. Above this level, the output voltage drops sharp-

ly. Within the 500-mA load range, the regulation is approximately 4 percent as measured from no load to full load. Not all Zener diodes provide equally good regulation, so it may be necessary to try several units or to increase the Zener-diode current-limiting resistor to obtain the indicated value of regulation. Better regulation could probably have been attained by increasing the ac input to the bridge rectifier to 18 volts. This was not done because it would increase the power dissipation in the transistors, necessitating the use of heat sinks. In its present configuration heat sinks are not required. The transistors are insulated from the chassis by the use of rubber grommets through which the mounting screws pass. With the power supply operating under full-load conditions, the power transistors do not become noticeably warm to the touch. This dual-voltage power supply has proved to be a most valuable addition to the workbench. — *Herbert L. Ley, ex-W3VYN*

IMPROVED REGULATOR CIRCUIT

While many amateurs are now using integrated-circuit voltage regulators, an external current-boosting transistor is usually required to increase the regulator current capacity. Normal current-boosting schemes, however, require additional active devices to duplicate some of the worthwhile regulator safety features (short-circuit protection, safe operating-area protection, and thermal shutdown). Here is a regulator circuit which retains these safety features through a current-sharing design. This regulator, intended for TTL circuits, has an output of 5 volts

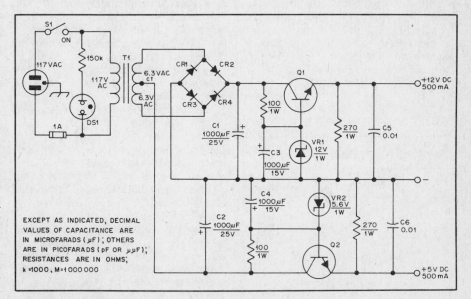

Schematic diagram of the economy power supply.
CR1-CR4, incl. — Silicon diode, 50 PRV, 3 A.
DS1 — Neon indicator lamp.
Q1, Q2 — Npn power transistor, 40 W (Radio Shack 276-592 or equiv.).
S1 — Spst switch.

T1 — 117-V pri., 12.6-V ct sec., 1.2 A (Radio Shack 273-1505 or equiv.).
VR1 — Zener diode, 12 V, 1 W.
VR2 — Zener diode, 5.6 V, 1 W.

at 5 amperes, and a typical load regulation of 1.4 percent.

R1 and R2 provide the necessary current division (assuming the transistor base-emitter voltage equals the diode drop). The voltage drops across R1 and R2 are equal, and the currents through R1 and R2 are inversely proportional to their resistances. In this circuit, R1 has four times the current flow of R2. For reasonable values of beta, the transistor emitter current will approximately equal its collector current, while the current through R2 will equal the current through the regulator. Under overload or short-circuit conditions, the protection circuitry of the regulator not only limits its own output current, but that of the external pass transistor too.

Thermal overload protection is extended to the external pass transistor when its heat sink has at least four times the capacity of the regulator (this is because both devices have almost the same input and output voltage and share the load current in a 4:1 ratio). For optimum current sharing between the regulator and transistor as temperature changes, the diode should be located physically near the pass transistor so its heat-sinking arrangement keeps it at the same temperature.

If the National LM340T regulator is used and mounted on the same heat sink as the transistor, the regulator should be electrically isolated from the heat sink as its case (pin 3) is grounded while the case (collector) of the transistor is at the regulator output potential. C1 prevents unwanted oscillations, while C2 improves the output impedance of the overall circuit. R3 is used to unload the excessive charge in the base region of the pass transistor when the regulator suddenly goes from full load to no load. The single-point ground system allows the regulator sense terminals (pins 2 and 3) to monitor load voltage directly rather than at some point along a possibly resistive ground-return path carrying up to 5 mA of load current. — *William R. Clabo, K9ASL/8*

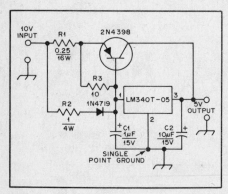

Short-circuit protection, safe operating-area protection, and thermal shutdown are safety features of this improved voltage regulator circuit.

FILM-CONTAINER BATTERY HOLDER

An excellent C cell battery holder, which offers the advantages of being inexpensive as well as easily attachable and separable, can be fabricated from 35-mm plastic film containers. Heavy-duty snap fasteners attached to both ends of the plastic container provide the terminals for a C cell, when placed in the battery holder.

Construction is simple; the fasteners consist of three parts: a ring, socket, and stud. The ring, with any paint removed, is centered and the prongs of the ring are forced through the plastic container and also through the plastic cap from the inside. A socket or stud is then centered on the protruding prongs of the ring. The entire assembly is then set against a hard surface and the ring is driven home with a hammer and a short section of 1/2-inch dowel rod. The choice of whether to use a socket- or stud-fastener configuration is left to the individual. Small pieces of aluminum foil folded several times and placed in the cap and container, flush with the end rings, provide excellent battery contact and also serve as spacers.

Several of the battery holders may be used in combination when needed, and the required voltage can be obtained by snapping the appropriate number of holders together. In addition, the recycled battery holders are inexpensive. Eight of the holders cost a total of fifty-five cents to construct. — *Allan Hale, WA9IRS/WB8UZG*

SIAMESE-TWIN POWER SUPPLY

A power supply for a high-power linear amplifier can contain a lot of metal and grow into a heavy, unwieldly monster. This became evident after a study of "Use Surplus and Save," October 1967 *QST*, in which W1ICP described a supply using two power transformers to obtain the desired voltages and current. A string of six high-capacitance electrolytic capacitors and associated items add to this bulk and weight.

An answer to problems of this nature is to build the equipment on two chassis, either of which is easier to move around. The transformers, switching system, and protective devices would go on one chassis; the rectifiers and filters on another. Interconnections should be made with high-voltage cabling and barrier strips. Quick-disconnect plugs might not be safe to use at these points. For flexibility, both chassis should be the same size, and if vertical stacking is more practical, heavy aluminum angle stock could be used on the corners. — *Julian N. Jablin, W9IWI*

A REGULATED POWER SUPPLY FOR FM TRANSCEIVERS

When a regulated power supply capable

of operating a 10-W 220-MHz fm transceiver from 117 volts ac was needed, all of the parts were rounded up locally in an hour and a half of shopping (including travel time). In any metropolitan area large enough to support a TV-service parts distributor and a Radio Shack store, it should be possible to duplicate this power supply at the same cost or less. The power supply was designed to provide up to 2 amperes continuously at 12 volts, although the output voltage may be adjusted internally within the range of 9 to 13 volts with the circuit constants shown in the diagram.

Circuit Description

Up to point A in the schematic drawing, the circuit is a fairly conventional; step-down transformer, full-wave bridge rectifier, and capacitor-input filter. The use of two transformers, rather than one, allows a certain degree of flexibility of operation, in that the supply may be used on either 117 or 235 volts ac with only minor differences in wiring. The dc voltage at point A is approximately 30. Q1 is used as a series pass transistor to drop the voltage at point A of the diagram to the desired 12-volt output value, and maintain that voltage over wide variations in the output load current. U2 is an integrated-circuit voltage regulator which, with the aid of a few external components, is capable of handling up to 600 mA of output current. Since an output current of 2 A is desired, however, U2 is used here to properly bias Q1, which has a much higher current rating. The inner circuitry of U2 can be divided into four basic elements: a fixed voltage reference, a variable voltage reference derived from the fixed reference, an error amplifier, and an output regulator. An internal Zener diode is used as the fixed reference. This reference voltage is applied to one input of a differential amplifier (a differential amplifier responds to the difference between two applied voltage levels), while the other input is connected to the junc-

An adjustable 12-V power supply.

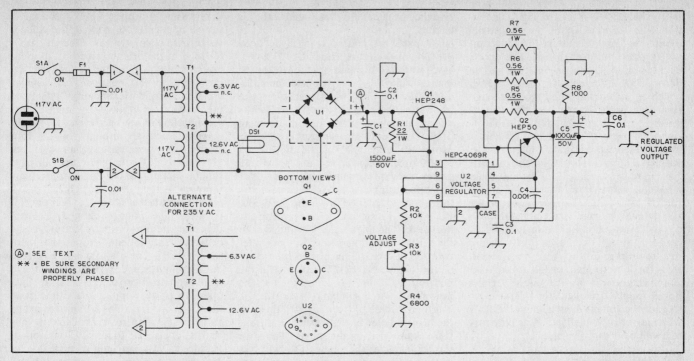

Circuit diagram for the power supply. Unless otherwise noted, all resistors are 1/2-watt composition. Component designations not listed below are for circuit-board layout purposes. Capacitors are disk ceramic except those with polarity marked, which are electrolytic.

C1 — 1500 µF electrolytic, 50 volts dc (Sprague TVA 1318).
C5 — 1000 µF electrolytic, 50 volts dc (Sprague TVA 1316).
DS1 — 12-volt pilot lamp.
F1 — 1.5 A, type 3AG fuse.
Q1 — Motorola HEP248 or equiv.

Q2 — Motorola HEP50, 2N706A, or equiv.
R3 — 10-kΩ printed-circuit-mounting pot (Radio Shack 271-218).
R5, R6, R7 — 0.56 Ω 1-watt wirewound resistor (Radio Shack 271-072).
S1 — Miniature dpst toggle.
T1 — 117-volt pri., 6.3-volt ct sec. (ct unused),

3 amperes (Radio Shack 273-1510).
T2 — 117-volt pri., 12.6-volt at sec. (ct unused), 3 amperes (Radio Shack 273-1511).
U1 — Full-wave bridge rectifier assembly, 50 volts, 10 amperes (Radio Shack 276-1156).
U2 — Motorola HEP C4069R, MC1469R, or MC1569R.

tion of R3 and R4 (pin 8 of U2). R3 (in series with R2) and R4 form an externally adjustable voltage divider, from the differential amplifier output (pin 9 of U2) to ground. Thus, the output of the differential amplifier will swing to the level that results in the voltage at pin 8 of U2 being identical to the fixed reference voltage.

A second differential amplifier serves as the error amplifier. One input (pin 6 of U2) is tied directly to pin 9, while the other input (pin 5 of U2) is connected to the power-supply output bus. The error-amplifier output controls the internal output-regulator bias of the IC, which in turn controls the bias applied to Q1. When connected in this manner, the error amplifier responds to any difference between the power-supply output level and the (previously adjusted) voltage reference level. The output regulator acts on Q1 to correct the discrepancy. C3 and C4 are used in the interest of maintaining amplifier stability. R5, R6, R7 and Q2 are included in the circuit to protect the power supply and regulator in the event of an inadvertent short circuit between the output terminals or if the current demanded by the load is too heavy for safe operation. The operation of the current-limiting feature is as follows: When the current flowing through the parallel combination of R5, R6 and R7 (equivalent parallel resistance of about 0.18 ohm) is large enough to produce a 0.6-volt drop across

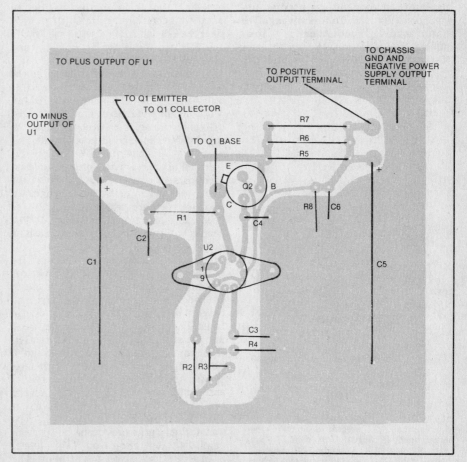

Foil pattern and parts layout for the regulated power supply.

the resistors, Q2 is biased into conduction. The action of Q2 on the IC internal output regulator results in the reduction of the current through Q1. The short-circuit output current in this case will be limited to 3.3 amperes (0.6/0.18 = 3.3), which is within the safe regulator/pass-transistor limits. The value of the current-sensing resistance required for short-circuit currents of other than 3.3 amperes is calculated as follows by Ohm's Law: $R_{SC} = 0.6/I_{SC}$ where R_{SC} is the current-sensing resistance and I_{SC} is the maximum allowable short-circuit current. If a long run of cable is used between the power supply and the load, the voltage drop in the cable may be large enough to be of concern. If this is the case, a separate remote voltage-sensing wire may be run from the load to pin 5 of U2, rather than connecting pin 5 to the output at the power supply. The regulator will compensate for the voltage drop in the cable. This wire may be of a small gauge, as little current will be drawn through it.

Construction Details

In the author's power supply, most of the components were mounted on an etched-circuit board (see the pattern drawing), although point-to-point wiring on a "perf" board would have sufficed. As the transistors inside the IC are capable of operation at vhf, it is good practice to use short leads for interconnecting the regulator components to prevent unwanted oscillations from occurring. The manufacturer recommends a low-inductance connection between the case of the HEP C4069R and ground. No

evidence of instability was noted with this circuit.

All parts are housed in an 8 × 6 × 3-1/2-inch Minibox (Bud CU-2109-A). Two standoff insulators support the pc board, while the power transformers, T1 and T2, are bolted directly to the Minibox. As Q1 dissipates several watts when maximum load current is being drawn, a heat sink is required. The Motorola HEP500, consisting of an MS-10 predrilled heat sink and an MK-15 power-transistor mounting kit, is ideal for this application. In accordance with the instructions supplied with the HEP500, the MK-15 socket is first installed on the heat sink. The mica washer included with the MK-15 should be coated on both sides with a thin layer of silicone thermal compound (Radio Shack 276-1372), with the bottom of Q1 and the center area of the heat sink treated similarly. After the Q1 emitter and base pins are inserted through the proper holes in the washer, the transistor is mounted in the socket. The mica washer insulates the case of Q1 (which is connected internally to the collector) electrically from the heat sink and chassis, while the silicone compound increases the thermal conductivity between Q1 and the heat sink. Care should be taken to prevent contact between the case of Q1 and any grounded object, as the full supply voltage appears on the transistor case. The current-limiting feature will not protect the device from destruction in event of an accidental short from Q1 to ground, since the current sensing resistors (R5, R6 and R7) are connected between Q1 and the power-supply output terminals.

The heat-sink assembly is bolted to the rear panel of the Minibox with no. 6 hardware. The MS-10 is 3 inches high and 4-1/2 inches wide, so it must be located off center in order to accommodate the fuse holder and the line cord on the rear panel. A 1-inch-diameter hole was punched in the rear panel prior to the heat sink installation to allow access to the transistor socket pins. Short lengths of hookup wire are used between the pc board and the transistor socket. U1 is coated with silicone compound and then bolted to one of the inside walls of the Minibox, which serves as a heat sink for the diodes. Ventilation of the Minibox is desirable. Large holes punched or cut in the sides and bottom of the box and covered with perforated metal stock can be used, or ventilation holes can be drilled individually in the metal enclosure. The regulator IC is mounted directly on the pc board, and it does not require a heat sink.

After the pilot lamp, the power switch, and the binding posts are installed on the front panel, T1 and T2 can be bolted in place near the front of the box. The transformer primaries can be tied in parallel for operation from 117 volts ac, or in series for 235-volt ac operation. The T1 and T2 secondaries must be connected

in series and in proper phase for the power supply to operate correctly. If the unloaded ac output voltage as measured with a VOM is in the neighborhood of 20 volts, the windings are connected properly. If, however, the VOM reads approximately 6 volts, the secondaries are out of phase and the leads from *one* of the transformer secondaries must be reversed. If the primary loads are brought out to four separate terminal posts, changing from 117-volt to 235-volt operation will be a simple matter of changing appropriate jumpers. Alternatively, a 117/235 switch may be installed easily on the rear panel if frequent line voltage changes are anticipated. In either case, attention should be paid to the matter of proper phasing of the windings. The use of a 3-wire ac cord installed in a properly grounded outlet is intelligent practice for this and any line-operated power supply. If a transformer with a secondary rating of approximately 18 volts at 3 amperes is available, it may be used in place of T1 and T2. It is not advisable to use an unmodified 24- or 25.2-volt transformer to replace T1 and T2. The maximum allowable dc input voltage to U2 is 35 volts, and the unloaded output voltage of a 24-volt transformer, full-wave bridge rectifier, and capacitor-input filter exceeds this value. If such a transformer is on hand, it may be possible to remove turns from the secondary winding to bring the voltage down to within bounds. A Stancor P-8388 open-frame transformer rated at 25.2 volts and 2.8 amperes was tried as a "guinea pig" for this procedure. Removal of the outer protective wrapping revealed that the secondary was wound over the primary, and that it was possible to remove turns from the secondary without difficulty. The unloaded secondary voltage was measured (the unloaded voltage will usually differ from the listed voltage at the rated load) and then 10 turns were removed and the secondary voltage measured again. The new voltage was 2 volts less than the original voltage, giving a figure of 0.2 volts per turn for that particular secondary. It was then possible to calculate the number of turns to be removed in order to reduce the unloaded voltage to 20 volts.

Operation

The supply as described will run continuously at 12 volts with 2 amperes of load current. The ripple voltage on the output is on the order of 30 mV peak to peak or less. If a higher output current is desired (8 amperes, for example), the only limiting factors in the present components are the transformer current rating and the value of the short-circuit current-limiting resistors (R5, R6, R7), which can be adjusted accordingly. If it is desired to have front-panel adjustment of the output voltage, R3 may be replaced by a conventional pot. — *Ed Kalin, WA1JZC*

Inside view of the no-junkbox regulated power supply. The use of the 4-inch-square pc board (visible in the right foreground) simplifies the interconnection of most of the parts. The full-wave bridge rectifier assembly (U1) and the heat sink for Q1 are bolted to the rear Minibox wall. T1 and T2 occupy the left foreground.

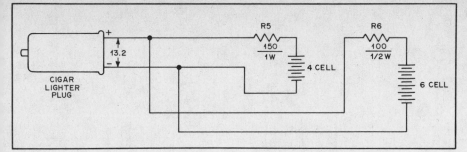

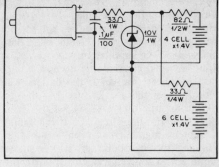

Schematic diagram of the circuit suggested for use in charging NiCad batteries from dc power source.

A modified version of the circuit given, which allows for recharging one set of batteries while using the second set in a mobile (hand-held) rig.

CHARGING THOSE NICADS

NiCad batteries offer an efficient yet compact power source which can provide greater design flexibility for portable equipment. An advantage of these cells is that the output voltage changes only slightly over the discharge cycle range — theoretically 0.15 volt. In an emergency one can discharge the battery below one volt, if the equipment will operate at that dc level: The practice is not recommended.

A question often asked is "How many times can a NiCad cell be recharged?" There is no definitive answer because of variables involved. A guestimation is 500 times or more for a cylindrical cell. End of life occurs when cells no longer provide 80 percent of original capacity. NiCads do have a tendency to self-discharge when not in use.

A precaution should be stressed in working with NiCad cells: Never attempt to solder to a NiCad cell or battery that does not have solder tabs. Heat from soldering or from a high charging current may cause a battery to explode. Use pressure connections for untabbed cells or batteries. A battery holder is recommended.

The method of charging is one area of confusion for many users of NiCad cells. If a charging unit is furnished with a purchased piece of NiCad-powered equipment, use the charger exactly as recommended.

Any transformer to be used for a NiCad charging circuit should provide a secondary voltage of about twice the dc voltage rating of the cell or battery to be charged. Never charge NiCads in parallel without placing an equalizing resistor in series with each battery.

When the batteries of a hand-held transceiver have run down and a charger is not readily available, the battery in your car can save the day. Using a 6 × 4 battery-pack configuration of a popular fm transceiver, you can charge your batteries from the cigarette lighter socket of your car. When charging in this manner, *keep the engine turned off!* In addition to variations in voltage, the spikes and other "garbage" on the 12-volt bus of the automotive electrical system are abundant.

Charging circuits are designed to provide a constant-current charging rate. This means that the resistance of the "outside world" circuit is many times larger than the internal resistance of the cell.

Actual design and construction of chargers can be quite simple. Table 1 gives ball-park figures to use for charger design parameters. For a completely discharged NiCad battery, a typical recharge period would be 14 hours. If a cell is to be on charge for more than 14 hours, switch the charger to a trickle rate. Remember, too, that only NiCads designed to take a fast charge should be fast-charged. — *Bud Meyer, K2PMA*

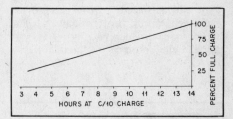

Curves for charge level vs. charge time (rate) for all methods discussed in the text, except fast-charge types.

SURGE PROTECTION

The 3000-volt power supply described in the *Handbook* (51st edition), uses a dc relay and a dropping resistor which protect the supply from the high inrush of current at turn-on time. Using the power supply on 117 volts ac, a simpler protection system, with fewer components, will provide an equivalent function. The diagram shows the change in the primary circuit. When K1A is energized, R1 introduces a voltage drop in the primary of T1 until the capacitor bank is nearly charged. When this occurs, the voltage drop across R1 lessens after a small time interval and allows K2B to pull in, thus applying full primary voltage as R1 is removed electrically from the circuit.

This change does away with the need for a 117-volt dc supply to energize the coil of K2, the large 300-Ω, 50-watt resistor, and one contact on K1, as it is not necessary to break both inputs of the primary. — *Bob Varone, WB2GLI*

Table 1

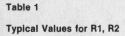

Typical Values for R1, R2

E_{ac}	mA C 10	n =	E_{batt}	R1	R_{dis} WATTS	R2	R_{dis} WATTS
7.1	22.5	2	—	75	1/4	N.A.	—
7.1	22.5	4	—	27	1/4	N.A.	—
7.1	50	4	—	12	1/4	33	1/4
14	22.5	—	5	150	1/4	N.A.	—
14	50	4	—	68	1/4	220	1/4
28	50	—	12	110	1/2	330	1/4
28	100	4	—	91	2	270	1/2
14	50	6	—	43	1/4	120	1/4
28	250	—	12	43	5	120	2

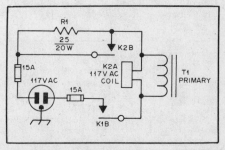

Simplified surge-protection circuit for use with power supply.

12 VOLTS THE EASY WAY

Power amplifiers designed for mobile operation generally require up to 10 amperes of current at 12-volts dc. Commercial power supplies in this range are quite expensive. A used automobile battery is an alternative. If the battery will not hold a charge, it is still usable to power an amplifier for OSCAR contacts.

If you try the circuit of the bargain-basement high-current supply shown in the illustration, the battery will be under constant slow charge except during transmitting periods. The switch in the positive lead permits the operator to place the battery in either a charge or operate position. The level of the electrolyte should be checked regularly and distilled water added as needed. Be sure to provide good ventilation for the battery. The hydrogen gas, which is a by-product of the charging process, is flammable. — *W1XZ*

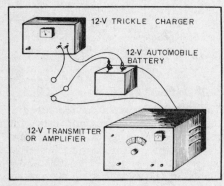

Bargain-basement high-current supply for 12-V linear amplifiers. The battery is charged constantly, except during the actual satellite pass.

REDUCING HUM FROM HWA-7-1 POWER SUPPLY

Many owners of equipment which uses the Heath HWA-7-1 power supply seem to be bothered by excessive hum. This problem applies particularly to the HW-7 receiver. A trick used to reduce hum and audio howl in old-time regenerative receivers is very effective in curing the problem with the HW-7. As shown in the illustration, two 0.01-mF capacitors are connected in series across the power-supply transformer secondary. The midpoint of the capacitor connection is grounded to the chassis. — *R. J. Beckwith, W1HHK*

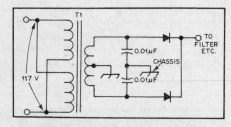

This HWA-7 modification reduces hum.

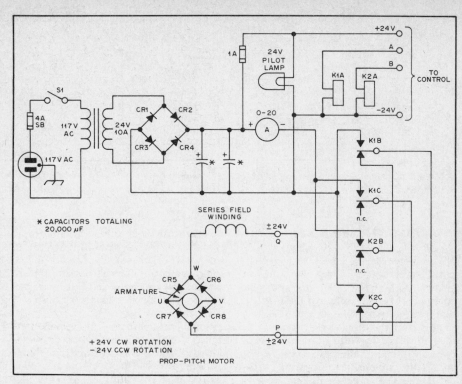

Power-supply and diode arrangement at the motor for two-wire control of a prop-pitch motor. Relays K1 and K2 are 24-V dc types. The letters P, Q, T, U, V and W refer to the terminals on the motor. Diodes CR1-CR8, incl. are 100 PRV, 15 A.

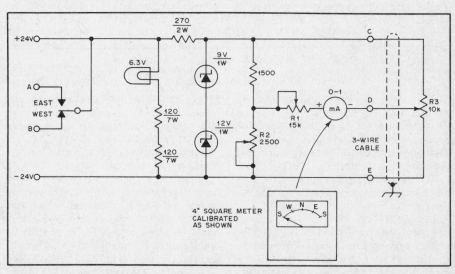

The control unit for the prop-pitch motor. R1 is used to calibrate the meter at full scale and R2 is used to set the meter for zero deflection. R3 is located at the rotator and is used for sensing direction.

TWO-WIRE CONTROL FOR PROP-PITCH MOTORS

Prop-pitch motor control usually involves the use of several wires. The system described here uses only two wires, which greatly simplifies this rotator system. Basically, all of the components are located at the shack. Only three wires are required for the direction indicator, and two for powering the motor. By using diode logic, only two wires are necessary. The motor speed is the same in either direction. The direction indicator, power supply, and the arrangement of the diodes at the motor, are shown in the accom-

panying diagrams.

The control system offered here need not be used, but the motor will run more efficiently with dc as compared to an ac voltage. The 24-volt secondary can be wound on an old TV power-transformer core, retaining the primary winding. Since the duty is intermittent, No. 14 copper wire is adequate for the secondary. The motor operates over a voltage range from 24 to 30. The current consumption in normal use is 6 to 9 amperes, and in very cold weather, 10 to 15 A. The starting current is in excess of 20 A. — *William M. Fugate, W8IYD*

Chapter 5

Antenna Tidbits

UPGRADE YOUR HAM-M WITH DELAYED BRAKING

Since I installed my Ham-M rotator some months ago, I have promised myself that I was going to install the modification which allows the brake solenoid to remain energized for a few seconds after ending rotation.

Now that I've had a chance to see the new Ham-M II control box, and the method used by CDE to solve the tower twisting problem, I was inspired to get started with a modification. In case you're not familiar with the Model II, it employs an additional brake-release switch requiring that you hold the brake-release switch a second or two after releasing the rotation switch.

Initially, I started out to use W1FBY's approach, but after thinking about the size of capacitor needed, I decided to design something that would fit inside the present control unit case. My design does that without drilling a hole or making any major changes to the original wiring. Mostly, leads are unsoldered and tied together and taped.

Circuit Operation

The 5000-ohm relay is energized by the operating switch and held closed after release for approximately 1-3/4 seconds by means of the 500-µF capacitor. The relay contacts supply primary 120 V to the main transformer, which continues to hold the brake off after rotation power is removed.

Note the addition of the 200-µF capacitor in parallel with the original 50-µF filter. This is required because the 500-µF capacitor across the relay coil increases the control voltage, thereby causing approximately a 15° error between readings. The additional 200-µF capacitor

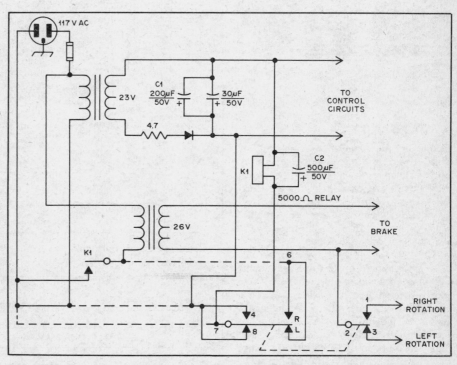

The Ham-M rotator electrical circuit can be modified as shown above for delayed braking. The dotted lines leading to the 117-V circuit represent original wiring.

increases the control voltage such that identical readings are obtained during rotation or at rest. My modification also causes the unit to read position whenever it is plugged in. I have a master switch which removes all accessories when the station is not in use.

To increase the indicator lamp life, I changed the lamps to 28-V types. The relay fits nicely near the left front just above the screwdriver-adjust calibration control. The capacitors are fitted easily near the rear of the meter. — *W.J. Short, WB4TBO*

SOURCE FOR INSULATORS

One item that is almost impossible to find, but is a necessary component for amateur work, is the common insulator. Feed-through, standoff, and antenna insulators just don't seem to exist anymore. One answer to the problem is to use sheet polystyrene. Nearly any plastic dealer or hobby shop stocks sheet poly, and the material can be cut and drilled to form almost any type of insulator. Polystyrene will handle any rf or dc voltage an amateur is likely to encounter and the material is extremely low loss. — *W1ICP*

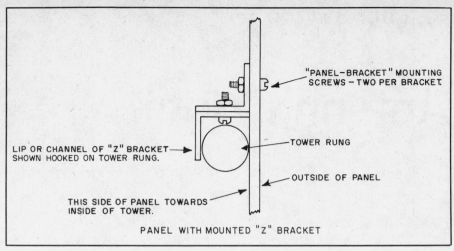

Installation of the shield on a tower rung.

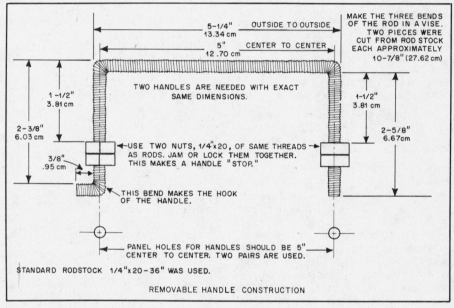

Removable handle construction.

A TOWER SHIELD

To prevent the "small-fry" from climbing your tower resulting in possible injuries and a legal suit, a tower shield will eliminate the appeal of climbing the structure. This tower shield is simple but effective. The low cost and easy construction make it well worth the protection and security that most hams need!

The tower shield is simply composed of panels that enclose the tower and make climbing practically impossible. These panels are five feet in height and are wide enough to fit snugly between the tower legs and flat against the rungs. A height of five feet is sufficient in most every case. The panels are constructed from 18-gauge galvanized sheet metal obtained and cut to proper dimensions from a local sheet-metal shop. A lighter gauge could probably be used, but the extra physical weight of the heavier gauge is an advantage if no additional means of securing the panels to the tower rungs are utilized. The three types of metals, used for the components of the shield, are supposedly rust proof and nonreactive. The panels are galvanized sheet steel, the brackets aluminum, and the screws and nuts are brass. Total cost of all parts was about $20. The tower shield consists of three panels, one for each of the three sides, supported by two brackets. These brackets are constructed from six-inch pieces of thin aluminum angle stock. Two

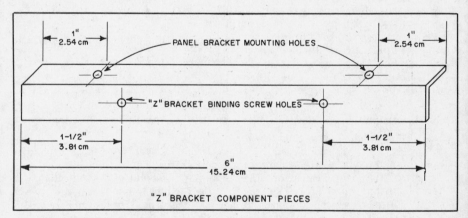

Mechanical features of the tower shield. At the top is the installation of the shield on a tower rung. In the middle drawing is the removable handle and at the bottom is the Z bracket.

of these pieces are bolted together to form a Z bracket. The Z brackets are bolted together with flat-head (binding-head) brass machine screws.

The panels were laid flat for the measuring, marking and drilling. The first measurement is from the top of the upper mounting rung on the tower to the top of the bottom rung. These mounting rungs were selected to position the panel on the

Panel with mounted Z bracket.

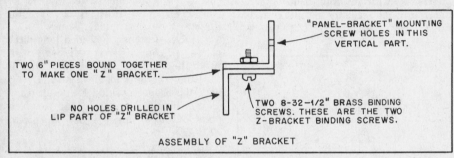

Assembly of the Z bracket for the tower shield.

tower. This distance from rung to rung was then marked on the panel. Using the same size brass screws and nuts, bolt the top vertical portion of each Z bracket to the panel. The mounting-screw holes were drilled about one inch from the end of the Z brackets so that an offset clearance occurred between the Z-bracket binding-screw holes and the panel-bracket mounting-screw holes. The panel holes were drilled to match the Z-bracket holes.

The panels are held on the tower by their own weight. They are not easy to grasp because they fit snugly between the tower legs. If the need exists for added safety against deliberate removal of the panels, this can be accomplished by means of tie wires. A small hole can be drilled in the panel just above, just below, and in the center of each Z bracket. Run a piece of heavy galvanized wire through the top hole, around the Z bracket, and then back through the hole just below the Z bracket. Twist together the two ends of the wire. One tie wire should be sufficient for each panel, but use two if desired.

The completed panels are rather bulky and difficult to handle. A feature that is useful if the panels have to be removed often for tower climbing or accessibility is a pair of removable handles. The removable handles can be constructed from one threaded rod and eight nuts. The two pairs of handle holes were drilled in the panels a few inches below the top Z bracket and several inches above the bot-

tom Z bracket. For panel placement or removal, the handles are hooked in these holes in the panels. The hook, on the top of the handle, fits into the top hole of each pair of the handle holes. The handle is optional, but for the effort required it certainly makes removal and replacement much safer and easier. — *Baker Springfield, W4HYY and Richard Ely, WA4VHM*

ALUMINUM TOWERS — SOME THINGS TO WATCH FOR!

Nine years ago I became the owner of my first tower and beam — a self-supporting spire, topped by a new tribander. It was 48 feet tall and set in concrete. It was made of aluminum (no painting or other maintenance problems)! Sounds wonderful, doesn't it?

Last fall, I noticed some extra flexing at the middle joint, 24 feet up. Early winter weather in Michigan was not conducive to thoughts of taking down and repairing the tower. Also, it had been up nearly nine years and a few more months wouldn't make it much worse, or so I thought!

In late March the condition was much more obvious. The tower had taken on a "dog leg" at the middle joint and watching it in the brisk March breezes scared me. A tower-lowering party was organized and once the system was

horizontal in the back yard, considerable damage was evident. The bolt holes in one leg were elongated beyond drilling out to a larger size, and on one of the opposing legs metal fatigue had cracked the material nearly three quarters of the way through. Also, we found two frost-splits in one leg. How could a hollow aluminum tower leg get frost-splits at 30 feet above ground? Don, WB8NUS, found the answer by pushing a length of electrical cord through the leg and finding several spiders' nests had been formed inside the leg. These had trapped the moisture which entered at the joints above this section and a hard freeze had done the rest.

Upon removing the bolts which held the two sections together at the joint where the elongation had occurred, the bolts were found to have been etched away from an original diameter of 3/8-inch to approximately 3/16-inch at the center. We removed all the bolts from the tower and found this reduction in diameter to be quite common, evidently due to electrolysis of the dissimilar metals.

The frost damage and crack were repaired by heli-arc welding and the two sections where the elongation had taken place were aligned and welded together. All the other original bolt holes were drilled out undersize, and new galvanized 7/16-inch bolts were driven in, replacing all the original ones. The coax runs on the tower were checked with the technique using a dummy load at the far end and a wattmeter at each end. The rotator and beams were reconditioned (using rust-resistant paint on the original plated fittings) and a hearty crew once again erected my "sky hooks."

If you have had a tower up for several years, please don't take it for granted that everything is still in good shape just because it withstood Mother Nature's last onslaught. Give your tower a good general inspection with a pair of binoculars at least twice a year, preferably during a stiff wind. If it is aluminum remove a bolt or two and check for deterioration. This would also be a good time to check the ground connections to make sure the ground clamps are in good condition and tight on the cable which ties the tower leg to the ground rod.

Aluminum ground conductors are not permitted within 18 inches of the earth (according to the National Electrical Code) and a few wraps of cable around a tower leg or a ground rod do not constitute a good electrical connection. — *H. J. Bell, WA8LAY*

ANOTHER SEALANT FOR ANTENNAS

There are many kinds of weatherproofing material available for sealing antenna connections and coaxial-cable fittings against moisture and corrosion-causing substances. Some of the compounds are messy to work with and result in an unsightly mess once they are applied.

During some recent experiments with various sealants, the writer tried a tube of Dupont no. 6111N clear windshield sealer. A 1-3/4-ounce tube was purchased for less than a dollar in the automotive department of a nearby variety store. The substance was applied to a 450-MHz Cushcraft 4-pole antenna to provide a protective coating over the mounting bolts and nuts (to prevent rusting), and over each of the gamma-rod joints to insure against corrosion. Finally, each of the coaxial connectors on the antenna were doped with the compound to keep moisture from entering them.

The result was excellent. After the sealant dried it was completely invisible, yet provided a thin, durable coating over the protected parts. The life span of the 6111N material should be similar to that of other compounds designed for outdoor use. — *W1FB*

THREE-BAND MATCHING SYSTEM FOR A 40-METER DOUBLET

A common method for energizing a half-wave antenna is to feed it at the center with parallel-conductor TV lead-in, or twin-lead as it is usually called, and to use an open stub for matching the 50- to 70-Ω antenna resistance to the 300-Ω impedance of the line. However, this technique, as described in the latest edition of *The ARRL Antenna Book*, generally gives proper matching on only one band.

After a number of trial-and-error calculations on a Smith Chart, along with lots of cut-and-try experimenting, I devised a three-stub matching scheme so that I could operate my 40-meter doublet on 40, 20 and 15 meters. The illustration shows this method and gives the lengths of the stubs and their positions along the feed line. The dimensions shown are for standard twin-lead, with a velocity factor of 0.82. All of the stubs are open at the ends and are made from the same type of line as the feed line. Note that the two lower stubs are connected at the same point on the feed line.

The length of the longest stub is fairly critical. It should first be cut to 17 feet and then trimmed no more than two inches at a time, until the SWR is minimum in the center or the desired portion of the 20-meter band. The feed line can then be matched with a 4:1 broadband balun to a 75-Ω coaxial cable from the transmitter. With my antenna, the described matching system gives an SWR of less than 2.5 to 1 over all of the three bands, with minimum values of 1.3 to 1 on 40 and 15 meters, and 1.7 to 1 on 20 meters. As with any multiband antenna, one must guard against harmonic radiation. — *Frank Stuart, K7UUC*

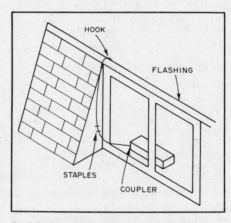

Roof flashing serves as antenna.

APARTMENT DWELLER'S ANTENNA

After trying several different indoor antenna configurations in my apartment with only mediocre results, I thought of using the metal flashing around the roof as an antenna. I simply formed a hook out of 1/16-inch model airplane "music wire" and hooked it over the edge of the roof. A flexible wire was attached to the music wire and brought into the shack to a conventional L-network coupler. The system performs remarkably well on all bands (80 through 10 meters); over 100 countries have been worked with it in less than eight months. In addition, it is quite inconspicuous. The antenna seems to exhibit directional properties favoring the longest dimension of the building, but is effective in all directions.

The only difficulty experienced so far has been corrosion of the music wire leading to poor contact with the metal flashing. This problem has been solved by soldering a piece of tinned copper wire (which appears to corrode more slowly than the iron wire) to the music wire and then wrapping it around the hook. — *Ira Lipton, WA2OAX*

HY-GAIN 18AVT/WB VERTICAL ANTENNA MODIFICATION

The Hy-Gain model 18AVT/WB is a vertical antenna, designed for use on the 80-through 10-meter amateur bands. Operation on 80 meters is possible because a mobile-type 75-meter loading coil and whip are mounted at the top of the antenna. Bandwidth on 80 is narrow, and the operating frequency is selected by adjusting the length of the whip. When the whip is cut to the proper length for 75-meter phone operation, it is not possible to obtain a proper match on the cw end of the band unless the whip is replaced with one of the proper length. Rather than purchase a new whip assembly, I fastened a 12-inch long piece of No. 12 copper wire to the whip with two Fahnestock clips. This allows me to slide the wire up and down on the whip until the proper position is found, using an SWR bridge connected at the feed point of the antenna. — *Al Skornicka, K8WXQ*

[Editor's Note: A more permanent method is to use small cable clamps to secure the added wire to the whip.]

A DIELECTRIC "NO-NO"

Let's call this a hint, rather than a hint and kink. In fact, I would like to hint strongly that certain kinds of insulating material, regardless of how good they look to the human eye, are definite members of the "no-no" family. Vhf and uhf men are especially cognizant of the need to select suitable insulating materials, as the effect of using an improper dielectric substance becomes more pronounced as the operating frequency is increased.

Among the worst offenders available to amateurs on a widespread basis is nylon. Polyvinylchloride (PVC) is a bad hombre also. Despite the physically durable nature of the materials, they are extremely lossy. In circuits where considerable rf power is used, they will absorb the rf energy, heat up rapidly, then warp or melt. Even though the insulating agent may not burn or melt (depending on the power level involved), the losses will be high.

The photograph shows the catastrophic result of using PVC tubing for building a loading coil for a top-loaded vertical antenna. When 300 watts of rf power were supplied to the antenna, there was an immediate and constant change in SWR. Eventually the SWR became so great that the transmitter would not load into the antenna system.

Examination of the vertical showed the

40-METER HALF-WAVE ANTENNA

4'4"

7'5"

3'

16'4" (SEE TEXT)

6'6"

300-OHM TWIN-LEAD

4 TO 1 BALUN

75-OHM COAX TO XMTR.

These matching stubs enable a 40-meter doublet antenna to work on 20 and 15 meters.

Melted PVC tubing.

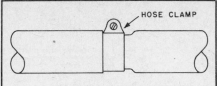

Hose clamp aids disassembly of tower.

top section (loading inductor and above) to be leaning at a 30-degree angle with respect to the lower member of the vertical. The inner PVC support tube for the coil had overheated, causing it to melt the plastic centering disk at the lower end of the coil. The photograph shows the warped inner tubing section — complete with rf burn holes!

The inductor was rewound on two-inch diameter solid phenolic rod (impregnated-cloth variety), and the problem was resolved. In an ideal situation (though frail, physically) an air-wound coil, or one placed on a ceramic form, would be used. — *W1CKK*

A CLOTHESLINE-SUPPORTED ANTENNA

Some of the old gang wanted to reactivate a Sunday morning round table on 75 meters, but a problem immediately became apparent. A dipole used for the purpose had long since met its demise during a New England ice storm and its successor hadn't fared much better. While the remains of the latter antenna worked on 75, performance was inadequate.

The alternative seemed to be climbing up on an icy roof to install something better, but this prospect was not met with much enthusiasm. However, a clothesline ran from the back porch to a pole in the backyard, and this seemed like a good possibility for supporting a temporary antenna. Approximately 100 feet of plastic-insulated hook-up wire were reeled out to the end of the line, and fastened every 10 feet or so with clothespins. The wire was then connected to a homemade matching network and the transceiver. Results were gratifying, and after the round table the wire was rolled up for future use. Since the stations contacted were within 60 miles, the high angle of radiation from the antenna, because the antenna was so low to the ground, proved to be a definite advantage. — *W1YNC*

DISASSEMBLY OF TOWER SECTIONS

Recently, I took down my aluminum tower and needed to take apart the tower sections. When I removed the bolts, I found that I could not just *pull* the sections apart. After the tower had been

standing for five or six years, the tubing of the three legs was rather firmly "jammed" together. After some blood, sweat and tears, I devised a disassembly method which worked just fine. The only tools required are three hose clamps of the type which tighten like a collet.

This drawing shows how the hose clamps are attached, one on each leg of the tower section. Put each clamp on the necked-down part of a tower leg, as close as possible to the full-size part of the leg on the adjacent tower section, and tighten securely. Then, with the tower lying with two of its legs on the ground, grab the third leg near the joint to be taken apart and lift. That joint will pull apart slightly. While holding the tower in the raised position, loosen the hose clamp on that leg and slide it down against the full-size part of the tower leg and retighten it. Roll the tower over so that the leg which you just loosened is now on the ground, and repeat the process. Continue with the third leg, and so on. I found that I could get from a quarter to a half inch of movement each time I did this, and after a few tries on each leg the sections came apart easily. — *H.H. Hunter, W8TYX*

USING 75-OHM LINE IN A 50-OHM SYSTEM

It is not uncommon these days to find bargain-priced 75-ohm coaxial line. Much of this coax is the type used in CATV installations, with foamed-polyethelene dielectric, aluminum or "hard-line" jacket, and acceptable loss figures even for rather lengthy runs at 220 MHz. Many amateurs pass up a potential bargain because they hesitate to install 75-ohm

line in an existing or planned 50-ohm system.

For fixed-frequency operation, such as at a repeater installation, stub matching can be used. The SWR will then be 1 to 1 in the 75-ohm line, and yet the input and output impedances will remain 50-ohms resistive. The stub matching scheme is shown in the illustration. To avoid the making up of multiple connectors for the 75-ohm portion (hard line can be difficult to work with), all stubbing is done with 50-ohm line. Great for running the bargain-priced stuff up a tall tower, eh?

It should be mentioned that this is not a lossless method of matching. With the SWR theoretically being infinite in the stub sections, there will be inherent losses when the matching sections are installed. If the 75-ohm line is of quite low loss in the first place, the total losses resulting from using it in a 50-ohm system may be less than those of the stub-matched arrangement. You can determine the trade-offs yourself, by comparing performance with the stubs connected *versus* with them removed. Of course you'll have to readjust the transmitter tuning and loading for the different conditions. — *K1TD*

INEXPENSIVE CAPACITORS FOR TRAP DIPOLES

Recently, I decided to put up a multiband trap dipole. Finding transmitting-type capacitors for the traps became a problem. Roy Purchase, W8RP, suggested that I might be able to use a piece of coaxial cable as a capacitor rather than the hard to obtain transmitting capacitors.

The proper length of coaxial cable needed to make the trap resonant at the desired frequency was determined experimentally. The method used to hold the trap assembly together can be seen in the accompanying drawing.

The antenna has been up approximately two months and no problems with the traps have developed. The RG-58/U cable seems able to handle the rf voltages developed on the antenna. It should be noted that I run 100 watts on ssb and cw,

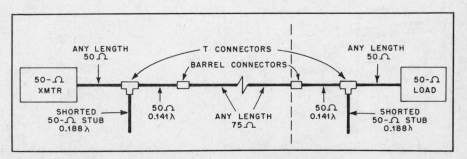

Stub-matching arrangement for intermediate run of 75-ohm line in a 50-ohm system. Dimensions shown in wavelengths are electrical lengths for the frequency of operation; the velocity factor of the line must be taken into account when calculating the physical length. See text. The portion drawn to the right of the vertical broken line may be replaced with a 75-ohm load.

and if higher power levels are to be run it might be necessary to use RG-8/U coaxial cable. Of course the transmitting type of capacitors could be used. — *Don R. Walters, WA8FCA*

REMOVING GROUND RODS

An easy way to remove a ground rod is to grasp the pipe or rod with a pipe wrench, then simultaneously twist and pull. Soaking the ground near the rod will also help loosen the ground rod. — *Bob Zavrel, Jr., WA9RAT/7*

COAXIAL-CABLE STRAPS

Strips cut from plastic bottles make excellent coaxial-cable and control-cable strapping. Use either aluminum tacks or brass screws to resist rusting.

Plastic bottles come in various thicknesses and colors and usually are not of uniform thickness so select the portion of the bottle best suited for your needs. Antifreeze bottles work very well. Wording on the bottle will not be seen since it does not show on the reverse side of the bottle. Paper cutters will do a better job than scissors or snips. — *Katashi Nose, KH6IJ*

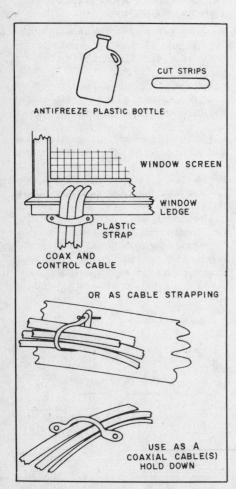

Inexpensive cable straps can be made from used plastic bottles.

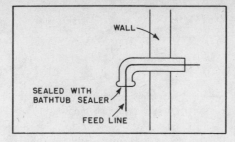

Plastic pipe elbow used as a feedthrough insulator.

FEED-LINE FEEDTHROUGH

I have found that plastic pipe available at hardware and plumbing-supply stores works well for running leads from your antenna system through a wall into the shack. It is available in a variety of diameters to suit your needs. I found that a 90° elbow on the outside helps prevent moisture problems and the pipe opening can be sealed with bathtub sealer. — *Keith Gilbertson, WBØLXM*

CENTER INSULATOR FOR DIPOLE ANTENNAS

I'm convinced that I've seen this general idea published elsewhere, and if it has been it is probably worth repeating for the benefit of people who are new to amateur radio. Nearly all amateurs use a half-wavelength dipole on at least one band, and finding a secure center insulator for coaxial feed is not always an easy assignment — if I may inject a truism!

While browsing recently through a local hardware store I spotted some bins filled with white plastic Ts and other unions for use with PVC plumbing pipe. The Ts looked especially interesting, as they came in a variety of sizes (OD). I purchased the two medium-size units, took them home, then performed minor surgery so that they would be suitable for my intended purpose.

I drilled two holes at each end of the horizontal part of the T. The two dipole wire elements would be threaded through

the holes and secured there. At the top dead center of the T I drilled a larger hole, through which I threaded the RG-58/U feed line. Following the assembly and soldering of the center section of the dipole (see accompanying sketch), I filled the vertical portion of the T with epoxy cement to assure minimum strain of the coaxial cable where it fanned out above the T to join the dipole elements. The cement was used also to seal the open part of the coax (braid and center conductor), thereby preventing water from entering the cable to degrade it.

Inverted-V enthusiasts may wish to invert the T and use the stem as the halyard connection point for the antenna. If that is done, the entry hole for the coaxial cable will be the first one which was used as an exit hole in the first example. — *W1FB*

LIGHTNING ARRESTORS FROM SPARK PLUGS

Though many ham stations have effective lightning protection in the form of directive antennas of all-metal construction, mounted on towers that are well-grounded, there are still uncounted random-length-wire and resonant-wire antenna systems in use. Many of these have no real protection against lightning, despite the well-publicized need for it. John Askew, W4AMK, who recently came back into amateur radio after 25 years away from it, was lightning conscious from "way back." But when he started looking in radio stores for lightning arrestors, he found nothing he wanted to trust in this critical role. Particularly, most of them were not suitable for outside installation, which John deemed a must.

Every issue of *The Radio Amateur's Handbook* shows spark-gap protection for wire antennas and feeders. W4AMK was about to make up something of this kind when he had a tune-up job done on his car and was left with a bag of old spark

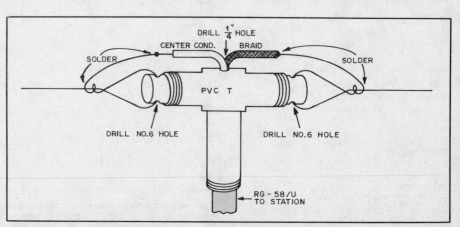

A dipole antenna center insulator made from a PVC plumbing T fitting.

plugs. Would these work? He called Headquarters for suggestions, and the writer "just happened" to have some old plugs rolling around in his car after a tune-up, too, so some checks were run.

With nothing more than a wire brushing and cleaning with some grease solvent, plugs were checked on the Lab's Q-Meter for capacitance and Q. The Q was nearly infinite, and the capacitance was 10 pF. The undersigned uses an end-fed random wire for occasional work on the bands from 21 through 3.5 MHz. It is ungrounded — but is its own protection, being of No. 24 wire eminently "meltable," and strung between two grounded towers. A spark plug was connected between this wire and the common ground, which includes everything metal in the house and an underground copper pipe to an outside well. No observable effect except a very small retuning for minimum reflected power resulted. The spark plug stays!

The gap, as the plug comes out of the car, is probably OK, though purists may want to file both parts to points, and adjust their spacing to the lowest that will stand the highest rf power used. Where balanced feed lines are used, mount two plugs on a grounded metal plate at approximately the feed-line spacing. The *Handbook* gives all important safety details. — W1HDQ

EASIER INSTALLATION OF CONNECTORS ON COAXIAL CABLE

If difficulty is experienced forcing the vinyl jacket of a coaxial cable into a connector or reducing sleeve, a shot of aerosol silicone spray on the jacket will usually allow the cable to be easily fitted into the connector. — Lee R. Wical, KH6BZF

OPEN-WIRE-SPREADER SOURCE

An excellent source of spreaders for open-wire feed line is fiberglass battens made for sailboats. The raw fiberglass comes in 10 or 12-foot lengths and sells for 70 cents per foot from Hard Sails, Inc., Islip, NY. It may be cut to size and drilled very easily. The finished product is quite strong and an excellent insulator. — Bob Fischer, WB2EUH

Fiberglass battens for sailboats make excellent feed-line spreaders.

An antenna feedthrough panel.

ANTENNA FEEDTHROUGH PANEL

It is not always convenient or desirable to bring antenna feeders into the shack by routing them under a window, to which an insert strip has been added for that purpose. The under-window method makes it difficult to seal against weather, and insects have a way of finding the smallest of cracks through which to gain entry to the house.

Homeowner-hams who aren't afraid to cut into the siding may fare better by using the technique described here. A saber saw is used to cut a square or rectangular hole in the wall of the house, after first using a stud locator or similar device to make sure the hole will be cut in a clear area of the wall. The hole should be approximately 1/2-inch smaller in vertical and horizontal diameter than the jack plate that will mount over it. This will provide ample "shoulder area" for screwing the plate to the wall, and will permit adding a gasket of cork or rubber for the purpose of weatherproofing the area.

After the hole is cut on the inner or outer house wall, find the approximate center of the hole by inserting a screwdriver or other long tool into the hole, bringing the tip to rest on the wall surface in which the mating hole will be cut. A level can be placed on the screwdriver blade to assure reasonable accuracy in finding dead center on the opposite wall surface. Mark that spot with a pencil; then with a long drill bit, bore a hole through the uncut wall. Use the hole to establish the center when laying out the borders of the second hole.

The jack plates (two) should have the coax fittings, steatite feedthrough bushings, ground terminal, and whatever placed in a symmetrical manner, remembering that one plate will be the mirror image of the other. Mount the antenna fittings on both plates, and add coaxial-cable and wire extensions to the fittings on one plate. Allow three inches more lead length than the wall thickness.

Attach one plate to the wall. Bring the leads through the wall and solder them to the mating jacks on the remaining plate. Attach the second plate to the wall.

If a feedthrough bushing is used to provide access to an end-fed wire, make sure the insulation on the wire is capable of handling high rf voltages. The writer uses Teflon-insulated No. 16 wire for the purpose, but the inner conductor and polyethylene insulation from a piece of RG-8/U coax cable can be used as a substitute.

SWR checks were made to see how much reactance was presented by the wall panel. A 50-ohm dummy load was connected to one side of the feedthrough assembly, and an SWR indicator and transmitter to the other. From 160 through 10 meters there was no indication of SWR. However, the jack panel may cause a "bump" in line impedance in the vhf spectrum. The vhf/uhf builder may want to mock up a set of plates and fittings and check them for SWR *before* cutting merrily away with a saber saw!

The accompanying photograph shows the author's feedthrough panel (outside the house) on which three coax fittings, one single-wire bushing, and one ground terminal have been mounted. GE Silastic compound was used to seal the edges of the plate and wall against weather, dust and insects. — W1FB

ANTENNA FEEDTHROUGH METHOD

I had a problem when running the end of a wire antenna into the basement shack without replacing a window pane with plastic sheet. I needed a weatherproof feedthrough, and the photo shows what I came up with. Materials used were a piece of 1/2-inch PVC pipe long enough to go through the wall, and a brass rod which was 1/8-inch diameter and two inches longer than the PVC pipe. It was threaded to accept 6-32 hardware. I used two no. 00 rubber stoppers, and two each no. 6 brass nuts and washers. Corks may be substituted for the rubber stoppers. Additional waterproofing is possible if silicone sealant is applied where the stoppers press into the pipe. — Art Mueller, WA3BKD

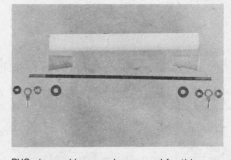
PVC pipe and brass rods are used for this feedthrough method.

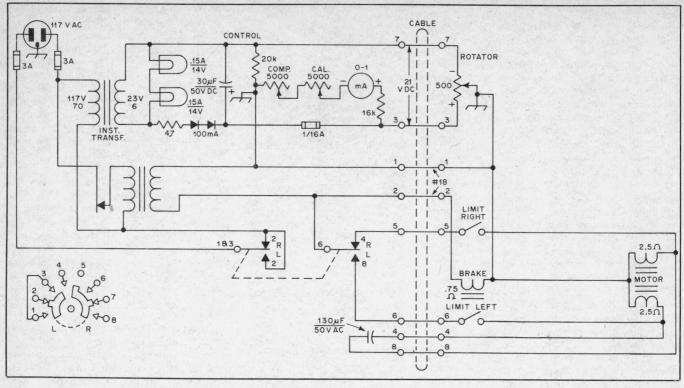

Schematic diagram of the CDR control circuit with the W7IC/K7IC modification.

HAM-M ROTATOR BRAKE MODIFICATION

Last fall I installed a Heights 72-foot free-standing aluminum tower with a TH6DXX Hy-Gain beam antenna. To swing this beam, I had a CDR rotator series no. 1 that had never been removed from the original carton. The immediate problem was the instant stop feature of the CDR with no way to install torsion bars (no guys), as recommended by Cornell-Dubilier, on the tower. I read with interest in *QST* for May, 1974, the article by K8CM as well as the conversion data by CDR to update the series no. 1 to series no. 3. My ultimate goal was to turn the beam and to be able to stop it without the sudden stop. I didn't fancy operating a separate switch on the control box to de-energize the brake. The CDR control box has a switch that, when turned right or left to the first position, turns on the panel light and energizes the meter circuit to give beam position indication. When pushed to the extreme right or left the brake releases, the beam turns and, immediately upon releasing the switch, the brake is applied while the beam is still turning.

The enclosed diagram shows the conversion wiring from series no. 1 to series no. 3, and also the rewiring of the direction control switch. The switch, when placed in the first position to the right or left, turns on the panel light, energizes the meter circuit and releases the brake. If the lever is pushed to the extreme right or left, the rotator will turn to the desired posi-

tion. When the lever is returned to the first position, the light and meter circuit is still on and the brake is off. The beam comes to a gentle stop. After a short delay, the lever may be returned to the center position, the brake-hold coil is then de-energized and the brake is applied.

I used this system last winter, even through some severe wind, and found it to be completely satisfactory. The wiring is simple and the results are great! A simple rewiring job gives complete control of rotation with the original switch arrangement, with no drilling or altering of the control box case and no need for torsion bars! — *George A. Onsum, W7IC/K7IC*

A BETTER GAMMA CAPACITOR

The gamma rod is fairly easy to make and fasten to the driven element of an antenna, but the gamma capacitor can present some difficult mechanical problems. While this capacitor need not have a very high voltage rating (the gamma-match feed point is usually at a high-current/low-voltage point), it must withstand the outdoor environment.

Common methods for weatherproofing include sealed metal, glass or plastic cans for air-variable capacitors, and the use of coaxial capacitors, with the gamma rod itself acting as one plate with an air or polystyrene tubing dielectric. Both of these methods require fairly sophisticated and painstaking design and construction techniques.

At my location, a gamma-matched wire

dipole has been in service for 18 months, exposed to the Southern California seashore environment. This antenna uses a fixed-value mica gamma capacitor that is fully exposed to the weather. There have been no observable adverse effects caused by temperature, moisture, salt or smog, and the mechanical installation is sturdy.

The mica capacitor used in this application was made by Elmenco, and has a hard-glazed, brown ceramic coating, with the wire leads brought out at right angles to the body of the capacitor. The required capacitance value is determined by temporarily clipping an air-variable capacitor to the terminals of the antenna and adjusting this capacitor and shorting bar location until the desired match is obtained. When a satisfactory match has been achieved, the variable capacitor can be removed, and the value determined visually (for example, if a 100-pF variable capacitor is used and the plates are about 60 percent meshed at the matched condition, 60 pF is a good starting point with the fixed-value capacitors).

Mica capacitors are stocked in MIL values and are rated at 1500-V dc for low values of capacitance, and 1000-V dc for intermediate values. At about 15 cents per unit, a dollar will buy an assortment that will certainly include the required value (and help replenish the junk box). A brief cut-and-try session should show which capacitor brings the desired match. The selected capacitor, which is light, compact and inherently weatherproof, can then be mounted permanently on solder legs or screw terminals and coated with silicone grease or acrylic lacquer to protect leads and solder joints from corrosion.

The same type of capacitor has been used in the trap circuits of a two-band trap dipole, at 500-watts input. In this application, high rf voltages were present across the traps, so it was necessary to connect three 1500-V units in series across the inductor. Adjustment can be accomplished most easily by using a dip oscillator to find the resonant frequency of the trap (as constructed from calculated values) and by compressing or expanding the inductor to achieve the desired setting. A heavy coat (or coats) of lacquer is recommended for corrosion protection for the inductor. — *Paul H. Weisz, K6YQ*

USING THE ALLIANCE U-100 ROTATOR FOR ELEVATING SATELLITE ANTENNAS

While it is possible to communicate through the OSCAR satellites using a fixed antenna elevation of 30 degrees, it is desirable to have some means of adjusting the antenna in order that it may be pointed more directly at the satellite. The rotator used should have a direct readout of angle of elevation and be of the type that allows the rotating mast to pass completely through the body of the rotor. The Alliance model U-100 is one rotator that fulfills these requirements. Dimensions for a mounting plate are shown in the drawing. The 1/4-inch thick aluminum plate is fastened to the support mast with two U-bolts and clamps (Radio Shack no. 15-826). One side of the rotor shell has a protrusion to keep the rotor from sliding down the mast when mounted normally. This part of the casting is removed with the aid of a hacksaw, and the rotor is mounted on the plate. The U-100 was not designed to withstand severe lateral force, and the loads on either side of the unit should be balanced. If it is desired to elevate a very heavy antenna, such as a 10-meter beam, some sort of thrust bearing should be devised to relieve pressure on the rotor bearings. Bear in mind, rotators of this type were designed for occasional turning of TV antennas. The internal gears will not tolerate excessive

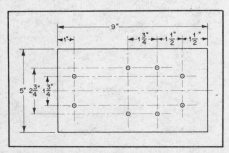

Dimensions for U-100 mounting plate.

torque resulting from attempting to elevate a heavy system. — *W1XZ*

CALCULATING ANTENNA TURNING RADIUS

Crowded living in the world today sometimes makes it necessary for the amateur to know if the turning radius of an antenna will permit rotating it in a limited space. As can be seen in the accompanying sketch, A is the longest (or at least half) part of the boom extending out from the mast or tower, B is one-half of the reflector length, and C is the turning radius. In other terms, C is the hypotenuse of the right triangle formed by A and B. You may remember from high school math that C equals the square root of $A^2 + B^2$. Or $C^2 = A^2 + B^2$ is its usual form.

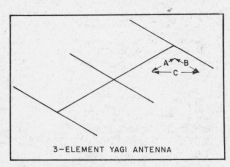

3-ELEMENT YAGI ANTENNA

Boom length and reflector length determine Yagi turning radius.

If you can't make the physical measurements for any reason, like not having the antenna yet, you will want to make sure it will fit your space before you acquire it. All you need do is study the literature or advertisements, determine the boom length that is applicable to the formula and the length of the reflector, and you are in business.

For beams of various length booms, the following formula can be used

$$\text{Radius in feet} = \frac{\text{Boom length}^2}{2} + \frac{\text{Reflector length}^2}{2}$$

If your available space prevents installing a "standard" commercial antenna, there are a few tricks you can use. Mounting the Yagi vertically is just one; the turning radius resulting will be 1/2 the boom length. — *Robert Weinstein, K4KXR*

CUSTOM-MADE WEATHERPROOF ENCLOSURES

Frequently a need exists for an easy-to-build outdoor box in which to put a matching network for an antenna. Some

A neat weatherproof enclosure for an antenna tuning network. This box was made with single-sided glass epoxy circuit board.

metal boxes, even if made weatherproof, tend to rust after long exposure to the elements. Aluminum boxes are subject to corrosion. Furthermore, it is not always possible to locate a ready-made container of the desired size for a given application.

The photograph shows a 10 × 10 × 10-inch (254 × 254 × 254 mm) housing made from single-sided glass-epoxy circuit board. The material was acquired at low cost from a vendor at a ham-radio flea market. One attractive feature in the use of circuit-board material is that a box of some specific size can be made readily. The copper surfaces are inside the container. A high-wattage soldering iron (100 W or greater) can be used to affix the walls in the desired position. The solder will seal the joints against the weather.

A tuning network for 160 meters is enclosed in the model shown here. A coating of spar varnish has been painted on the box to help preserve the glass epoxy. Weatherproof tape has been used to offer additional protection where the walls have been joined. A variable capacitor shaft protrudes from the front of the box (knob at right). A rubber grommet provides a tight fit around the variable-capacitor shaft to keep dirt and moisture out of the housing. The assembly is affixed to one tower leg by means of two U bolts and an aluminum plate. Caulking material is used to seal the bolt holes at the mounting point. — *W1FB*

CORRECTING ERRATIC DIRECTION INDICATORS

The resistance wire in the direction indicator potentiometer in CDR rotators is terminated at each end with a rivet. The connection between the wire and the rivet often corrodes, resulting in erratic indication, or no indication at all. My solution for the problem does not require the operator to remove the rotator. After determining which terminals on the control box connect to the ends of the potentiometer, I charged up an 80-μF, 450-volt electrolytic capacitor and discharged it across the potentiometer. The brief, high current will actually weld the connection between the wire and the rivets, without damaging the potentiometer. In one case, the connection at one end was completely open when measured with an ohmmeter, but after one "shock treatment" normal operation was restored. — *Maryan W. Plaza, W9TMU*

USING A HOCKEY PUCK TO INSTALL WIRE ANTENNAS

A hole is drilled in the center of a hockey puck, and a string is tied through the hole. By tying the end of a wire antenna to the string and throwing the puck over a tree branch, an antenna may be installed without climbing the tree. The aerodynamic qualities of a hockey puck make it better suited for the application than the commonly used rock or baseball. — *WA4FIB*

TRANSMISSION-LINE LOSSES

The subject of transmission-line losses in the presence of standing waves has always held an aura of mystery for some amateurs, even though much information has been published on the subject. The attenuation chart shown may help dispel all mysteries, for it provides a convenient means of determining total losses if the SWR at either the input or the load is known and if the loss in the line without standing waves is known. (This latter factor may be obtained from manufacturers' data or from transmission-line data such as appears in *The Radio Amateur's Handbook, The ARRL Antenna Book* or *The Radio Amateur's VHF Manual*.) Conversely, if the SWR values at the input to the line and at the load are measured with a reliable instrument, the total line loss and the loss of the line without standing waves (matched loss) may be determined from the graph.

The horizontal axis of the graph is calibrated in values representing the SWR at the load, while the vertical axis represents total loss in the line in decibels. The curves which are predominantly vertical (dotted lines) in the body of the graph represent the SWR value at the line input, and the curves which are predominantly horizontal in the lower portion of the graph (solid lines) represent the matched-line loss. Interpolation of values may be made between the curves, and the curves are interrelated so that each set or family may be considered as another "axis" of the overall graph.

A couple of examples best illustrate use of the graph. If we had, say 100 feet of RG-8/U feed line connected between a 10-meter transmitter and its load, and if the SWR as measured *at the load* is 3:1, what is the total line loss and what is the

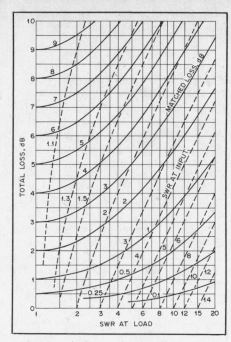

This graph relates the matched-line attenuation loss in dB to the total line loss and to SWR values at the line input and load.

SWR at the line input? First we must determine the matched loss of the length of coaxial line. Data tables tell us that RG-8/U has a 1.0 decibel of loss per hundred feet at 30 MHz, a value close enough for our needs. Now we proceed by running a finger along the scale at the bottom of the graph and locate the value of 3, representing the 3:1 SWR at the load. We follow the vertical "3" line up until we meet its intersection with the "1" solid-line curve which represents 1 dB of matched-line loss. At this intersection we may read from the calibration scale at the left that the total line loss under these SWR conditions is 1.5 dB. At this same intersection, by interpolating between the dotted-line curves, we may also see that the SWR at the line input is approximately 2.3:1.

As another example, assume that we are using a length of line with a matched loss of 3 dB and that we measure the SWR *at the line input* to be 2:1. What is the total line loss and the SWR at the load? In this case we begin as before, by running a finger along the scale at the bottom of the graph until we locate the value of 2 for SWR at the load (it'll be the same at the line input if the line is lossless, or has 0 dB of matched loss). This time, however, we proceed by following the "2" *dotted* line up and slightly to the right, as this dotted line represents a 2:1 SWR at the line input. We follow this line until we reach its intersection with the "3" solid curve, representing the matched loss of our feeder. From this intersection we may read (scale at left) that the total line loss here is just a tad more than 5 dB, and (scale at bottom) that the SWR at the load

is 5:1. If we had not known any attenuation values in this example, but were able to measure the SWR at the load as 5:1 and at the line input as 2:1, we would be able to determine the matched loss and the total loss from the intersection of the "5" SWR-at-load vertical line and the 2 SWR-at-input curve. There's no mystery here, is there? — *K1TD*

EASY GROUND-ROD INSTALLATION

Dig a hole five or six inches deep and six inches in diameter. Fill the hole with water. Set the pointed end of the rod in the center of the hole and start tamping with the rod as though you were tamping a post. Pull the rod up so the water goes down in the hole. Insert the rod in the same hole and push down again. Repeat this procedure until the rod is down to the desired depth. — *Clarence E. Berry, K9TAT*

A plastic block mounted on a right-angle bracket at the tower base serves to support an antenna loading coil.

HY-TOWER LOADING COIL

Shown in the photographs is the method that I used to mount a loading coil for my Hy-Tower but it is a system that could be used with any tower. I feel it is superior to the method recommended by Hy-Gain because there is no mechanical strain on the coil.

A plastic block is bolted to the base of the tower using a right-angle bracket as shown. Holes are drilled in the plastic for coil-support points, plus the block edges

The coil is mounted over the block. Note the clip lead used for making initial adjustments.

A weatherproof cover is installed.

are rounded so that the coil is a press fit over the plastic. The coil is not electrically connected at the bottom end — the nut and bolt are for mechanical support. The wire that runs the length of the tower section is connected to the upper end of the coil at the upper support screw. The coil tap is electrically connected at the tower-base feed point. Rain protection is provided by a plastic juice container, inverted over the coil. — *Larry Price, W4DQD*

ANOTHER CLIFF-DWELLER ANTENNA

Most transmitters are designed to work into 50-ohm loads. Some amateurs, particularly newcomers, don't realize that a simple antenna that provides a low-impedance load in the 50-ohm region is an end-fed wire that is a quarter wavelength or odd multiple of a quarter wavelength for the desired band. When using such an antenna, simply connect one end to the output terminal on the rig, and get the other end as high as possible. Be sure to use an earth ground on the transmitter. — *W1ICP*

ALUMINUM WIRE CONNECTIONS

When using aluminum wire for elements and matching stubs on a 220-MHz Yagi, I needed a way to make easily adjustable connections to the Twin-Lead and to the shorting stub. The solution was to use large Fahnestock clips, slipped over the ends of the wire before the array was assembled. A pair of clips were soldered together to make the shorting stub. Incidentally, the insulators shown were made of plastic pipe fittings, drilled to fit over the 7/8-inch boom, and slotted with a saw to take the stub wires. — *Donn G. Shankland, W8WVS*

LOW-COST CABLE HANGERS

There is a frequent need for bringing coaxial cables and assorted control wires into the ham shack, or from one equipment rack to another in the same room. A neat installation will help to keep the numerous conductors from creating an octopus of disarray.

This writer recently purchased 12 plastic shower-curtain hooks for 79 cents at a nearby discount store, hoping to solve a problem the OM was having. It seems that he was trying to bring three coaxial cables, a rotator control line, and a shielded pair for controlling a remote tower-mounted antenna switch into the shack from outdoors. The cables were hanging in disorderly fashion between the tower and the entrance panel on the rear wall of the house. It was suggested that the lines be dressed neatly under the overhang of the house, approximately six feet above ground.

Plastic shower-curtain hooks provide an inexpensive means of supporting cables.

The shower-curtain hooks (see photo) turned out to be ideal for the application. A piece of heavy-duty guy line was stretched between the lower tower section and a support member for the sun porch, anchored in place, and equipped with six of the shower-curtain hooks. The cables were then run through the hooks to the point where they could be dropped down to the entry panel leading to the shack.

The style of hooks shown here are of the snap-together variety, thereby permitting them to be opened easily when it is necessary to add or delete a cable. One thing for sure, it beats holding bundles of wire together with vinyl-plastic electrical tape. The latter creates a sticky, disgusting mess after being exposed to the sun in warm weather. — *W1CKK*

ANOTHER LOOP ANTENNA FOR HUNTERS

The general use of frequency modulation (fm) on the vhf and uhf amateur bands has complicated the problem of direction finding (DF). The limiter circuit used in fm receivers leaves no easy point in the receiver from which monitoring of signal levels can be accomplished. The use of some other circuit source for indicating the DF steer is required.

Most fm receivers include the use of a squelch circuit. An adjustable sensitivity control sets the minimum level at which the squelch will "open" and the audio from the receiver will be heard. With the antenna described here connected to the receiver, rotating the antenna will cause the signal to "pop" in and out. To improve this effect, some control over the amount of signal the receiver "hears," and proper adjustment of the squelch threshold, is needed. The latter is usually performed by the operator and the former is accomplished by inductively coupling the feed line from the receiver to the antenna.

The loop is made from 40 inches of 3/8-inch OD copper tubing, bent into a circle with the ends about one inch apart. The coupling link is a piece of hard-drawn copper wire, fastened to the center of a bulkhead fitting from a small boat. The size of the coupling link should be kept as small as possible since it also might function as a very small loop, rather than a coupling device for the antenna.

To use the loop, it is connected to the receiver by a length of coaxial cable, with the coupling link parallel to the loop for maximum coupling of the antenna to the feed line. After the signal is tuned in, rotation of the coupling link will attenuate the signal until a point is found where a sharp null will be indicated as the antenna is rotated. PVC plumbing fittings were used to give the antenna a "finished" appearance; nothing is unusually critical about the design. The antenna has been used to "home" on the transmitter, a 25-watt, 2-meter signal from as close as 50 feet, and also on the 162.55-MHz Weather Service broadcast station in New York, a distance of over 60 miles. — *B. C. Algeo, Jr., W3EM*

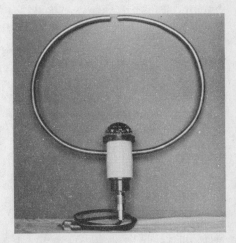

View of the completed loop antenna. The compass adds magnetic heading indication to the antenna operation, useful when plotting a "steering" heading.

Chapter 6

Thoughts for CW Operators

KEY JACK FOR ACCU-KEYER

I saved a little space in the construction of my Accu-Keyer, built from instructions in *QST* for August, 1973, by using a key jack instead of a switch for tuning adjustment. It is convenient to just plug my key in: It is less expensive too! — *Skip Turner, WB4YXN*

THE HEATH TWO-KEY KEYER

When my new HD-1410 keyer arrived, I was pleased to find that assembling it was not difficult. What I did not realize was that this was one of those newfangled squeeze keyers intended for iambic operation. Although it is true that the built-in paddles may be used for traditional noniambic operation, I found that trying to adapt my style of sending to the use of the paddles was not easy: I did not care for iambic.

From a discussion with Steve Harney, W9IHH, I learned that the keyer could be modified for use with a Vibroplex Vibro-Keyer. The simple arrangement is shown in the diagram. I now have a well-engineered keying device with the option of using a fast external key or the built-in paddles. — *Sam LeBow, WB6FJZ*

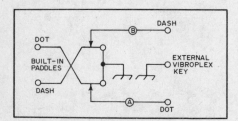

Modification of the Heath HD-1410 keyer for use with a Vibroplex Vibro-Keyer is shown here. Paddles are tapped at A and B. Ground for the Vibroplex is obtained from the phono socket at the rear of the keyer.

ANTI-VOX IMPROVEMENT FOR CW OPERATION

There have been many hints toward speeding up the pull-in time of VOX relays while operating transceivers in the cw mode. None of them solve the basic problem. In some types of equipment the anti-VOX circuits are not disabled during cw operation and a bucking voltage is built up during reception which must dissipate through the timing circuits of the VOX control. The result is that part of the first dot or dash (or all of it) is not transmitted.

My own Heath SB-401 suffers this defect as does the HW-100, the HW-101, the SB-102. I suspect the earlier SB-300 and SB-301 as well as other manufacturers' transceivers do also.

The solution is to kill the anti-VOX amplifiers or the anti-VOX rectifiers (if no amplifier is used) during cw reception only. This is accomplished by opening the screen or plate circuit to the anti-VOX amplifier, disconnecting the audio to the amplifier, or even disabling the anti-VOX rectifier. The voltage to a transistor amplifier may also be interrupted. There are usually extra contacts available on mode switches or relays. Either an opening or closing circuit can be adapted.

In the SB-401, contacts on mode switch M1R can be used. First, remove the yellow wire from M1R contact no. 11. Also remove the jumper from contact no. 12 of M1R to contact no. 9 of M1F. Discard the jumper wire and connect the yellow wire to contact no. 9 of M1F. This frees contacts no. 11 and no. 12 of M1R.

Next, break the foil on the carrier generator circuit board between R142 and C136. This opens the screen circuit of anti-VOX amplifier V13A. Connect a short wire from the hot end of C136 to terminal 11 of switch M1R and another

short wire from R142 to terminal 12 of M1R. The screen circuit of V13A will now be closed during ssb operation and open during cw operation. — *Kenneth J. Gardner, W2BGN*

CURE FOR THE WANDERING KEY

Another way to keep a paddle or bug from emigrating around the operating desk is to use one of those floppy disks sold as bottle or jar sure-grip openers. These openers are approximately 4-1/2 inches in diameter. No marks are left on the desk after use. A disk may also be cut apart and a piece glued to the bottom of each foot. — *Ray Day, WB6JFD*

USING THE HD-1410 WITH A TRITON IV

After purchasing my new Ten-Tec Triton IV transceiver I found that my Heath HD-1410 electronic keyer would not key the transmitter. Apparently this was the result of a fairly high key-line voltage. My solution was to short out diode D5 and resistor R27. — *Richard Gubanich, K3YLI*

RF IN THE ACCU-KEYER

Erratic operation of an Accu-Keyer can be caused by rf. To prevent rf from entering the unit, an all-metal box should be used for the cabinet. A good ground circuit is essential. The TTLs in the Accu-Keyer are easily affected by rf. I also found with my keyer that reducing the length of the RG174/U coaxial line from the keyer to transmitter (4 feet to 1 foot) effectively nullified another source of rf pickup. — *Jay Kobelin, WA2FIJ*

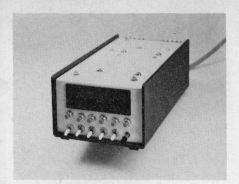

WA1JZC built this Accu-Memory and keyer inside a Bud RC-11100 cabinet measuring 3-1/4 × 5 × 10 inches (83 × 127 × 254 mm). The six push-button switches are for the RUN, STOP and MEMORY QUADRANT SELECT functions. The toggle switches provide for loading the memories, for activating the automatic character-space feature, for transmitter tuning and for switching the readout devices off to lower power consumption. The speed control is located at the bottom right.

THE WA1JZC ACCU-STOP

A simple modification to the WB4VVF Accu-Memory[1,2] will allow the keyer paddle to perform the same function as the STOP button. One of the four NOR gates that compose U21 (located on the driver circuit board) is unused in the original circuit. The modification involves the following: Connect a jumper wire between pin 2 of U21 and pin 1 of U3 on the memory board; connect a jumper wire between pin 3 of U21 and pin 8 of U6 on the original Accu-Keyer board; connect one lead of a 0.001-μF disk-ceramic capacitor to pin 1 of U21; and run a jumper from the other lead of the capacitor to U7, pin 6 on the memory board.

When the contents of a memory register are being read out, it is now necessary only to tap the keyer paddle either to the dot or dash side to interrupt the memory output. The output can be continued from the point at which it was interrupted by pushing the RUN button, or alternatively, a different memory quadrant can be selected by pushing the appropriate RESET switch. — *Edward B. Kalin, K1RT*

[1]Garrett, "The WB4VVF Accu-Keyer," *QST*, August, 1973.
[2]Garrett and Contini, "The Accu-Memory," *QST*, August, 1975.

TO U3, PIN 1 ON MEMORY — 2
TO U6, PIN 8 ON ACCU-KEYER — 3
7402 U21A — .001 — TO U7, PIN 6 ON MEMORY

Wiring of U21 for the WA1JZC Accu-Stop. This section of U21 is unused in its original version of the Accu-Memory, but is employed for another purpose if the information above by Garrett is followed. If the builder wishes to incorporate both changes, an additional 7402 IC may be added.

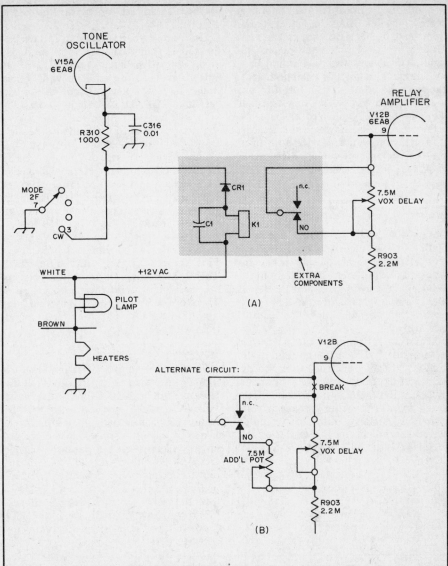

(A)

(B)

A circuit modification for the HW-101 to allow different VOX-delay time constants for cw and ssb operation. A variation of the circuit is shown at the bottom.
C1 — 100 μF, 25 V dc.
D1 — Silicon rectifier, 1A, 400 PIV. 1N4936 or equivalent.
K1 — Spdt relay, 12 V dc, 1200 ohms. Radio Shack no. 275-003.

CW AND THE HW-101

No drilling or additional controls are required for this modification of a Heath HW-101 to permit the use of two different VOX delay time constants for cw and ssb operation. In cw operation, particularly in traffic nets, fast VOX response is desirable in order to approach semi break-in operation. In ssb operation, when using VOX, this same response is unusable because it allows the TR relays to drop in and out during pauses in speech. Unfortunately, VOX delay is an awkward parameter to adjust on the side of the rig.

One solution would be to connect a switch across the VOX DELAY potentiometer, shorting it out for cw use and permitting normal VOX delays for ssb. However, there is no convenient place to mount such a switch without drilling holes in the front panel. This would be

undesirable. One could be installed on the rear apron, but that would be awkward.

The circuit described here makes this switch operable via the mode switch on the front panel and a relay. Relay contacts are connected across the VOX DELAY potentiometer, as would a pair of switch contacts. When cw is selected, one of the mode switch functions completes the tone-oscillator cathode circuit. These same contacts are employed in this modification to complete the relay coil circuit and energize the relay. Power for the relay coil comes from the 12-V ac heater pilot-lamp line, which is rectified by the diode and filtered by the capacitor to provide the necessary dc coil voltage. The diode prevents the tone-oscillator cathode circuit from being completed through the 12-V ac line when cw is not being used.

I constructed the little circuit on a small piece of pc board and mounted it on a homemade bracket fastened to the screw holding the socket for the meter pilot light. An obvious variation would be to mount an extra 7.5 MΩ potentiometer in the spare hole on the rear apron to provide a second VOX-delay time constant. This would be connected through the relay contacts as shown in the attached diagram, and would provide adjustment for the response of the VOX in cw. — *Edwin G. Solov, WA2DIW*

LAZY MAN'S ADDITION TO THE ACCU-MEMORY

During a Delaware QSO Party I decided that it would be nice to have an automatic recycle feature to periodically restart my Accu-Memory that complements a WB4VVF Accu-Keyer. After all it took *such* effort to reach over and push the restart button for the "CQ DEL" message!

The relatively simple circuit is designed to use a 74123 dual-retriggerable, monostable multivibrator. U1A is triggered during transmission by logic transitions in the output keying circuit of the keyer board. When the message is completed, U1A starts timing to the preset period determined by the setting of R1. When R1 is at the minimum setting, R2 determines the minimum recycle time. At the end of the period, U1A triggers U1B which "hiccups" a pulse that shuts off a manufactured AND gate (U3D and U3C) to start the memory. Since only one message will be repeated, the connections in the diagram are for message quadrant no. 1.

The values for R1, R2 and C1 give approximate range of 5 to 30 seconds, depending on the actual value of C1. You might want to experiment with other values to suit your needs, but do not use less than 5000 ohms for R2. Otherwise, U1A will lock.

A low to pin 11 of U1B inhibits the start pulse from reaching the memory. The "allow" latch consists of U3A and U3B. S1 sets the latch, taking U1B high at pin 11 and lighting the LED. This indicates that the recycle feature is active. The latch is reset by merely tapping the dit side of the keyer paddle. This takes U1B low at pin 11 and turns off the LED.

Setting the latch again does two things. First, the allow circuit is turned on again. Then U2A is triggered to send a pulse to the memory to send the message again. Therefore, one must press only one button to get back into the "round and round" mode.

Operation

To use the recycle feature, load a message into area no. 1. Press S1 and the message will be sent as you enable the "allow" circuit. The message will be restarted as often as you desire, determined by the setting of R1. When you get an answer, just tap a dit and the recycle feature will be disabled, allowing the contact to be made. To start calling again, press S1 and that's it.

By the way, I received a nice certificate for my participation in the Delaware QSO Party. But with so many events coming up it may be a long time before I treat my keyer to a professional-appearing installation in a metal chassis and cabinet, unless some kind soul wants to help a lazy and poor metal craftsman! — *Charles Trice, WA4RRB*

LIGHT DOTS WITH THE TR-4C

Have you been told that your dots are too light? Perhaps if you have a Drake TR-4C, the transmitter-mixer V4 is being biased too far below cutoff during the space period. When the key closes about 20 milliseconds are required for this bias to decay to where rf output begins. However, when the key opens, rf output almost instantly stops. Wave shaping to avoid key clicks prevents this cutoff from being completely instantaneous.

The 20-millisecond foreshortening becomes evident as chopped or light dots at moderate keying speeds or faster. The problem is especially evident on the first dot following the initial key closure for sending.

Curing this annoying condition may be achieved by means of this modification: Change R19 from 300 kΩ to 1.0 MΩ and connect a 200-kΩ resistor across C31. The voltage divider thus formed cuts the bias on V4 to near cutoff but lets rf flow almost instantly when the key closes. Waveshaping, as mentioned previously, prevents the rf from starting in a true, instant manner. The time constant for discharge of C31 is shorter following the modification. Keying is crisper but not near keyclick hardness when the key closes. The original keying characteristic is on the soft side. — *Ted Chernin, KH6GI*

CAPACITOR CURES DIT PROBLEM

When I began to use a speed key with my code-practice oscillator made from a commonly available module, the oscillator gave a higher frequency for dit than a dah. Placing a 3-μF capacitor across the single dry-cell power source cured the problem. — *Skip Turner, WB4YXN*

MAKING A SQUEEZE KEY ON A LEAN BUDGET

I recently built the WB4VVF Accu-Keyer but could not make use of the iambic operation because the price of a commercially made squeeze key was beyond this student's budget. My money-saving project that resulted provided me with a device with more exact operation and requiring less effort.

The circuit functions simply as a dc switch. The negative voltage on the gates of Q1 and Q2 reverse biases the FETs, which leaves the outputs to R11 and R12 open. When contact is made across either

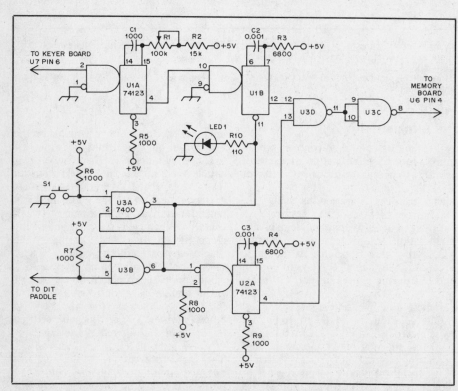

Schematic diagram for an automatic recycling feature for the Accu-Memory.

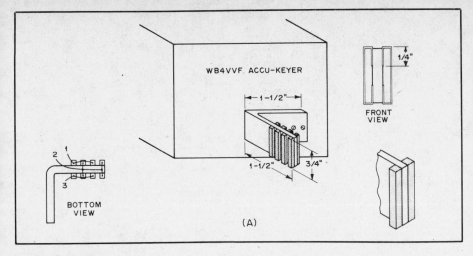

A novel squeeze key built within a student's budget.

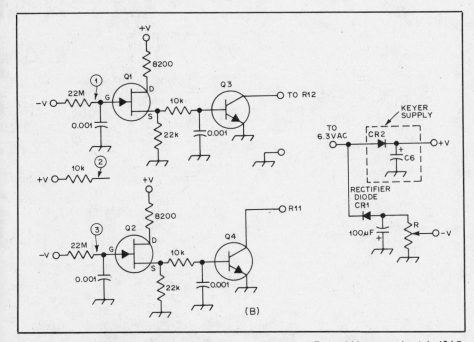

Circuit for the Squeeze Key on a Lean Budget. Sensitivity control R should be approximately 10 kΩ. The touchpoints 1 and 2 are for dots, and 2 and 3 are for dashes.

Q1, Q2 — N-channel JFET transistors, 20 V 200 mW, 15 mA, Motorola HEP801.

Q3, Q4 — Npn silicon transistors, Motorola HEP704.

chosen over etching a design on small sections of pc board. Otherwise, the perspiration from my fingers remaining between the edges of the foil after a long night of DX work was enough to make the pc touch plate stay on. The wires from the plate are brought into the keyer housing which is mounted on rubber feet. The leads are then attached to the circuit inputs. Thanks are due W6NKY for his comments on the circuit and construction. — *J. Gary Sparks, K3ZKH/6*

THE ACCU-START

When James Garrett, WB4VVF, introduced the Accu-Memory at the Dayton Hamvention in 1975, he may have set the standard for electronic keyers of the future. There are always the innovative individuals to dream up an additional touch. K1RT proved again the need for a valuable feature when he introduced his Accu-Stop circuit.

After hours of experimenting with an NE555 timer IC and the SN74123 monostable device, we designed and produced the Accu-Start circuit. In the final design the Motorola MC9601/8601 proved to be the logical choice for this unit. It has the ability to be retriggered or disabled during operation. The MC9601/8601 monostable multivibrator is designed to produce an accurate output pulse with a wide range of pulse widths from either edge of an input pulse. This one-shot circuit will retrigger when it is in an active timing state and reestablish the timing cycle from the last input pulse received. The MC9601/8601 provides the user with sufficient inputs, thus deleting additional gating circuitry.

All normal functions of the Accu-Keyer

side or both sides of the touch switch, a positive voltage overcomes the negative bias, turns on the FETs and one or both of the output transistors, resulting in the grounding of the outputs and turning on the keyer. Sensitivity control R adjusts the FET's negative-bias level and can be set for a given skin resistance to give the touch switch the proper action.

A small prepunched Bakelite board, used for the circuit construction, was mounted inside the keyer housing. I used a Minibox which provided ample room for the parts. The parts values are not critical. Substitutions may be made freely. The bypass capacitors, indicated in the diagram, eliminated any possible trouble with rf.

Mechanical construction is not as

tricky as it may appear. I bought some 1/8 × 1/8-inch (3 × 3-mm) balsa wood at a hobby shop as well as some 0.12-inch, instant circuit-board foil. The touch switch is made by cutting eight pieces of the balsa 3/4-inch (19-mm) long and then taping the instant circuit-board foil along one long edge, over the ends, and then onto each end of the opposite long foil-covered edge for a distance of 1/4 inch (6 mm). (See the front view illustration.) Then cement the metal covered pieces onto a piece of angled plastic at a spacing adequate for your range of touch. Electrical connections are made by soldering lengths of thin, enameled wire (I used No. 28) to the bottom (foil-covered) edges of the wooden supports as shown in the bottom view. This construction method was

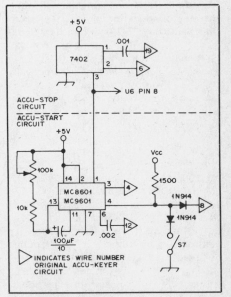

The monostable multivibrator circuit for the Accu-Start is shown here. Numbers shown in the triangles indicate the wire number in the original Accu-Keyer.

with memory and the Accu-Stop are maintained. S7 disables the Accu-Start circuit for all normal operation. Enabling S7 allows one to provide an automatic start pulse to the memory after manual entry of data is completed and after the desired time delay has been satisfied. The variable resistor sets the time delay after the last paddle closure before the start pulse is initiated. The timing cycle may be reset at any time before timeout occurs. Our use has proved that an appropriate time is 1 to 1-1/2 seconds. However, with component values shown, delays as long as five seconds can be reached. But with that amount of delay the chap at the other station may think you fell asleep and start his call-up. — *Gus Gaglio, WB8TJB and Joe Stout, W8HID*

A COMPUTER-TYPE ACTIVE FILTER

The advent of low-cost operational amplifiers in the past few years has excited interest in their use in RC active filter circuits. Typically, excellent Qs in the audio range have been achieved without any use of inductors. For band-pass and band-reject filters, resistors and capacitors are chosen to achieve a given center frequency and Q. However, there are several drawbacks to this approach. First, variable-frequency operation is difficult, requiring either ganged potentiometers or acceptance of severely reduced Q. Secondly, matching of capacitors or resistors may be required in some designs to realize high Q and good peak response or notch depth.

There is, however, an alternative. Instead of using one operational amplifier and an RC input-feedback network configuration, it is possible to use three op-amp networks to achieve virtually any second-order transfer function. A good example of what can be done is a notch filter using three 741 op amps. Center frequency can be varied (using one control) up to approximately 4 kHz, with circuit Q and notch depth remaining practically constant over the range. Component matching is not required. Only one setup adjustment is needed: a variable control adjusted for best notch depth.

The Circuit

In the circuit, U1 and U2 serve as integrators with a dc gain of about 25,000. U3 serves as a summing device. The 1000-ohm control, R2, is used as the Q control and is adjusted only once for deepest notch. R1 serves as the frequency control by controlling the "gain" of the differential equation, which the system is solving in effect. For easiest tuning, this should be a 10-turn precision-type potentiometer.

The results are impressive for a circuit of such simplicity. Notch depth is at least 50 dB. Measurement of absolute depth

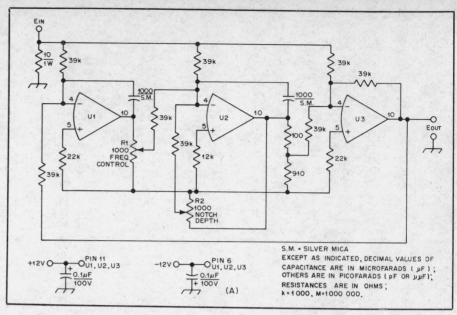

Schematic diagram of the active filter. The preferable tolerance of the 39-kΩ resistors is two percent. All others can be 10 percent. Tolerance of the silver-mica capacitors should be five percent.
R1 — See text.
R2 — Circuit-board type.
U1, U2, U3 — Op amp, type 741. Pin numbers are shown for 14-pin, DIP package (Motorola MC1741L or MC1741P2). For the 8-pin types (MC1741G and MC1741P1), substitute pin 7 for pin 11 on the drawing, pin 4 for pin 6, pin 3 for pin 5, pin 2 for pin 4 and pin 6 for pin 10, respectively.

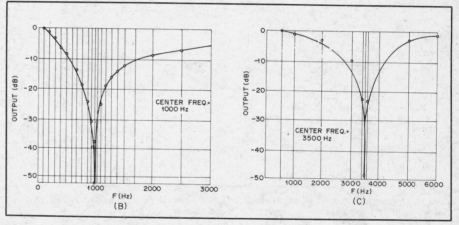

Response plot for the active filter. The output voltage a 0-dB reference was 0.48 and the input voltage was 0.5 V pk-pk. Response plot for a center frequency of 3500 Hz.

was difficult because the test oscillator used had a harmonic content suppressed by only 50 dB.

Notch depth remains approximately constant over the tuning range, with Q seeming to increase somewhat with center frequency. In determining experimentally the two plots shown, the Q control was untouched.

In operation, the input to the filter may be taken from the speaker or headphone jack of a receiver. Because a 741 op amp will deliver approximately 12 V pk-pk across 2000 ohms, a high-impedance headset may be connected directly across the output. If required, a suitable buffer stage could be added to drive a lower impedance speaker or headset. Best results in notching out an offending heterodyne can be achieved when the receiver agc is turned off. Otherwise, the strongly interfering carrier would heavily activate the agc and reduce the receiver gain, pulling the desired signal down with it. This filter would be a useful accessory for an ordinary ssb transceiver, which normally lacks provision for i-f notching. In my setup, I am able to take the required voltages for the filter from the VOX accessory socket of the Swan 350. A 10-turn tuning control makes adjustment swift. The total cost including such a control and the op amps should not exceed $15. — *Allen Taflove, WA9JLV*

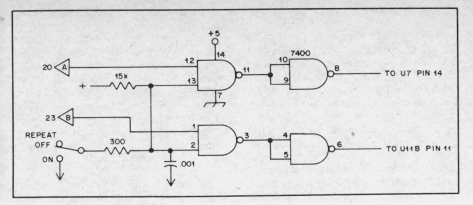

Circuit modification for continuous- or repeat-mode operation of the Accu-Memory.

CONTINUOUS OPERATION FOR THE ACCU-MEMORY

Some amateurs should be interested in a modification of the Accu-Memory (*QST* for August, 1975) that permits repeat mode or continuous operation of the device. Such use is applicable, for example, in sending "TEST DE W6QNB" over and over while the operator is inside the house or next door observing the reception on a TV set.

The modification consists of two parts: One is to avoid causing the device to stop after nine zero bits, and the second prevents rollover from one message readout into the next. Minor surgery and one more IC are required. Break the connection to pin 14 of U7 and pin 11 of U11 (refer to Fig. 4 in the original article). Then add the circuit that is illustrated here.

After the modification is completed, load the message to be repeated in the normal mode. Use the run button to pad the text as desired. Switch to the repeat mode and hit the message number desired to start the device. The four-message capability is retained in either normal or repeat modes. — *Daniel G. Drath, W6QNB*

IMPROVED CW PERFORMANCE FOR THE SB-401 TRANSMITTER

While trying to provide my SB-401/SB-301 combination with a full break-in system, several problems came to light. The SB-301 combination is an excellent ssb transmitter but leaves something to be desired on cw. The first problem tackled was elimination of chirp on the signal. It seems that the chirp is not uncommon in the SB-400/SB-401 series of transmitters. Investigation disclosed that the problem was poor voltage regulation, with the most critical area being the regulation on the line to the LMO. The input voltage to the LMO dropped 10 volts when the key was closed. Regulated voltage is supplied to the LMO by VR tube V7 and resistor R18 (4000 ohms).

Using information from *The Radio Amateur's Handbook* I determined that this resistor had much resistance and should be lowered to 2000 ohms. It was replaced with a 20-W resistor. In addition, a 100-μF, 450-V capacitor was installed in parallel with C77A to provide additional regulation at the output of the low-voltage power supply. The chirp was eliminated.

The following changes were made to improve the keyed waveform to eliminate a mushy sound and a key thump. Indications were that the rise time was too long and the fall time was too short. C211 (0.02 μF) which determines the waveform rise time was replaced with a 0.01-μF disk ceramic capacitor. A 1-μF, 200-V capacitor was installed in parallel with C304: It determines the wave form decay time. The replacements achieved the purpose of shortening the rise time and lengthening the decay time.

These modifications are easily performed. They are well worth the substantial increase in the quality of the cw signal. Ssb operation is not affected by these changes. — *G. A. Steward, K3ZOL*

A MONITOR FOR HEARING YOUR CW

To provide a sidetone monitor for my old Galaxy V transceiver and to key it at the same time, I built a unit that is also capable of keying a DX-100. W7MME has used the same design for keying a pair of 1625s in an old converted TCS being operated in the MARS network.

The NE555 is at the heart of my device. It operates well as a sidetone generator from a 9- or 12-volt dc supply. The additional circuitry shown in the schematic diagram is designed for blocked-grid or

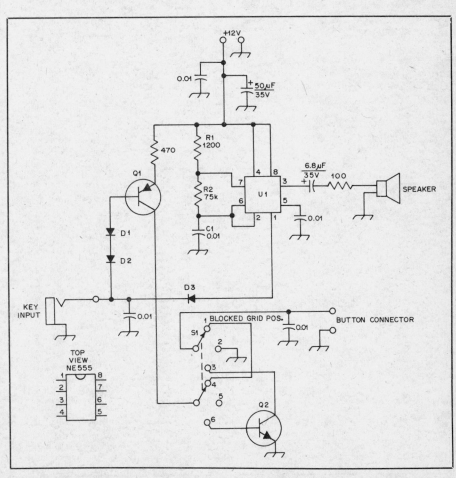

A sidetone generator and transistorized keying unit. S1 is shown in position for keying negative voltages (blocked-grid keying). All resistors are 1/4 watt. Capacitor values are in μF. S1 is a two-pole, three-position switch.
D1, D2 — Silicon diodes, 1N4005.
U1 — Signetics NE555.
Q1 — 2N2905 silicon pnp transistor.
Q2 — 2N5157 germanium pnp transistor.

cathode keying. Transistor Q1, chosen for positive keying, is a 2N5157. It is rated for 700 V at 3 A maximum, which is adequate for use with a pair of 807s or 6146s.

Closing the key circuit causes the NE555 to operate as a free-running multivibrator and turns on Q1 for blocked-grid keying when the rotary switch, S1, is in position 1. Position 2 is for tuning and position 3 is for cathode keying. On my model I labelled these positions G, T and C, respectively.

The unit is assembled in a 5-1/2 × 8-1/2 × 2-1/2-inch (140 mm × 216 mm × 64 mm) box. A speaker from a defunct transistor radio was installed. All input circuits were bypassed as shown in the diagram. Good shielding is essential.

The tone frequency is a function of the values of R1, R2 and C1, while the volume is determined by the operating voltage and the resistor in series with the speaker. A selected inductor in series with the speaker might do wonders for producing a sine-wave tone. This circuit drew about 35 mA in the key-down position when operated from a 9-V battery. — *Herb Ash, K7ARR*

IDEAS FOR THE SB-301

I have improved the performance of my SB-301 by means of these modifications. The first gives greater selectivity by the addition of another filter. The other changes allow the keying monitor in the SB-401 to be connected to the headphone circuit of the SB-301 and the use of audio filters without the requirement of transformers.

To obtain greater skirt selectivity, a second 400-Hz crystal filter may be added in series with the existing filter in the set. An isolation amplifier is added to properly terminate the filters and make up for the added insertion loss. The filter is mounted in the a-m filter holes. A small perforated board, about one-inch square, is suitable for mounting the amplifier. The board is supported easily by means of the leads connected to it. The amplifier has a gain of 3 or 4 dB and an input and output impedance of 2000 ohms. Skirt selectivity and ultimate rejection are much improved by this addition. Although I have not tried it, I presume an ssb filter could be added in a similar fashion.

As shown in the second drawing, shorting the 15 kilohm resistor gives a low-impedance driving source for audio filters such as the surplus beam filters. The other modification connects the sidetone output from the SB-401 to the headphone jack on the SB-301. A spare hole in the back panel of the SB-301 may be used for installing an additional phone jack which should be connected with shielded wire to the transformer tap as indicated in the drawing. — *Ed Jensen, K9HDP*

SEVEN BITS FOR THIS IDEA

Eight bits are required to store an insert feature in a message and for spacing between words when using the Accu-Memory as originally designed. A bit is equal to the dot element in length. But, to me words fit together more comfortably with seven-bit spacing than with eight. From my early code training days I learned that the "proper" word spacing is seven bits.

To modify the Accu-Memory to seven-bit word spacing, I simply connected both inputs (pins 9 and 10) of NAND gate U3C (7400) to pin 11 of U7, the D or 23 output of the 7490 decade counter. This output will go high when the count reaches 8 in the 7490 counter, the chip having started counting at the start of a word being loaded. Thus, both inputs of U3C go high at a count of 1000_2 and the output of the gate goes low, causing the address counters to stop. The eighth bit becomes the first element of the next character loaded and we now have a seven-bit word space.

An additional bonus is provided when one wishes to program a pause in the message. With the counter output at 100 (equivalent to 8_{10}), actuation of the run button provides a one-shot pulse to the counter, moving it to 1001 and storing a one-bit space in the memory chip. At 1001, however, gate U3C is still forced low, the D output of the 7490 is still high, and no further bits are needed to record the pause. A second actuation of the run button resets the 7490 to 0000 and it counts back up to 1000 before being stopped. This second consecutive closure takes up seven bits of memory, but should never be needed. In the author's circuit each actuation of the button resets the decade counter to 0000 and each such action

Greater selectivity for the SB-301 is provided by the addition of another filter as shown in this diagram. Q1 may be any small-signal npn transistor such as a 2N3565. The dotted lines surround the added circuitry. This drawing shows a low-impedance driving source for using the SB-301 with audio filters. Darkened lines indicate the added circuits.

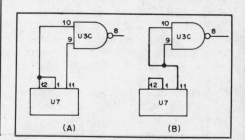

Modification of the Accu-Memory for seven-bit word spacing. The original circuit is shown at the left, while the modified version is at the right.

resulted in the waste of eight bits of valuable memory space.

For those Accu users who employed the same circuit board design as was made available by the authors, the modification is extremely simple. Cut the foil which extends between pins 1 and 12 of U7 and pin 10 of U3. At a point beyond the cut, make a solder bridge between this foil and the adjacent foil which connects pin 11 of U7 and pin 9 of U3. — *Harold Kalkstein, WA3QQZ*

AN OLD TIMER'S SOLID-STATE BREAK-IN AND KEYING SYSTEM

Many years ago I installed a break-in system on my HRO-5, similar to the one shown on p. 358 of the 1976 edition of *The Radio Amateur's Handbook*. I have replaced the relay with a 4016A COS/MOS switch and a 2N2222 npn silicon transistor to activate the auxiliary rf gain control. This improved operation.

Less rf reaches the receiver since there are two parallel sections of the 4016A that open up. The other two parallel sections ground the antenna terminal.

My transmitter is the 75 to 120-watt rig shown on page 172 of the *Handbook*. Since I key the cathode of the 6146B output stage as well as a two stage solid-state amplifier in the VFO, I am also presenting a circuit of the complete keying system. Some old timers like myself, who enjoy break-in operation, may be interested in this arrangement. — *Wayne H. Sandford, Jr., K3EQ*

A SOLID-STATE KEYER FOR CATHODE-KEYED TRANSMITTERS

When I finally made the decision to build an all-electronic keyer, the design had to offer compatible interface with my cathode-keyed transmitter. This meant a switching function capable of handling higher current than that found in a grid-block keying system. So, off to the parts catalog I went. Rechecking the surplus ads, I found that, sure enough, silicon-controlled rectifiers were readily available and units capable of handling quite high voltages and currents were inexpensive. For example, units that would withstand 600 volts and carry 6 amperes were available for less than a dollar apiece. Of course, using a silicon-controlled rectifier to key a transmitter required that it be turned off at the end of every character; but this minor problem was solved and the circuit shown resulted.

How It Works

The character (dot and dash) generator is essentially the same as the one described in pre-1974 editions of *The ARRL Radio Amateur's Handbook* except for the minor variations required to adapt it to the TTL ICs available and the needs of the SCRs. Since the *Handbook* describes the operation in some detail, the character generator will be described only briefly here.

Transistors Q1-Q3, along with their associated circuitry, comprise a pulse generator that generates a negative pulse immediately when the key is closed, and at regular intervals thereafter until shut down. The pulses are then applied to two flip-flops that act as a counter. Q4 is wired as a two-input NOR gate, and shuts down the pulse generator at the end of a dot or dash plus space unless the key is still closed. The character output appears at the collector of Q5, and the complementary output at the collector of Q4.

At the beginning of a character, the positive-going transition at the collector of Q5 is converted into a positive pulse by C1 and applied (through emitter follower Q7) to the gate of SCR Q9, turning it on, and thus keying the transmitter. SCR Q8 is off at this time, and C2 is charged to 15

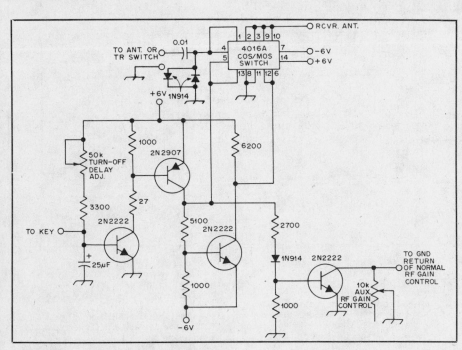

A solid-state break-in receiver control system.

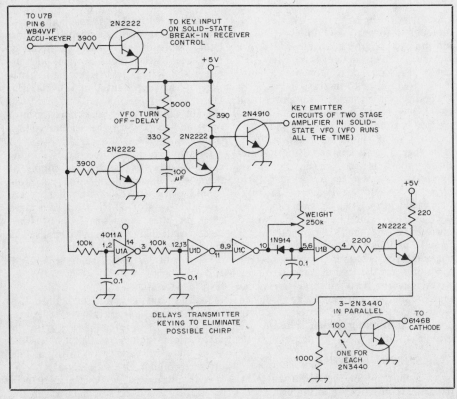

A solid-state keying system.

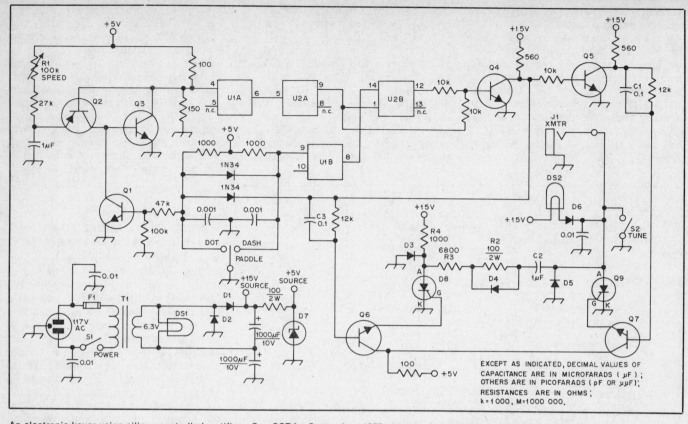

An electronic keyer using silicon-controlled rectifiers. See *QST* for September, 1977, page 11, for explanation of logic symbols.

C1, C2 — For text reference.
D1-D6, incl. — Silicon diodes, 600 PRV, 2 A 1N3191 or equiv.
D7 — Zener diode, 5.1-V, 400 mW, 1N751 or equiv.
DS1 — Pilot lamp, 6.3 V (no. 47).
DS2 — Pilot lamp, 14 V (no. 1815).
F1 — 0.75 A.
J1 — Phono or phone jack.

Q1 — 2N560 or equiv.
Q2 — 2N404 or equiv.
Q3-Q7, incl. — 2N585 or equiv.
Q8, Q9 — Silicon-controlled, rectifiers; 600-V, 6-A devices used by the author, equiv. to Motorola HEP R1223, but lower rated devices may be suitable for particular applications.
R1 — Linear taper.

R2, R3, R4 — See text.
S1, S2 — Spst toggle.
T1 — Filament transformer, 6.3 V, 1-A secondary.
U1 — Quad 2-input positive NAND gate, type 7400; 2 sections unused. Connect pin 7 to ground and pin 14 to +5 V.
U2 — Dual J-K flip-flop, type 7473. Connect pin 11 to ground and pin 4 to +5 V.

volts through R2, R3 and R4.

At the end of a character, a positive pulse (derived from the positive-going transition at the collector of Q4) is applied to the gate of Q8, turning Q8 on. C2 can now discharge through the path formed by D5, Q8, R3 and D4. The direction of current flow is such that the cathode of D5 and the anode of Q9 are slightly negative with respect to ground for the few microseconds it takes C2 to discharge — which is enough to turn Q9 off.

Q8 is turned off at the beginning of the next character when Q9 discharges C2 in the opposite direction. At this time D4 is back biased, and R2 limits the current surge through Q9 to a safe value.

DS2 is included to assure sufficient current flow through Q9 to maintain it in the "on" state when devices that draw only low currents are being keyed, e.g., a code-practice oscillator. A resistor of the proper value could be substituted for DS2, but a pilot lamp also serves as a TRANSMITTER ON indicator.

In the present setup, the keyer handles about 150 mA from the transmitter, 5 mA from the monitor oscillator and the 200 mA from DS2. No tests were made to determine the maximum current-switching

capacity with the component values used, although I suspect it is about twice the amount mentioned above. If more current-handling capacity is required, DS2 could be disconnected. However, a better method would be to increase the value of C2 and decrease that of R3 in proportion to the current to be switched. If C2 is increased beyond about 2 μF, R4 should be replaced by a 100-ohm, 2-watt resistor. Note that C2 gets charged in both directions, so that for larger values of capacitance, where an electrolytic capacitor would be required, a non-polarized electrolytic, or two capacitors back to back, would be required. I would not recommend that C2 be made larger than 10 μF, because then either the time constants for charging it would become too long, or excessive current surges would have to be handled. However, at that point the current being switched would be measured in amperes, and no *amateur* transmitter should require any greater amount.

Component Specifications

As mentioned in the *Handbook*, the diodes marked "1N34" in the paddle circuit *must* be germanium diodes. Also

mentioned in the *Handbook*, and just as important, Q1 must be a silicon transistor. Other than this, almost any parts can be used, keeping in mind the voltage and current requirements to be met, particularly the current surges through D3, D4, D5, Q8 and Q9. Note that D4, D5, D6, C2, Q9, and the 0.01-μF bypass capacitor must withstand the key-up open-circuit voltage of the transmitter.

Germanium transistors were used in the author's unit because a good supply of them was on hand. Silicon transistors should work as well. Q4 should have a minimum beta of 60 to assure saturation when on. It is also desirable that Q4 *not* have good high-frequency response. A good audio response is adequate, and will prevent spurious pulses being sent to Q6 and Q8 during a dash, when both flip-flops change state.

As TTL units have rapid response, it is important that all leads into the keyer case be bypassed, to prevent rf energy in the shack from taking over control of the keyer. Imagine trying to key the rig on and off seven million times a second!

A monitor was available elsewhere in the station, so none was included in the keyer. One may be connected to the collector of Q4, with sufficient series resistance to limit the current drawn by it.

The SCRs used in the author's unit required some amplification of the pulses available to turn them on. If SCRs with more sensitive gates are used, Q6 and Q7 may be eliminated, and the pulses applied directly from the capacitors C1 and C3 to the gates.

The power supply is conventional and straightforward. The +15-volt line has considerable ripple, because of the simple filter used, but this has no effect on the operation of the circuit.

Conclusion

The keyer has been in use for some time now, and has been behaving quite satisfactorily. Even though no heat sinks were used on the SCRs, the currents they handle are so low compared to their capabilities that no problems have been encountered or are anticipated.

In addition to the convenience of using an electronic keyer, it is comforting to know that the code being sent is as near "ideal" as the hand of man can manage. — *Howard Mark, WA2TNZ*

IMPROVED TRANSCEIVER SELECTIVITY

As a proud owner of a commercially made, single-sideband transceiver and having a keen interest in cw, I sought to improve the selectivity without replacing the factory-installed sideband filter. Allen Taflove's active notch filter (*QST* for May, 1975) provided the impetus that resulted in the circuit to be described. I utilized the notch circuit with variable center frequency and negative feedback for an additional amplifier stage. The additional amplifier was a 741 operational amplifier. Because polarity was reversed through the notch filter a non-inverting adder circuit was chosen for the fourth

741. The input signal and feedback signal buck each other except at the notch frequency, providing amplitude reduction of all but notch-frequency signals. Feedback level (selectivity) is controlled by the 5000-ohm potentiometer in the feedback loop. A single dpdt switch can be employed as shown to switch the notch filter from the feedback loop to precede the adder. This allows the device to perform as a notch filter with additional gain.

Power is supplied by two 9-V transistor-radio batteries. As with the notch filter alone, high impedance earphones should be used unless an impedance-matching stage is provided. In the diagram the box indicating the active filter does not include the 10-ohm input resistor that I installed at the input of the overall circuit.

The selectivity appears to be in the range of 50 to 100 Hz. Approximately $30 was spent for construction of the unit. It has greatly enhanced the performance of my transceiver when I tune in signals on a crowded band. — *Art Silvers, WA1UAH*

BETTER PERFORMANCE FOR THE MFJ CW FILTER

Amateurs who operate from fixed stations using the MFJ cw filter will find the following modifications improve the performance of the unit. My first recommendation is to replace the battery with an ac power supply. The Audiovox Corporation manufactures a plug-in type that delivers 15 volts. An alternative would be to make a power unit such as the one described on page 365 of any edition of *The Radio Amateur's Handbook* for 1974 through 1978.

For those operators who have high-impedance headphones an audio output transformer should be installed in the MFJ for proper matching. I used one sold by Radio Shack (part no. 273-1378) which

has a 2000-ohm primary and a 10-kΩ secondary. The transformer secondary provides a good match for the headset.

In order to reduce the effect of noise I added the noise limiter/clipper shown on page 253 of any *Handbook* for 1973 through 1978. A Minibox accommodated the components. When properly adjusted blasting is overcome, the initial thump is reduced, and there is an improvement in the resulting effect of agc when used with cw. — *Walden Pierson, K9BJA*

A HOLD SWITCH FOR THE K. E. ELECTRONICS KEYER

What I needed for my K. E. Electronics Memo-512-R keyer was a hold switch with which to tune up my exciter. After perusing the box and searching through the diagram in hope of finding a clue to the whereabouts of the missing switch I decided on this modification.

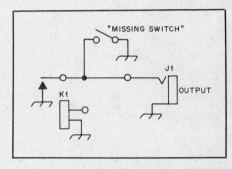

A "tune-up" key for the K.E. Electronics Memo 512-R keyer.

The junk box contained a small, but adequate, miniature spdt toggle switch with which to do the job. I garnered my 3/8-inch hand drill, plus a 1/4-inch bit, and went to work. Several minutes later a nice round hole appeared equidistant between the side-tone switch and the output jack.

After I mounted the switch, all that remained was the addition of a couple of wires in parallel with the keyer output jack and some attractive rub-on letters. *Voila, c'est tout!* Work time was 12 minutes. — *Rick Olsen, N6NR*

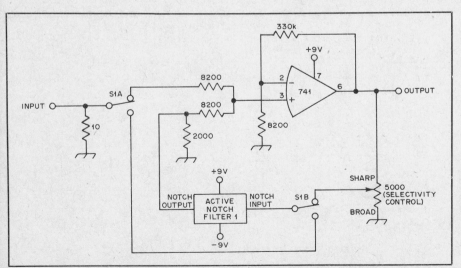

Transceiver selectivity is improved with the use of this filter, adapted from Allen Taflove's active notch filter (*QST* for May, 1975).

Hold switch for Memo keyer.

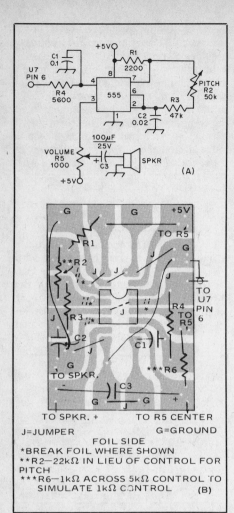

A model of a paddle constructed in the Hq. lab.

At A is shown the schematic diagram of the NE555 sidetone oscillator. At B is shown the modified Radio Shack printed circuit board used to mount the NE555 IC and its associated parts. The user of this hint should have the parts on hand and drill the mounting holes for the placement of those particular parts.

that those using this idea have the parts on hand and drill the board to suit those parts. — *Ron Mays, WA3WAE*

DOT INSERTION FOR THE ACCU-KEYER

The WB4VVF Accu-Keyer (*QST* for August, 1973) is a fine addition to the ham shack. However, the relative ease of sending code with a dot- and dash-memory keyer is debatable, particularly among those of us who are accustomed to operating dot-memory keyers.

The WB4VVF Accu-Keyer may be modified, quite simply, to provide dot insertion *only* by disabling the dash insertion input to the appropriate NAND gate in the iambic section of the keyer. This logic change may be accomplished by removing pin 5 from U2 (7400) or by bending the pin upward so that it cannot enter the IC socket. — *David A. Danello, WB4ONS*

MUTING A DRAKE R-4C WITH AN ACCU-KEYER

Here is a circuit I am using for muting with my Accu-Keyer. It duplicates the keying circuit in the Drake R-4C. Inverting is provided by connecting the unused gate on the 7410 as shown. Since the mute line on the receiver has —70 volts, the scarce 2N4888 was replaced with a 2N4354. No objectionable key clicks are evident. — *Dan Whitman, WB4FHT*

A KEY YOU CAN'T BUY — YET

You play this key with two fingers on the levers. It won't slide around, even on a glass tabletop, because the operating force is toward the base, not parallel to it. It is

light and may be held in one hand while sending code with two fingers of the other hand. That's real armchair sending! It is also human engineered, because it requires fewer muscles to operate.

The base is made from soft aluminum about 0.09-inch thick. The panel of those old war-surplus tuning units is just right. However, it could be made from wood, Plexiglas, Micarta or any suitable, non-magnetic material.

Make the shaft from an 8- or 10-penny nail, cut to fit between the bent-up sides of the base. The paddles should be made from 0.035-inch steel, each about 7/16 × 4 inches in size. Bend one end of each strip around the nail so the two make a good electrical connection, but not so tightly that the paddles move stiffly.

Cut a 1/4 × 1/2-inch piece of Plexiglas to fit snugly in the space between the bent-up sides. Round off the lower edge at the ends so it will fit flat against the base. Place one side of it to line up with the edge of the bent-up parts as illustrated and use a No. 29 drill to make a hole through the Plexiglas and the base. The other two

SIDETONE FOR THE ACCU-KEYER PC-BOARD STYLE

When building the sidetone oscillator for my keyer, the ubiquitous Accu-Keyer, I used a construction method which may be of interest to builders of most any keyer which requires a sidetone. Radio Shack offers a small (1-1/2 × 2-inch or 38 × 51-mm) experimenter's printed-circuit board with pads for a 16-pin in-line IC package. The IC pads are drilled and have feeders to 16 larger pads at the edges of the board. I found that all of the sidetone components fit easily on the circuit board and, since the circuit uses an 8-pin NE555 timer IC (see recent editions of the *Handbook*), that the sidetone circuit could be reproduced by cutting the foil at four places and using the eight left-over pads as connection and mounting points. The result is a professional-looking board with no etching required. The schematic diagram and modified Radio Shack circuit board are shown. I strongly recommend

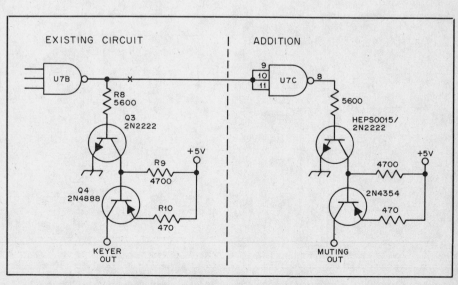

A muting circuit for the Drake R-4C when used with an Accu-Keyer.

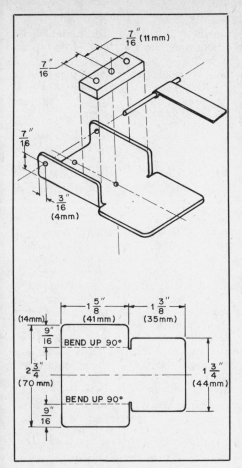

Dimensions of the paddle.

View of the Accu-Keyer component area.

down so the levers have about 1/16 inch of throw. Then drill and mount the cover. Two plastic tabs cemented to the levers and a piece of felt fastened to the bottom will finish the key. Hook it up so that the index finger of whichever hand will be used closes the dot contact, since that finger is usually more agile.

As for learning to send with the key my advice is to make haste slowly. Start at about seven wpm and practice *each* letter until you can send it perfectly 10 consecutive times. Then go on to the next letter. Only after you become accurate at this speed should you attempt higher speeds. — *John S. Lewis, W5TS*

[Editor's Note: A copy of this paddle was built in the ARRL lab and was the hit of the day. One by one, nimble-fingered employees and visitors tried their hand at sending with the key. No one seemed to experience difficulty adapting to pushing, instead of waggling, the paddles. Bug senders who wish to use an electronic keyer without fouling up their bug fists should find this little paddle ideal.]

WEIGHTS FOR YOUR BUG

If your bug weights are too light to make the dots readable, take some lead sinkers (which can be purchased at most hardware stores) and flatten them to about 1/4 inch or so. The weights that I used in my case were of one-ounce size. After the weights are flattened, saw a slit in the sinker and add it to the existing weight on the bug. — *Jeff J. Walters, WN8GNY*

PACKAGING THE ACCU-KEYER

This is not meant to be a how-to-do-it article, but rather a source of ideas. The power supply for the Accu-Keyer is a commercially available ac adaptor, the type used to power portable tape recorders, radios and calculators. It measures 1-3/4 × 2 × 1-3/8 inches (44 × 51 × 35 mm) and furnishes 7.5 V dc at 130 mA. After several hours of operation

the power supply package gets warm, but not hot, to the touch.

As can be seen in the photograph, the main circuit board, Brown Brothers key assembly, and monitor subassembly fit neatly inside a "mini" utility box which is available from Radio Shack. The box measures 7-3/4 × 4-3/8 × 2-3/8 inches (197 × 111 × 60 mm) and is rugged, attractive and priced reasonably. The gray hammertone finish and rubber feet help give the completed Accu-Keyer a professional appearance.

The schematic diagram shown was provided with the drilled circuit board obtained from WB4VVF. My monitor-oscillator was built on a 1-3/4 × 2-inch (44 × 51 mm) scrap of "perf" board, and was then epoxied to the rear of a two-inch round speaker. The speaker was mounted to the rear panel by using a scrap of copper window screening as a protective grill. Also located on the rear apron are two miniature phone jacks, one providing a connection for keyer output and the other for dc input.

The Accu-Keyer has an automatic character-space feature. After briefly disabling it during the pre-packaging stage of this project, I decided to use it without provisions to switch it in and out of the circuit. However, if one is interested in retaining the in-out feature of automatic character spacing, there is ample room for

holes in the Plexiglas only are for no. 6 self-tapping, hex-head screws, 1/4-inch long. Remove the hex-head screws from the Plexiglas and fill the heads with soft solder. Countersink the hole in the base for a no. 6 flat-head screw. Put a solder lug on each of the self-tapping screws and return them to their holes, with the lugs pointing toward the back. Mount the strip, being sure the screws don't short to the base.

After the pivot-pin holes are drilled, put the pin through one hole; thread on a washer, both levers and another washer. Separate the levers and determine the length of the required spacer. Additional washers or a piece of 1/4-inch copper tubing will do. Drill for a screw in the rear center of the base and countersink on the bottom side. Solder a 1-1/2-inch piece of flexible wire or braid for coiled pigtails to each lever near the end wrapped around the pin. Solder the other ends and a wire (for common to the keyer) to a lug, and fasten the lug to the hole just drilled. The other two wires to the keyer are connected to the lugs on the hex-head screws.

The cover may be bent from thin (about 0.020-inch) aluminum or anything handy that is not magnetic. The magnet (Radio Shack no. 64-1875) is glued to the front edge of the cover in the center, long edge crosswise. The cover is adjusted up or

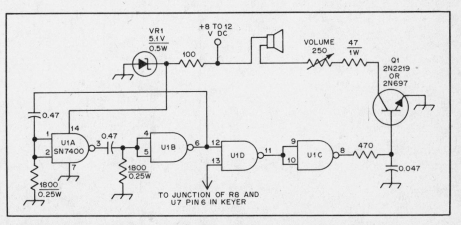

The WB4VVF circuit board diagram. These are the Radio Shack part numbers used in the assembly.
IC 7400 Quad NAND Gate no. 276-1801.
Two-inch, 8-ohm speaker no. 40-245.
Perf board assortment no. 276-1391.

Subminiature toggle switch no. 275-324.
Mini utility box no. 270-232.
Miniature jack and plug asst. no. 274-335.

A copy of *QST* serves to illustrate the compactness of the Accu-Keyer and power supply.

individually at 15 wpm. This way students learn by the sound of each letter instead of counting dots and dashes. Moving from 5 to 13 wpm presents the difficulty of proper spacing of characters if a stop-watch is being used. I devised this simple timer circuit; it might well be called an Accu-Space for the Accu-Keyer. By timing the length of the spaces while listening to practice transmissions, I am able to send tape-perfect code. Timing with a triggered scope is the best approach.

The pulse from the 2N2222 triggers the

NE555 timer and also resets it as long as anything is being sent. So the NE555 starts timing just at the end of the last code element and holds the regular auto-space feature on for a longer time through the OR gate. The LED helps me know the thing is holding and I can double the LED's time on for word spaces. — *David E. Allen, WBØTAQ*

BREAK-IN DELAY FOR THE HT-46

Owners of the Hallicrafters HT-46 transmitter, treated in "Recent Equipment" some years ago (*QST* for August, 1966), may be interested in the circuit described here. It is easy to build and is not expensive. Break-in delay is provided during cw operation through addition of this unit, and antenna changeover from transmit to receive is made possible by the plate relay used in the new circuit. Although we have no information to offer about use of this circuit with similar types of commercially made transmitting equipment, chances are the accessory could be adapted easily for addition to other kinds of gear.

This assembly is *not* a VOX box. Hallicrafters did manufacture such an accessory (model HA-16) for ssb operation, and the circuit of that item is contained in the HT-46 instruction manual for those who may want to build one.

a switch on either the front or rear panel. The front panel switch labeled TONE is the monitor disable switch. If your rig has a built-in sidetone oscillator, it will not be necessary to use the keyer monitor.

Included on the schematic diagram is a listing of the components with Radio Shack part numbers. It is given for those interested in duplicating this packaging scheme. — *Hal Morris, W4VUO/3*

NOW AN ACCU-SPACE

I'm teaching beginning and intermediate code classes for our local club. From the start I have been sending code characters

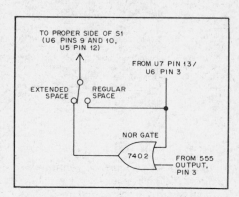

Switch arrangement for regular or extended space.

All of the operating voltages for the break-in delay "gizmo" are borrowed from the HT-46; they're taken through the VOX accessory socket on the rear apron of the transmitter (J6 on the HT-46 diagram). Plate voltage for V1 is obtained from pin 6 (+ 260 V), and heater voltage is taken via pin 3 (12.6 V ac). Pin 5 of J6 serves as the ground connection after the lead originally connected to it is unsoldered from terminal 9 of K1 and connected to chassis ground in the HT-46. Pin 1 of J6 is connected to the keying line at J2 after being unsoldered from C4 in the transmitter. The foregoing modifications make J6 unsuitable for use with the HA-16 VOX unit. Those wishing to retain the VOX-connection facility of J6 may elect to add a four-terminal connector on the rear apron of the HT-46 chassis for connection to the circuit shown here.

One other change was made to the HT-46 by the writer: A jumper was placed across terminals 5 and 6 of S1A to maintain cutoff bias on the HT-46 keying line during standby (function switch in STANDBY mode). Without the change the outboard break-in delay will actuate when the HT-46 is in standby, as V1A will conduct unless the grid is supplied with negative voltage.

Almost any plate relay will suffice at K2A, provided it is a spdt variety. The relay contacts should have good insulating material (ample for up to 100 watts of rf power), and the contacts should be rated

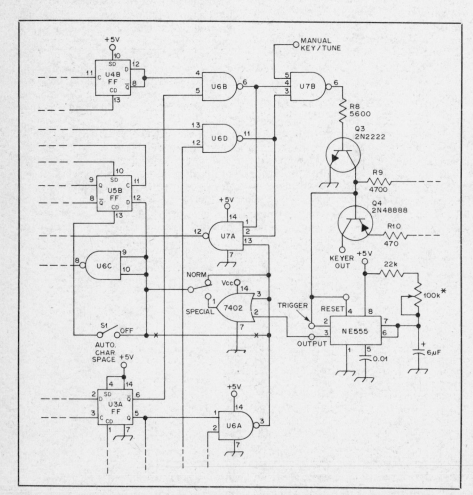

A portion of the original Accu-Keyer circuit is shown here with the addition of an NE555 timer circuit. The 100-kΩ potentiometer should have a linear taper. For extended space, the auto space should be ON.

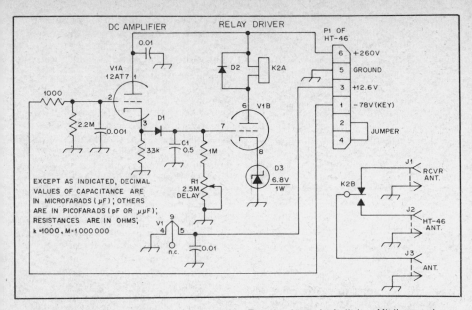

Schematic diagram of the break-in delay assembly. The circuit can be built in a Minibox, and should be shielded to prevent rf energy from causing adverse effects. Fixed-value capacitors are disk ceramic. Decimal-value capacitors are in μF. Fixed-value resistors are 1/2-watt composition types.

C1 — High-quality 0.5 μF, 100 volt or greater. Mylar, polystyrene, or glass capacitor recommended.
D1, D2 — Low-voltage silicon diode; 1N914 or power-supply type rectifier diode suitable.
D3 — 6.8-volt Zener diode.
J1-J3, incl. — Chassis-mount coaxial fitting of builder's choice. Phono connectors suitable.
K2 — Plate relay. See text. (Advance GHE-2C-10,000 used by writer.)
P1 — Plug furnished with HT-46.
R1 — Linear-taper, 2.5-megohm control, carbon type.

at 2 amperes or more. The builder can use a 5000- or 10,000-ohm relay, or any value in between those ohmic amounts.

R1 is the delay control. With the component values specified, the delay range is on par with most commercial break-in delay circuits. Shorter delays can be had by making C1 lower in value, or vice versa. If receiver muting is of interest, use a dpdt relay at K2A. The second set of relay contacts can be used for that application.
— W1FB

COMPLETE FLEXIBILITY FOR THE ACCU-MEMORY

I have found a small change in the WB4VVF Accu-Memory that is probably in great demand from those who prefer a completely flexible keyer with no compromises. The change is accomplished with the third section of the triple, three-input, NAND 7410 used on the main keyer board and two additional parts.

To interface the keyer and the memory, one must utilize the manual key gate. It can no longer act as the manual input since by so doing a TTL output gate would be brought forcefully and fatally to ground. Solutions involving output connections are not satisfactory since more than one type of output may very well be employed. In my version I have both grid-blocked and cathode outputs selected from the front panel. Switching the output and the various straight key and tune functions at the same time was too involv-

ed. Moreover, my front panel was already laid out. The solution came from the NAND truth table.

The output from the 7420 will go low when true via the keyer logic, the tune switch, or the straight key. This means that the normal state is high or floating for TTL. Therefore a NAND can become an OR with inverted inputs as shown in the illustration. The table defines any low input as producing a high output. All that would then need be done is to invert and feed the original manual key gate input. The two diagrams show the circuit arrangement before and after modification.

To make the simple changes, these steps were followed: Remove the wire connected to pin 5 of U7 and connect it to pin 9 of U7. Attach a wire to pin 10 of U7 for a manual tune switch. Next connect a wire to pin 11 of U7 and the memory circuit. Prepare a 2N3904 (or similar npn plastic switching transistor) as shown in B. Solder the emitter to the ground foil and the collector to pin 5 of U7. This connection can be made at the manual key pad. A 5600-ohm, 1/4-W resistor is then connected from the base lead to pin 8 of U7. This completes the modification. It leaves the operator with the choice of normal operation, or by grounding either the memory lead, the manual key, or the tune switch, the output is turned on. — Edward Tanton, WA4BAA

HEARING AID FOR THE TEN-TEC KR5 KEYER

A Radio Shack code-oscillator module for under $2 provided me with the basic unit for a sidetone monitor for my Ten-Tec KR5 keyer. The small module fits easily into the KR5 cabinet, and may be placed

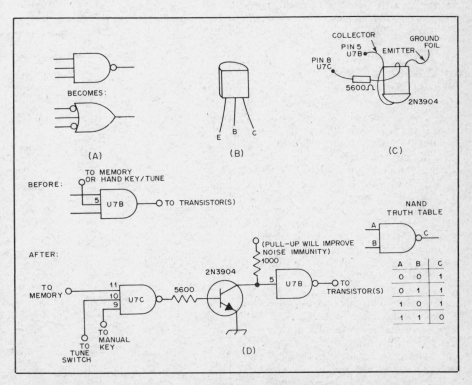

Accu-Memory circuit modifications for normal operation or activation of the memory output by grounding the memory key, using the manual key, or operating the tune switch. A NAND truth table is shown for reference. Lead connections for the 2N3904 are illustrated at D. The resistor leads are shorter than indicated (for clarity). The leads should be routed directly across the IC.

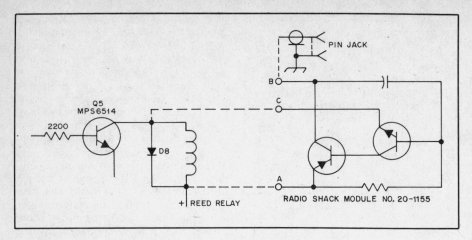

An inexpensive Radio Shack code oscillator can be converted to a sidetone monitor for the Ten-Tec KR5 keyer by using this circuit.

near the keyer relay. The simple wiring involves connecting terminal A on the module to the + side of the relay coil. B is connected to the pin plug that is added. C is connected to the minus side of the relay coil.

A phono jack was installed under the KR5 TRANS pin plug. A miniature pushbutton was mounted under the 6-12 V pin plug. This spst pushbutton switch was connected across the TRANS pin plug.

While I chose to keep the speaker outside the KR5 box, a small speaker could be placed inside the box. Since I already had an old transistor radio with a speaker mounted in the cover, I arranged to have it plug into the KR5 sidetone pin plug. During the first month of operation, performance was faultless. — *Velio S. Bussicone, W9IIL*

HEATH HD-10 KEYER MODIFICATION

I have been using a modified Heath HD-10 keyer for several years now and have a simple modification which permits easy, fast sending, and also provides for cathode keying. Here are the details, which should help other HD-10 owners.

First see page 16 of the assembly manual. Then remove the leaf springs and the shoulder spacer. Center the key level in the center of the slot by adjustment of bracket L. Loosen the screws that hold L to the plate, adjust the bracket so that the level falls in the center of the slot and tighten the screws.

Next, adjust brackets N and P so that the operating buttons of the microswitches are against the key lever and *partly depressed*. A short movement of the lever toward one side should snap the microswitch on that side closed, and releasing the lever should allow it to reopen, which pushes the lever back to center. A little "fiddling" will get this adjustment just right.

When this is done, you may find that it takes a little more force to snap one microswitch than the other. If this bothers

you, loosen L, and adjust it so that there is a little spring pressure on the side that needs help. Retighten L.

If cathode keying is desired, move the black lead from hole C to the next foil (the other side of R9). This is the only wiring change.

Connect the keying relay between KEYED LINE and BATTERY NEGATIVE on the external terminal board. I used a Magnecraft 132MPCX4 mercury-wetted reed relay with a 1000-ohm coil. (See the Allied Radio Industrial catalog.) I mounted this directly on the terminal board by means of two short pieces of No. 14 wire running from the relay coil to the terminals. The relay contacts then key a 50-watt buffer (in the cathode) on the rig.

The electrical change and relay can be omitted if you have only grid-block keyed rigs within the voltage limits of the keyer

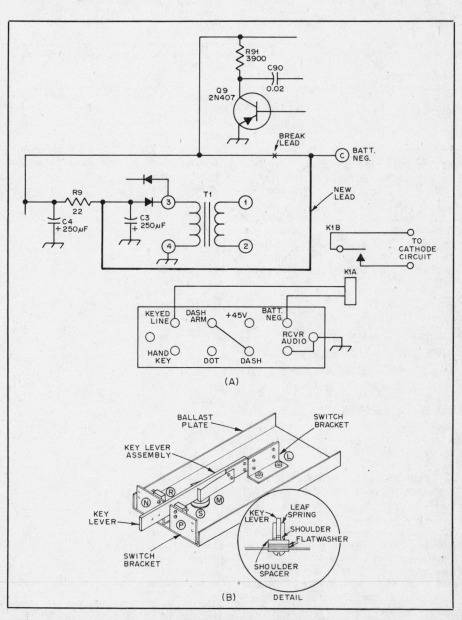

Fast, easy sending with provision for cathode keying for the Heath HD-10 keyer is made possible with this circuit shown at A. Mechanical changes for the HD-10 paddle illustrated at B.

output transistor. The relay, of course, permits keying anything within the limits of the relay contacts. — *Albert B. Booth, W4SSM*

AUTO-RECALIBRATION FOR CW DECODER

I have built two cw-to-alphanumeric decoders from the original article by Thomas Riley, WA1BYM (*QST* for October, November and December, 1975). They drive Burroughs self-scan displays and the following Auto-Cal circuit. Under live and test conditions both units are able to resynchronize using the Auto-Cal from six to in excess of 100 wpm from a single clock.

The loss of system lock or change in received speed can cause various out-of-sync conditions: up/down counter too small or large resulting in all Ts or Es, or character-spacing loss resulting in C = TETE. The decoding of all Ts or Es, or any combination of both, will increment the binary counter, U35, until a count of eight. This will cause an automatic Recal through U7D. Any dot/dash pattern that is decoded and shifted into the dot/dash registers will reset the counter through U36B. — *Thomas W. Hart, WB5OHM*

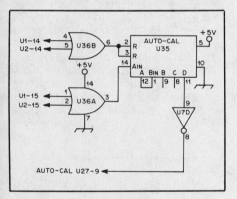

An Auto-Recalibration circuit that will synchronize the Riley cw-to-alphanumeric converter.

AN OLD CW FAVORITE

The sideswiper is the forerunner of the modern paddle used with electronic keyers. As is the paddle, the sideswiper is essentially a spdt switch with a return-to-neutral feature that assures you that your carrier doesn't remain on the air between dots and dashes. With it, a practiced operator can sideswipe along at a good clip, well above the speed anyone without a rubber wrist can achieve with a straight key. In use, one swings the arm of the key back and forth between the contacts, with elements of Morse character being formed alternately at right and left (left and right does just as well). It's a dot if your dwell time on the contact is shorter than your dash dwell time — although sometimes

dots tend to come out longer than dashes. Sideswiping compared to straight keying is something like flag waving as compared to using a well hand pump, a waggling versus a pumping motion.

One of the important characteristics of this basic instrument is that its action is faster than that of a straight key. On the other hand, perhaps a most important feature (which sets aglow the warm feeling many of us have for the sideswiper) is that it gives real character to one's fist. Such character isn't achievable with modern keyers by any but the most dogged — and it's impossible with a keyboard. The accent was a much more reliable identifier of the operator than was his chirp or his 120-cycle note (in sideswiper days 120-Hz hum was virtually unknown). The accent was almost better than a fingerprint. It never was clear why the FCC didn't record a little bit of each operator's sideswiper fist for its gumshoe operations (maybe they did!) since his accent couldn't be faked as can a call sign.

With a sideswiper there's an opportunity for each cw operator to do his own thing that is much more in harmony with modern ideas of individuality than is the homogenization of fists resulting from the use of such modern electronic aids as keyers and keyboards. It is suggested that each cw operator review his own fist objectives and consider the sideswiper, particularly the modernized version that is described below, for code character building.

Construction Details

The classical homebrew sideswiper is built from fundamental items found in any ham's workshop 35 years ago: a porcelain-base dpst knife switch (just try to find one now!), a hacksaw blade, a 6-32 × 1/4-inch machine screw and nut, and about two feet of friction tape. The switch is disassembled, the two blades are used to form a pair of rear supports for the sideswiper arm, and the terminals are reformed to make the opposing contacts spaced about 3/32-inch apart. The exact dimensions are unimportant. A hacksaw blade is then selected (those with a number of teeth missing are preferred over new blades, but the number of teeth per inch is unimportant since they are ground off anyway), cut to length, and mounted as shown. Finally, the classical key is completed by winding the friction tape over the end of the blade to produce a soft, comfortable "knob" (much better than the cold feel of a plastic knob). Experienced users will mount the key on a wooden baseplate that is large enough to prevent the key from scooting around in use and that is finished to match the decor of the shack.

Basic Design Improvement

After lengthy experimentation during the building program, required by an in-

ability to find in the junk box any non-dried-out friction tape of the type required for the classical design, it was determined that the currently available plastic electrician's tape is an entirely satisfactory substitute — and in fact provides the basic modernization. One's fingers no longer stick to the knob when the key is first made. Instead, the smooth plastic tape encourages the use of the sideswiper immediately on completion and does not require dirty fingers to eliminate the stickiness, as was necessary with tape of the earlier specifications. Experienced sideswipers will recognize this basic improvement in the homebrew key as a valuable contribution to the evolution of the instrument. — *John Myers, W9LA*

ANOTHER ANTI-SLIDE IDEA

To keep a keyer or bug in place, I glue two pieces of fine-grade sandpaper back to back. The keying unit was placed on the paper and remained in the same position throughout long slugfests of cw operation. The sandpaper won't scratch the table either! — *Chris G. Skuza, WA2ISO*

BUG TO KEYER PADDLE, AND BACK TO BUG

Here is an idea for modifying your bug for use as an electronic keyer paddle. This modification will allow you to change the bug back and forth between bug and paddle quickly without much effort.

Remove the weights from the vibrator arm. Glue a small fiber block from behind the dot contact to the vibrator arm. This prevents the dot contact spring from operating. Underneath the base-plate, remove the bus bar connecting the dash and dot terminals. Adjust the key arm so that as the dot contact is made the vibrator arm touches the damper assembly. Wiring is straightforward. Reverse the above procedure to restore the unit to its original configuration. — *Robert Anderson, WB9FTA*

KEYING A TRANSMITTER WITH A TAPE RECORDER

This simple envelope detector and wave-shaping circuit uses a low-cost quad-NAND gate module to enable "instant replay" of recorded cw transmissions. Diodes D1 and D2 protect the gate from excessive input voltage swings. (Type 1N270 diodes were used, although any small-signal switching or general-purpose diode should be suitable.) R3, C2 and D3 provide envelope detection of the amplified and clipped audio input. R6 provides positive feedback to suppress output oscillations which can occur when TTL gates are subjected to slow rise- and

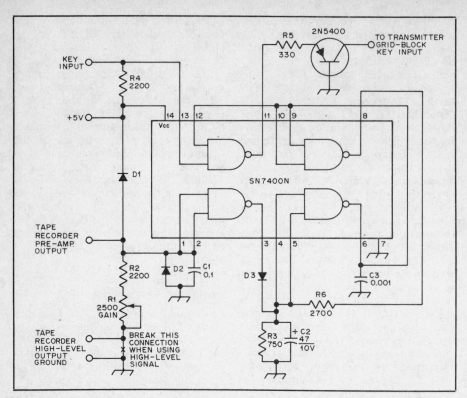

A simple envelope detector and wave-shaping circuit for instant replay of recorded cw transmissions.

fall-time signals. R1 is used to lower the "floating" input threshold to the gate and increase circuit sensitivity.

For low-impedance recorder outputs or high-level audio outputs, the low side of R1 should be disconnected from ground and used as the audio input point; the value of R2 should be increased if amplifier hum or background noise is still sufficient to trigger the circuit falsely. Of course, an audio-filtered and impedance-matched input to the tape recorder greatly assists in generating a perfect noise-free output replica of the original input signal. — *Andrew H. Kilpatrick, K4YKZ*

VE3CJB KEYER PADDLE

The Canadian amateur who purchases parts manufactured outside Canada naturally has to pay import taxes; when faced with the cost of purchasing a keyer paddle plus the tax, I balked! One solution to this problem seemed to be to come up with a scheme to build a keyer paddle. I finally made one that looks and feels as good as the commercially manufactured units. I got to thinking that maybe there are other hams who, for one reason or another, would be interested in my design layout.

The paddle's construction is such that it does not require the use of any uncommon household workshop tool. The only power tool required is a hand drill (naturally a drill press would be preferred,

especially if a steel base is used). The main parts are made of 3/8-inch, cold-rolled-steel rod, cut and filed to fit as called for on the drawing. — *Jim Baker, VE3CJB*

EXPANDING THE ACCU-MEMORY

After operating my Accu-Memory for a while, I realized that an enlarged memory capacity would be desirable. It seemed to me that most of the logic in the Accu-Memory was devoted to timing and operating the RAM. Because of the nature of the tri-state RAM, installing two additional RAMs in the memory circuit did not seem foreboding. The main problem was physical — how to accomplish this feat without disassembling the unit and without cutting leads on the existing RAM. Another consideration was to retain the rf immunity of the keyer memory.

My plan was to attach a piggy-back, 16-pin socket to the existing RAM, since all leads of the pair would be connected in common except for pin 13, the chip selector of $\overline{CE}$, according to the IC manual. A 7432 quad-NOR gate was chosen for selecting the pair of RAMs. The total memory, after modification was ample for most situations.

Fortunately, my Accu-Memory was constructed with sockets which eliminated the need to unsolder connections on the underside of the board. Installation of the additional RAMs was done according to the following sequence: Remove the existing RAM from its socket. Bend pin 13 at right angles to the other pins. Place it back in the socket. Bend pin 13 of the new 16-pin IC socket at right angles also. Place that over the existing RAM, lining up the bent pins. Solder the new IC socket to the existing RAM, waiting 20 seconds between finishing one pin and working on the next. Pin 13 is not soldered. Care must also be exercised to avoid soldering the existing RAM into the original socket.

At this point, the additional RAM and the piggy-back socket are removed from the existing socket. Insert a piece of wire firmly into pin hole 13 of the existing socket. Solder a length of wire to pin 13 of

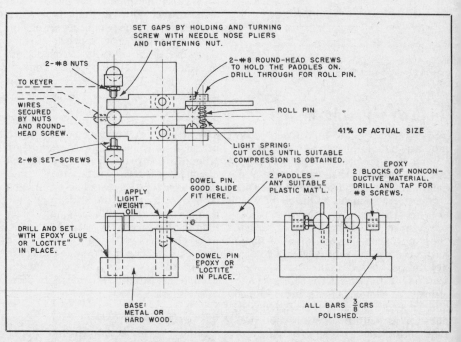

Mechanical drawing of the VE3CJB keyer paddle.

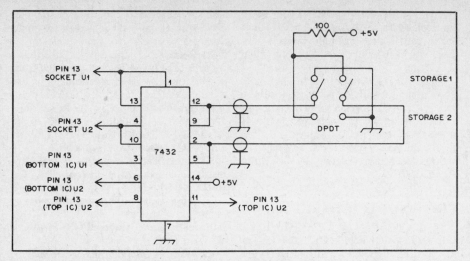

An enlarged memory is achieved for the Accu-Memory by incorporating this circuit.

the old RAM and another length to pin 13 of the piggy-back socket. Reinsert the old RAM in the original socket. The new RAM should be inserted in the piggy-back socket in the same direction as the original RAM. Installation procedure is the same for both new RAMs.

The 7432 was wired without the use of printed circuits by using the dead-bug method. Simply bend all leads of the IC 90 degrees so that they are pointing away from the device. Necessary jumpers were added. The IC was secured with acrylic 10-second glue to the top of U6.

Except for the short jumpers, shielded wire was used throughout the project to avoid rf pickup. After completion the keyer retained immunity to rf. I was able to mount the miniature dpdt switch, indicated in the drawing, on the front panel.

This modification provided one keyer with two independent memories. Each will function the same as the original memory. Moreover, the four RAMs provide 4096 bits of storage. — *Jake Gold, WB2AFS*

METEOR-SCATTER TIMING MODIFICATION FOR THE ACCU-KEYER MEMORY

My primary interest is operation in the 2-meter band. Therefore, I spend much time calling CQ, so the Accu-Memory is quite helpful. Meteor-scatter contacts are much simpler: The memory takes care of the repetitious transmitting of my exchange. I developed the modification shown in the schematic diagram to eliminate the need to synchronize pressing the appropriate memory switch with the sweep second hand of a clock. U1, an NE555 timer, provides timing pulses at intervals determined by the setting of R1. U1 "clocks" U2, a flip-flop, the Q output of which stops the memory of the keyer. The output of U1 is applied through the five-position switch to the RESET switch-

es in the keyer. Every second pulse from the timer resets the memory. Fifteen seconds (or whatever interval is desired) later, the memory is stopped, and after 15 seconds is restarted for as many cycles as desired. The unused position on the rotary switch allows the operator to disconnect the timing circuit from the keyer, for synchronization with WWV.

This circuit works very well and takes much of the hassle out of meteor-scatter work. It may also be of interest to EME (moonbounce) workers, with appropriate changes in the time constants. — *Michael R. Owen, WB5DOJ*

RF IN AN ELECTRONIC KEYER

When I operate my Hallicrafters FPM-300 Mark-II transceiver in the 40-meter band and above, rf apparently enters my Heath HD-1410 keyer. The trouble was eliminated by connecting a 0.01-μF, 1 kV, bypass capacitor from one of the 117-V ac supply leads to ground as shown in the diagram. — *A. D. McMahone, WB9FCK*

KEYER WEIGHTING

Charlie, an old friend who just received his Novice license, asked me a question: "How fast can you copy?" As I started to reply, I realized that there was no simple pat answer. There was no unqualified number I could give him. It required a little discussion that went something like this:

My cw receiving speed is almost wholly dependent on the sender's quality or articulation, his rhythm, spacing, and keyer weighting. I can read a super operator such as Flo, W7QYA, at 50 words per minute and there are some hams I strain to copy at 10 words per minute. And some of the hard-to-copy hams are not beginners, either, but old timers who have exacerbated their bad habits. And the trouble is that it takes a lot of courage to tell a friend that he has a lousy fist — sort of like telling him he needs a deodorant.

A few years ago, I was involved in some rather elaborate measurements of speech intelligibility conducted by Cruft Laboratory of Harvard University. The "articulation percentage" was the percent of words understood with different amounts of noise and with various frequency responses. From these tests came an understanding of just what was required for accurate, articulate speech under various conditions.

The same general observations apply to cw. The pitch, for one thing, should be centered around 1 kHz where the ear is the most sensitive, especially at low levels of sound. It acts as a band-pass filter of sorts.

An all-important factor in producing easy-to-read cw is the "weighting" of the keyer or the setting of a bug. This is the ratio of the dit and dah length to the space between them. The classical ratio is 1:3, in which the dit is 1/3 the length of a dah and equal to a space. However, in practice, it is a bit choppy in the range of 15-20 wpm where most of us work. Increasing the character length about 15 percent

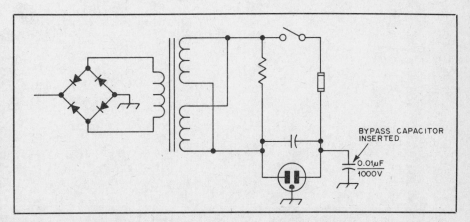

Reduction of troublesome rf in the HD-1410 may be obtained by connecting a 0.01 μF, 1-kV capacitor from the 117-V line to ground as shown in this diagram. An alternative would be to connect two 0.01-μF capacitors in series across the line, grounding the common connection between the two capacitors.

gives about the same readability but is a lot more pleasant to read for it is smoother and a little musical.

For speeds above 25 wpm, weighting becomes extremely important. Shortening the characters with respect to space increases the articulation and the greater the speed, the shorter the bit lengths should be to make it easy for the ham at the other end. The greatest problem for an operator of a DX station is to read the call signs of stations calling in a pile-up, especially under "wide open" band conditions. Sometimes a call is discernible only for a second or so. To be read, it must be clean. If the signal is fairly weak, (in a pile-up of loud signals, all often appear weak) the right combination of moderate speed and short weighting will often bring a reply to the station that is several S units below the others who are pounding away with slurred signals.

An easy way of visually determining proper weighting is to connect an ohmmeter across the keyed output. When the dit side is actuated, the meter will read half scale for a 1:3 ratio. This is, of course, because a dit is equal to a space. This is the basing point.

Some electronic keyers have variable weighting; others have factory preset weighting. Most can be modified to provide the ideal weighting for your particular style of operating. If your normal operation is in the 15-20 wpm range, you will find that an increase of about 15 percent will give you the best balance of articulation and smoothness. You will sound great, be easy to copy. If, however, you are QSOing some pretty fast company, reduce the characters by the same amount and you will be doing a favor for

the ham at the receiving end. If your keyer has a preset factory adjustment, by changing a resistor or installing a variable control, you can tailor it to your individual preference.

With the increased interest in higher code speed these days, perhaps we need a new Q signal to request advice on optimum setting. Or to suggest a change. If it was in general use, it would be a help in producing more legible cw at any speed as well as less strain and tension. — *Albert Kahn, K4FW*

CLEANING CAPACITANCE-ACTIVATED KEYER PADDLES

Capacitance-activated keyer paddles, such as the Data Engineering Electronic Feather Touch, become erratic in operation when dirt and oxide build up on the metal grid. The dirt may be removed with a soft cloth moistened with denatured alcohol. — *Wayne E. Whitman, W9HFR*

THE YAESU FL-101

The Yaesu FL-101, when using full break-in with the T-R switch in the ARRL *Handbook*, operates beautifully except for an annoying backwave that will mask weak signals. The finals and the driver are grid-block keyed. To correct the backwave problem, I decided to key an additional stage. The heterodyne oscillator was selected because of the construction of the unit and convenience.

1) Remove PB-1407 from its socket.

2) On the socket, disconnect the ground lead from pin 5.

3) On PB-1407 use a sharp-edged knife

and slice through the foil leading to pin 5. Drill a small hole at the top of the pin 5 foil.

4) Remove R7, and jumper pin 5 to the emitter of Q3 with a small insulated wire.

5) Mount a 50-kΩ potentiometer on top of the chassis. I taped this in to prevent damage and to preserve trade-in value. One side of the potentiometer goes to pin 4 of PB-1407 and the other to the center pin of J4, which is the key input.

6) Underneath the chassis, wire a transistor as shown in the diagram. I used a 2N2222A with long leads.

7) Adjust the 50-kΩ potentiometer to remove the backwave. The Yaesu FL-101 will now operate beautiful QSK, as there was never any hash and now no backwave. — *Max Cornell, WAØSIG*

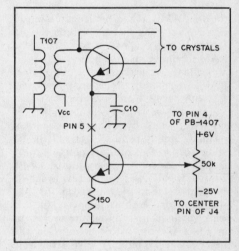

Backwave on the Yaesu FL-101 eliminated with this circuit.

Chapter 7

Portable and Mobile Quickies

BATTERY CONSUMPTION SAVING

When using hand-held and other battery-operated equipment over extended periods of time it is clearly desirable to keep consumption to the minimum possible that allows the system to function without significant loss of efficiency. One technique that for some years has been fairly widely used in professional equipments is the use of a low duty cycle during standby operation of the receiver, automatically switching the equipment to normal receive conditions when a signal appears. In other words, this means that the muted receiver "listens" for perhaps 10 percent of the total time, taking a brief look at the frequency every few seconds. If the squelch or muting circuit then indicates that there is a signal coming in, the interrupt condition is disabled and the receiver stays on until perhaps 10 seconds after the signal has gone, when the sampling process is restarted.

A number of suitable "battery saver" circuits that accomplish this sampling process have been described: for example, one by Dr. D. A. Tong, G8ENN, was given in *Wireless World* for March, 1972, pp. 124-5; another by Intech Inc. in *Electronic Design*; and the latest by John Rumsey, ZL2TNK, and Peter Williams, ZL2ARW, in *Break-In* for August, 1975. This one is basically similar to the G8ENN design but uses rather less components. The New Zealand design was intended for use with a specific group-project walkie-talkie but there is no reason why it should not be used, possibly with minor modifications, for other equipments.

All these systems depend on an astable multivibrator to provide the basic 1:10 duty cycle and use this to control a transistor power switch which interrupts the power to the active devices in the receiver.

In operation the receiver is held on either initially or after transmission for

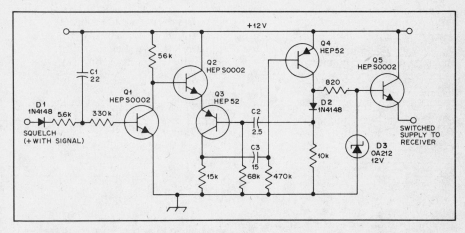

A battery-saver device can reduce the consumption of walkie-talkie and hand-held equipment during standby by a factor of 10 by using an astable multivibrator to switch the receiver off except for brief "sampling" periods every few seconds. When the presence of a signal is detected by the receiver squelch or muting circuits the receiver remains "on".

about 25 seconds before the sampling cycle begins. The following notes on circuit operations and necessary precautions are based directly on the *Break-In* article.

When the receiver is switched on, C1 is initially discharged but then charges slowly through the 330-kΩ resistor and the base-emitter junction of Q1, holding Q1 on which in turn forces Q2 off. Eventually C1 becomes fully charged, so that base current ceases to flow in Q1, turning this transistor off and causing Q2 to switch on, which in turn works through the system until Q5 is turned on, so providing power for the receiver. If during the sample listening period there is a signal present, the squelch circuit in the equipment provides an input voltage to D1. This causes current to flow through D1 and the 5600-ohm resistor, so that base current flows in Q1, turning Q2 off and holding the receiver on. When the signal disappears, however, C1 again charges through the 330-kΩ resistor and the

original cycle of events reoccurs. Q5 acts not only as a switch but, in conjunction with D3, as a voltage regulator.

The authors state that it is important to use high-gain transistors throughout since low-gain types, e.g., BC237, BC307 (HEP 729, HEP 715) do not switch effectively and can give rise to unpleasant noises from the receiver as it switches. It is suggested that tantalum capacitors should be used for C1, C2 and C3; they are smaller and have lower leakage. Since the sampling time and duty cycle is affected by both capacitor values and transistor gains, some experimentation may be needed, especially with C3, to get the desired results. The original unit was built on a piece of paxolin less than one inch square with 0.1-W resistors, and was able to fit into quite a compact walkie-talkie.

The current drawn in this particular unit with the mute closed is normally 40 mA, but with the battery saver in operation the average current drops to 4 mA, thus providing a very worthwhile extension of battery life, particularly where the equipment is required to operate for extended periods on standby.

On the subject of battery economy, it is interesting to note that the range of Varta batteries, made in Germany, now includes a miniature sealed NiCad 9-V battery, type TR7/8. It is the same size as the well-known PP3 transistor battery, with similar connections, but can be recharged some hundreds of times (provided care is taken). The capacity is 90 mAH; unfortunately details of the price are lacking: obviously NiCad units are expensive compared with primary cells but for anyone using a lot of batteries it should work out cheaper in the long run. — Radio Communication, *December, 1975, RSGB*

SHOCK MOUNTING FOR MOBILE RIGS

A large percentage of mobile-equipment failures may be caused by vibration damage while in motion. Before installing my new mobile rig, I placed a rubber grommet over each mounting bolt, to act as a shock absorber. The grommets are installed so that they are compressed between the mounting bracket and the dashboard of the vehicle. — *Howard A. Johnson, WA8QBJ*

INTERFERENCE-FREE CAR REGULATOR

Electronic solid-state voltage regulators as a part of "car electrics" are attractive for a number of reasons — not least because they have no mechanical contacts to produce sparks that can be a difficult-to-eliminate source of interference to mobile operation.

John King, G4CFJ, when using a 1.8 MHz mobile rig in a car with a fiberglass

(glass reinforced-plastics) body, found it impossible to suppress the voltage regulator with any of the usual techniques. So in the end he adopted the solid-state regulator arrangement shown in the illustration.

In this system the battery volts are compared with the reference volts across a 6-8 V Zener diode. When the battery voltage is low, the 741 operational amplifier IC provides an output of about + 12 V, turning on C1 and C2. This causes generator field current to flow and the generator output to charge the battery. As soon as the battery volts rise beyond that of the Zener reference, the 741 output drops to about + 2 V and the field current is turned off. The battery is prevented from discharging through the generator by diode D1 which should have a current rating of at least 20 A.

G4CFJ mentions that when he installed the new regulator he left the original one in place and simply placed cardboard between its contacts to stop it from working. The wires to A, F and D connections were soldered to those already on the old regulator. It should be noted that the circuit as shown is suitable only for negative-earth systems, but by changing npn to pnp types and suitably connecting the diodes, it should be possible to adapt the system for positive-earth vehicles.

If the generator output is too low (or high) it can be adjusted by changing the value of R1 (1.5 ohms nominal); R1 should be set to give 13.5 to 14 V from the battery. — *Radio Communication, March, 1976, RSGB*

MOUNTING MOBILE EQUIPMENT

A convenient place to mount mobile equipment is below the instrument panel. The mount is constructed from aluminum angle stock and a piano hinge, both of which should be available from the do-it-

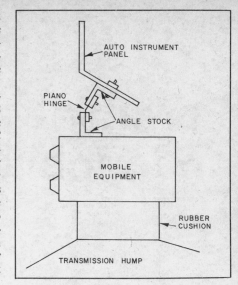

W5TBC's mobile mount.

yourself counter at most hardware stores. This scheme makes a rigid mount, yet equipment may be removed easily by pulling out the pin in the piano hinge. — *Robert T. Paige, W5TBC*

LOCKING ACTION FOR MOBILE MICS

A simple modification to my mobile mic has made long-winded QSOs a bit easier. By carefully filing a notch in the push-to-talk button, a locking action can be added to almost any mobile mic. The sketch shows the placement of the notch. Care should be taken to keep filings from falling into the mic case. With my mic, it wasn't necessary to remove any more than 1/16 inch from the control button. Be sure to check frequently for locking action. — *Gene Kusluski, WA8YIT*

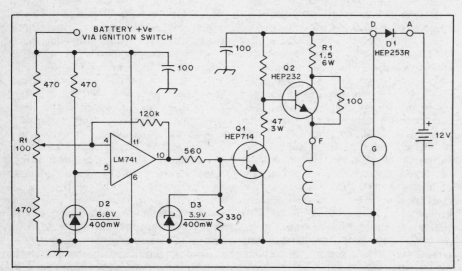

Solid-state voltage regulator used by G4CFJ to overcome the problem of regulator interference to 1.8 MHz mobile operation. Unmarked resistor to base of Q2 is 20 ohms.

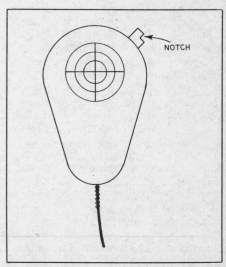

Notch in PTT button removes need to press the switch continually during QSO.

The complete system showing bike, wooden frame, generator, VOM and so forth. Lest anyone trespass, that is K2PLT's basset hound, Josephine, keeping watch.

This shows the method of suspending and bracing the rear of the bike.

MAN + BIKE = POWER

Is it possible and practical to devise an electric generating system using man-power and a bicycle mechanism to deliver enough energy — 100 watts or more — so that it would be a meaningful source of communications power in a time of need? After conducting a few simple experiments the answer to the question was manifestly — yes. The jury-rigged, garden-variety mechanical system described here hopefully will serve to encourage more sophisticated experimentation and design that would inevitably result in a more efficient application of the principle.

The system is basic and simple. The rear wheel of a five-speed bicycle is used to friction drive a small-treaded lawn mower wheel which was force-threaded directly onto the shaft of an old 12-V dc automobile generator, from the junk box, of course. Power was taken directly off the generator to run an amateur hf

transceiver — an FT-101B. Voltage regulation was accomplished by connecting a VOM across the generator and pedaling so as to maintain a voltage reading of 13.5 volts or so.

The generator was mounted so that the wheel on its shaft would be in line and make direct contact with the bicycle wheel. The amount of contact pressure was found to be important if not critical, and this pressure was varied by spring-loading the generator to the bike wheel and adjusting the tension in the spring with a turnbuckle. Another advantage derived from the spring was that it allowed compensation for the circumferential irregularities of the wheels. The orientation of the generator to the wheel was such as to ensure that the direction of the bicycle wheel rotation would tend to push the generator away from the contact point. A function of the spring was to apply an opposing force and thereby maintain the needed contact and pressure. For this to be possible the generator had to be mounted on a pivot which allowed it to rotate a few degrees horizontally toward the wheel when the spring was attached.

With the 27-inch (686 mm) bicycle wheel driving a 5-3/4-inch (146 mm) generator wheel, and with the derailleur type gear system set at the fastest speed, this ad-lib system allowed for the generator to be rotated about 1125 rpm when delivering full output under man-power conditions. A refinement was to add 32 μF of capacitance across the output terminals of the generator to reduce the armature-caused hash to an insignificant level.

The mounting of the bicycle was accomplished by building a frame of two-by-fours. A 1-inch pipe was U-bolted to

the top bar of the bicycle frame allowing about 12 inches to extend out over the rear wheel. The rear of the bicycle was then suspended from the frame and stabilized at the wheel hub, using improvised brackets on each side. The front wheel was removed to facilitate portability and to improve vertical stability when a solid log or block was placed under it. A long aluminum bar was used to provide additional stability from the rear to the top of the wooden frame.

Some design considerations suggesting themselves are: use of a direct drive system from pedals to generator shaft; the determination of optimum rates of pedaling incorporating proper ratios of associated sprockets or gears; use of low-friction bearings and high-quality gears; mechanically linking the individual's arms to the system to assist the legs (when leg muscles began to tire we simply pushed on our knees with our hands); exploitation of the flywheel principle; careful choice of a

This shows the contact point between the bike wheel and generator wheel. The long threaded bolt is the vertical axle that allows the generator to rotate horizontally toward the bike wheel, because of the pressure from the spring. The probes are from the VOM.

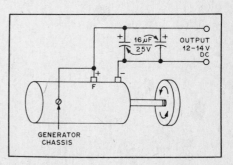

"F" is the field terminal of the generator. For this application the field terminal is connected directly to the frame. "F" is also the B+ terminal. The remaining terminal is B−. The generator used was a Delco-Remy, 12-V dc, model 1100304.

generator for the system so as to obtain the highest possible efficiency; choice of an efficient voltage-regulator circuit; inclusion of a battery-storage system.

Perhaps the most interesting of the items mentioned is that of the flywheel, which, through energy-storage properties, can offer several advantages to a man-powered system. For example, a flywheel would tend to act as a mechanical voltage regulator. This results from the fact that in a one-man pedal system there are two power strokes per pedaled cycle which produce voltage irregularities in pace with each pedal stroke. Once rotating, a flywheel would tend to apply a relatively constant force to the rotating mechanical system, resulting in a more regular rotation of the generator shaft, therefore diminishing the voltage irregularities.

Lest anyone be misled, it is a dramatic experience to "ride" the bike and pedal up to about 13 volts without a load, and then to suddenly feel the drain of 90 to 120 watts being taken from the system when the switches are thrown, filaments heated, and key pressed. It is a good bit like suddenly having to pedal at a fast pace up a steep hill. — *Edward Yadzinski, W2DNZ*

MATCHING TO HF MOBILE ANTENNAS

Many hf mobile antennas will not present a good match for the 50-ohm output impedance of a transceiver. Feed-point impedances range from 12 to 35 ohms and, while SWR is often high, losses are small because of the short length of coaxial cable between the rig and antenna. When using a transceiver with broadband tuned circuits, the high SWR may result in erratic operation, because of the mismatch that exists between the rig and the antenna. The author designed an rf autotransformer to allow better matching when operating a 1-kW mobile rig. T1 has seven bifilar turns of No. 12 enameled or Teflon-insulated wire, on an Amidon T200-2 core. The winding (see drawing) is tapped at 2, 3, 4 and 5 turns from the cold, or ground, end. A single winding will suffice for power levels under 500 watts. S1 may be used to select the tap which provides the best impedance match,

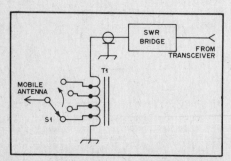

A method for matching an hf mobile antenna.

determined by minimum reflected power indication on the SWR bridge. Alternatively, the correct tap may be found by experimentation, and the wires soldered in place. An enclosure is not necessary, though desirable. — *Alan Applegate, WBØBHE*

TRANSCEIVER MOUNTING BRACKETS

My problem has been to find suitable mounting facilities for two transceivers that I use for mobile operation. I own a Swan 350 and I have a Poly-Comm 6-meter transceiver on loan from c.d. I wanted some type of mounting brackets that would hold either rig, in spite of the fact that there is a difference of 2-1/2 inches in the widths of the transceivers. In addition, I wanted to answer my wife's complaint that the Swan mounting bracket kept gouging her knee when no rig was in the car.

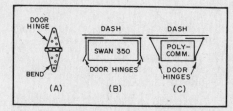

Two triangular hinges are bent as shown in A, and mounted under the dash. B shows the position of the brackets with the Swan 350 in place, and C shows the brackets with the Poly-Comm 6-meter rig installed.

After a couple of experiments with plumber's pipe strap, I thought about trying hinges. Sure enough, by mounting a pair of 4-inch long, triangular door hinges, I solved my problems. I didn't even have to drill extra holes in the hinges, as there were four holes to choose from for installing the rigs. To accommodate the Poly-Comm, the smaller of the two transceivers, I simply bent the hanging portion of the hinges slightly near the bottom. When not in use, the hinges can be folded up and held against the dash with magnets or strips of tape. — *James Hoffer, WA8OVC*

CONTEST LOGGING WHILE MOBILE

During mobile contest operation, nothing is more difficult than logging stations. At one or two contacts a minute, it can become tiring to search for the logbook and grope for a pencil. However, there is a solution to the problem: the Mobile Desk.

The Mobile Desk snaps onto the front of the steering wheel and eliminates the need for finding a place to write on. It was built from a 10 × 12-inch (254 ×

305-mm) piece of 1/8-inch thick Masonite. The board is held to the wheel by two Sears type 34 K 6123 cable clamps, and an ordinary spring clip is used to secure the logbook to the board. For added convenience a hole was drilled in the board, and a beaded chain like those used on key chains was passed through it. A pencil was then taped to the free end of the chain. To prevent marring the steering wheel, masking tape should be wrapped around that part of the wheel over which the clamps are to be snapped. — *Ron Dagavarian, WA2FLO*

OPERATING 12-VOLT EQUIPMENT FROM THE CAR BATTERY

Some manufactured amateur radio equipment is designed for operation at 12-volts dc, *maximum*. At operating voltages higher than 12 volts, damage can occur to some of the components, especially the transistors and ICs, and circuit performance can be degraded significantly.

Since most fully-charged automobile batteries provide something in excess of 12 volts — usually 13 volts or more — some means should be employed to lower the potential to 12 volts, thus protecting the equipment from possible damage. A case in point is the Motorola P33BAM fm transceiver. The driver tubes will exhibit very short life if the filaments are operated at more than 12 volts for a period of time.

Tests with a commercially built, solid-state cw transceiver showed that severe chirp resulted when the unit was operated (VFO-activated) at any voltage higher than 12 volts. A simple way to lower the operating voltage is to take advantage of the forward voltage drops of one or more silicon diodes. Usually the voltage drop is between 0.4 to 0.7 volt per diode. The more diodes used, the greater the voltage drop across the series string. The diode current rating is chosen according to the total current drain of the equipment; the diodes should be rated at twice the current taken by the equipment, or greater, to provide a margin of safety for the diodes. Diodes with a 50-PRV rating are fine for this application.

The diodes offer an added benefit — protection against circuit damage should the supply leads mistakenly become reversed! — *W1FB*

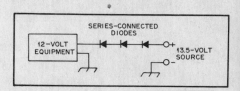

Equipment that is designed to be operated at a maximum of 12-volts dc can be safely operated from a fully charged car battery (13 volts or more), if a suitable number of diodes is connected as shown. See text for diode specifications.

is possible to generate all the required tones for the typical patch.

Circuit Details

The heart of the encoder is the IC and while I use a 12-switch keyboard, four-row and three-column inputs, the chip will accept a four-by-four switchboard. The MC1441OP is designed to accept digital inputs in a two-of-eight code format and to digitally synthesize the high- and low-band sine waves specified by the telephone tone-dialing systems. The chip doesn't have adequate output to drive a speaker so two transistors, Q1 and Q2, are connected in a compound series mode to drive an 8-ohm speaker. Operating from a 9-volt battery, total current drain is 35 mA idling, and slightly over 100 mA when driving the speaker to full audio capability.

Construction Details

If it is not already obvious from the photographs, the encoder was constructed in a transistor radio case. There are plenty of "burnt-out" radios around and they make good housings for projects such as this. I was able to use the speaker. Also, the case was chosen because it met my "shirt-pocket" size requirement. Garage and tag sales are good sources of transistor radios.

All the components were assembled on Vectorboard, and all the wiring for the IC is to a socket, rather than directly to the chip. Although the IC has internal protection against high-static voltages or electric fields, it is advisable that the chip not be removed from the conductive foam "shipper" until it is ready for use.

The speaker in the radio was moved to the back of the case (some holes were made in the back for audio to escape)

The completed encoder is shown here. The Touch-Tone pad is just the right size to fit on the average small transistor radio case.

AN ACOUSTICALLY COUPLED ENCODER

A Touch-Tone encoder can be built using acoustic coupling to the transceiver, thus avoiding direct modification of the transceiver itself. The Motorola IC, MC1441OP, makes the project feasible. It is a unique IC that contains all gating, dividing, decoding and driving circuitry in one package. Also included in the package are all the components necessary for a crystal, L-C or external oscillator input. Incidentally, by using the MC1441OP, it

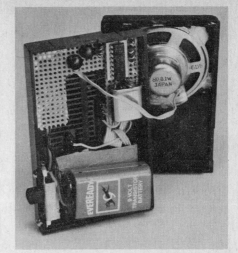

The view shows the inside of the encoder. The IC and transistors are mounted on a piece of Vectorboard at one end of the case.

because the flat front of the radio was needed to mount the keyboard. Also, with the speaker mounted by itself, only two leads are required from the encoder board to the case back. (The encoder board is mounted on the keyboard side and there is less chance of breaking leads when changing batteries.) I used RTV bathtub caulk to mount the circuit board and speaker in the radio case. This method has been used successfully on other projects.

Alignment and Operation

Because all major wiring is done inside the chip, and a crystal is used as the frequency-determining element, no tweaking is necessary. If no tones are heard when a key is depressed, check all the connections.

The encoder has worked successfully with all the local machines on the first try. With any reasonable signal into the repeater, it is a simple matter to hold the encoder to the mic and set up the auto-patch. — *Chet Gorski, K1MYQ*

CODE FOR COMMUTERS?

Many amateurs have found that it is one thing to struggle through the Morse test to obtain the coveted Class A (Extra Class) permit; something rather different to feel really at home with cw operation. It makes all the difference if you persevere until 12 wpm seems a little like flag-waving. There is a common belief that a short spell of cw operation on the bands will quickly convert a 12 wpm capability into 20 wpm; this is only partly true — so much amateur "traffic" follows well-defined patterns that it is by no means the ideal way of bringing up your speed.

This brings a note received from Dick Rollema, PA0SE, putting forward some thoughts on a novel way of finding time

Circuit diagram of the low-cost encoder. All resistors are 1/4 watt.
KB1 — Keyboard (Poly Paks no. 92CU3149).
Q1,Q2 — 2N3643 or equiv.
U1 — Motorola MC14410P.

Y1 — 1.000 MHz (Mariann Labs no. ML18P, Sherold Crystal no. HC-6).

for regular practice sessions, originally suggested in his *Reflecties* column in *Electron*. He writes:

"Many commuters spend considerable time each day in their cars. PA0WV has suggested that this largely lost time could be put to good use by listening to taped Morse as an exercise in copying cw. Some suitable practice material is recorded on a cassette recorder and replayed in the car.

"I have put this idea into practice and find it most useful. The almost daily practice soon results in good progress. My own favorite material is the 40-minute news bulletin transmitted daily by PCH for Dutch ships. If there is any question of copyright, as arises with the PCH material, it is better to ask permission to use transmissions in this way. — Radio Communication, *March, 1976, RSGB*

DUAL-FUNCTION COAX

To permit use of my mobile antenna when running the mobile rig on the workbench, I installed a length of RG-8/U from the cellar to the garage with a wall-mounted SO-239 on each end. Also, I use a short RG-8/U patch cable from the car antenna to the SO-239 fitting in the garage. As an extra benefit, I find this coax handy for piping 12-volts dc from the bench power supply to the car battery for an occasional overnight charge. — *Raymond DeMers, W2KVP*

MOBILE LOG DEVICE

I have found one solution to the problem of keeping a log when operating mobile. The unit is a pilot's flight-plan log holder that has a curved bottom that fits snugly on the operator's leg. A leg strap is provided to make sure the log stays put! A clip at the top and bottom of the device holds the log sheets in place. The gadget holds two pencils and even has a built-in pencil sharpener. A night light powered by two small batteries is also included. My unit was manufactured by Jeppesen & Co., and probably can be purchased at aircraft supply houses or the local airport. — *Alan R. Haywood, K6AUE*

RETURNING A CAR USED FOR MOBILE OPERATION TO ITS ORIGINAL CONDITION

Recently I was about to trade automobiles, when the car appraiser stated he would have to deduct $10 for filling in the holes on the rear deck where my antenna was mounted and painting the refilled area. Having on hand part of a can of touch-up paint as well as a good-sized junk box, I went to work. First I removed the antenna and used the base as a pattern for a backup plate, which I cut

from a piece of 24-gauge galvanized steel. Next I beveled the large center hole in the body with a half-round file, and countersunk the three mounting holes so that no. 10-32 flathead machine screws would drop in slightly below the body surface. After mounting the plate, I put a couple of coats of spot putty (available in automotive stores) over the indentations, sanded and painted the area, and proceeded with the trade. — *Gene Halvorson, WA9UAU*

MOBILE HINT: A PENCIL WHEN YOU NEED IT

Ever hunted for a pencil while mobiling? Keep one on the top surface of the dashboard. A piece of magnet from an old speaker will stick to any convenient location on the dash. And an ordinary wooden pencil with about three wide-spaced turns of baling wire or equivalent (not copper) around the shaft will cling to the magnet. For long trips a piece of scratch paper can be placed beneath the magnet, which will hold the paper firmly enough for quick operation notes. — *Harold A. Thomas, W5HJM*

REMOTE CONTROL FOR A MOBILE TRANSCEIVER

Why clutter up the front seat of your car with mobile gear? It can be installed easily back in the trunk compartment, out of the way, and still be controlled from the dashboard. Running the speaker, volume control, and mic leads up front is relative-

ly simple, but frequency control is more difficult. This article shows one method of how the latter can be done with a Swan Cygnet 260.

Two surplus-type, CRV-23253, receiver-tuning controls are needed, along with 12 feet (4.6 m) of flexible control cable, type MC215. These can be obtained from Fair Radio Sales in Lima, OH. Other components necessary are a flexible coupling to fit a 1/4-inch shaft and hardware to mount one of the receiver heads on the transceiver.

The dial assembly from one of the receiver heads is removed and the head is mounted on front of the transceiver as shown in the photograph. The author drilled a hole in the front panel of the 260 and fastened a flange directly to the transceiver dial, as shown. This was necessary since the dial drive on this transceiver was of the friction type and some slippage occurred. Only minor modifications may be necessary with transceivers that use other types of drives.

The flexible cable is then run up to the dash where the other receiver head is mounted. Before the setup is installed, the calibration on the dashboard head should be changed so that it matches up with the one on the transceiver. A new one was made by the author and consisted of a plastic base with a shoulder and a dust cover. Sandwiched in between is an opaque dial with the new calibration marks. These can be of the builder's choice and decal-type numbers were used in the unit shown. — *George Tamer, W4BAD*

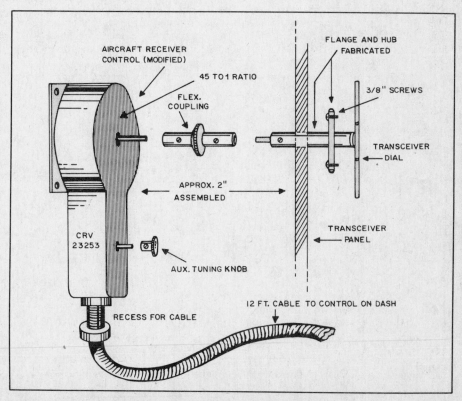

AIRCRAFT RECEIVER CONTROL (MODIFIED)
45 TO 1 RATIO
FLEX. COUPLING
FLANGE AND HUB FABRICATED
3/8" SCREWS
TRANSCEIVER DIAL
APPROX. 2" ASSEMBLED
CRV 23253
AUX. TUNING KNOB
TRANSCEIVER PANEL
RECESS FOR CABLE
12 FT. CABLE TO CONTROL ON DASH

Detailed drawings showing how the receiver head is coupled to the transceiver dial.

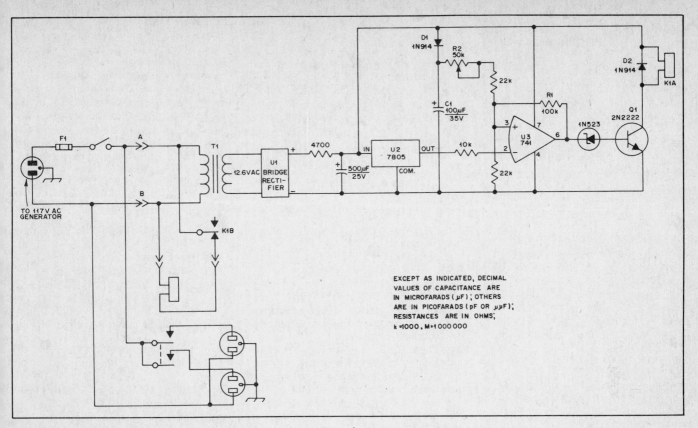

Circuit for protecting equipment from overvoltage.

OVERVOLTAGE CUTOUT FOR FIELD DAY GENERATORS

When powering equipment from small gasoline generators, the line-voltage regulation usually leaves something to be desired. Since our club was not well enough endowed to afford a magnetic regulator, some other means of protecting the equipment from overvoltage was needed. The circuit I developed is shown in the schematic diagram.

The 117-V ac output from the generator is applied to a 12.6 V filament transformer. U1 and U2 rectify and regulate one input to U3, which is used as a comparator. D1 and C1 act as a peak line-voltage monitor. When the voltage applied to the noninverting input of U3 exceeds the 5 volts applied to the inverting input, the output of U3 goes positive, turning on Q1, which applies power to the coil of K1, a small 12-V dc relay. The normally closed contact of K1 opens, removing power from the coil of K2, a 115-V ac relay. The contacts of K2 must be capable of passing the current demands of the equipment in use. VR1, a 5-volt Zener diode, is required because the output of U3 is slightly above the negative supply terminal (pin 4) when saturated. If a Zener diode is not used, Q1 cannot be turned off. R1 provides the necessary hysteresis to prevent the relays from chattering when the input line voltage is close to the threshold.

To adjust the circuit, connect a variable ac source to points A and B. With 125 volts applied to the circuit, adjust R2 until K2 drops out. When the applied ac voltage is reduced, K2 will again pull in. The pin numbers for U3 shown in the diagram are for the TO-5 package. D2 shorts out the reverse-polarity voltage which results when power is removed from K1. F1 should be able to pass the normal load imposed by the equipment used. Power requirement of the overvoltage protection circuit is insignificant. — *P. Hansen, W8TWA*

A "FIXED-LOCATION" POWER SUPPLY FOR MOBILE EQUIPMENT

Mobile equipment permanently mounted in a car can usually be operated "fixed location" for extended periods of time only at the expense of either an overheated engine or a run-down battery. And, of course, gallons of gasoline can be consumed while the car motor is being used to generate primary power for the mobile supply. If operation takes place during a hot afternoon, you're also in for some personal discomfort caused by the extra heat radiated from the motor. Ignition noise generated by your own car is still another annoyance that results from "leave-your-motor-running" operation.

Most of these problems may be minimized or completely eliminated by us-ing a field-type battery charger as suggested by W7FVI. Our version of this supply is used to charge the car battery, but the same unit may be used to keep life in any storage battery being used in the field.

The charger consists of a small gasoline engine, an old auto generator and a voltage regulator. These are mounted on a plywood base equipped with handles. Output from the generator is coupled to the car battery through a long length of heavy duty two-wire cable. Naturally, the length of the cable will be determined by how much you want to separate the charger and the battery. If you want lots of separation so that racket from the charger can be kept in the background as much as possible, just remember that the cable may have to carry 30 amperes or more if the generator-battery system is designed for 6 volts. Figure on a wire size that will handle 15 or 20 amperes if the charger is a 12-volt affair. — *Jack Miller, W9WTY*

VHF MOBILE

Recently we mentioned an American review of professional vhf mobile radio developments during the past few years (*TT*, October). This month it is possible to come a little nearer home and draw attention to a very detailed survey "Mobile vhf and uhf radio systems in the UK," by D. A. S. Drybrough, G8HEV, *IEE Reviews,*

Table 1
Propagation Losses From Large Obstructions

H/(√d) ADDITIONAL LOSS (dB)	12	24	36	48	72	120
80 MHz	3·5	5·5	7·5	10	12·5	17
125 MHz	4	6·5	9	11·5	14	19
170 MHz	4·5	7·5	10	13	16	20·5
460 MHz	6·5	11·5	14	16·5	20	24·5

H is height above line-of-sight path (in meters); d is distance to obstruction from nearest terminal (km).

Vol. 122, no. 10R, October, 1975 (a special issue of *Proc. IEE*). It traces the development, current practice and possible future trends over the whole field of private and public-service mobile operation. For example, a detailed table lists all the frequencies used, including channel widths and the paired channels for various types of services, typical ranges with fm and a-m systems (showing significant advantages to fm despite its vulnerability to flutter losses). For the future still narrower bands are forecast (aided by phase-locking techniques) together with a continued search for improving reception in the presence of interference and fading.

Among all the data is an interesting table of the signal losses that can be expected from large obstructions in the propagation path, showing how these vary at different frequencies.

In VHF Communications, Vol. 7, no. 3, 1975, T. Bittan, DJØBQ/G3JVQ, reports some of his findings on aerials used for mobile telecommunications. He may set a few dovecots fluttering with some interesting conclusions on the advantages of horizontal polarization, and intends to follow this up with designs in future issues for circularly polarized omnidirectional mobile aerials. Conventional vertically polarized mobile aerials, he suggests, can result in signal fluctuations of more than 70 dB due to multipath propagation effects while a vehicle is in motion. At high speeds he also found that the 1/4-wavelength whip gives significantly better performance than the 5/8-wavelength whip, mainly due to an additional bending caused by the extra length. He believes that for mobile applications, the field strength of a horizontally polarized signal is usually far more constant than with a vertically polarized one, due to less attenuation of the direct wave (vertically polarized signals are particularly subject to attenuation by trees), and because fewer multiple reflections are present. Further, radiation characteristics do not vary as much as with vertical whips, so long as the horizontally polarized aerials are at least 1/2 wavelength above the car roof. If it were not for repeaters, apparently, he would have everyone using halos; but as things are, the best of both worlds seems to be found

in circular polarization (or perhaps diversity techniques). — Radio Communication, *December, 1975, RSGB*

MOBILE NOISE SUPPRESSION

Coaxial capacitors for ignition spark coil primary filtering must be installed with the shortest leads possible. I found that the capacitors with threaded terminals have the same thread as the screws projecting from the spark coil. The capacitors may be threaded directly onto the coil terminals resulting in no leads at all! Of course, the capacitor's metal case must be grounded to the coil case. This can be done with copper straps soldered to the capacitor and coil cases. — *James W. Stuckey, W5ZJO*

SUB-AUDIBLE TONE GENERATOR

The following circuit is an unusual method for generating a subaudible tone, commonly known as P/L, Channel-Guard, CTCSS, etc. The circuit is unusual in that a 2235-kHz crystal is used with a counter chip to produce a 136.5 Hz (EIA no. 4) tone. The signal from the oscillator goes through 14 divide-by-two flip-flops to produce the low-frequency square-wave output on pin 3 of the IC. The square wave is then put through several stages of low-pass filtering to develop a

sine wave. The subaudible tone should be introduced into the transmitter just after the deviation control. Since most audio is cut off in the low-frequency ranges, it is necessary to inject the tone after any audio processing. Two output filters are shown. It will be necessary to select the filter that performs best with a particular rig. For other subaudible tones, use crystals that are 16,384 times the desired frequency. — *Edward Gellender, WB2EAV and Manny Marcel, WB2BON*

USING A CENTER-LOADED LOW-BAND WHIP ON 50 MHZ.

When I had my 3.9-MHz loading coil in my Master Mount mobile antenna, I accidentally turned my multiband, 3-watt rig to 50 MHz. On hearing a station, I gave him a call, and much to my surprise, he came back and gave me a fair report. Since then I have had several dozen 50-MHz contacts using this combination, some of them with stations that were more than 30 miles distant.

After my initial vhf QSO with the low-band antenna, I tried each of the available coils in making a test with one station. We discovered that the 7-MHz coil gave a small but noticeable improvement whereas the 14-MHz coil or a jumper across a loading coil gave a serious decrease in signal strength.

Somewhat later I put an SWR bridge at the input of the 50-ohm coaxial cable which feeds the antenna. The measurements were consistent with these observations: The SWR was the least (2:1) with the 7-MHz coil and only slightly higher with the 3.9-MHz coil. Perhaps the SWR could be lowered by trimming a coil exactly, but the inconvenience seems hardly worthwhile since losses in a short line are insignificant when the SWR is down to 2:1.

While at 50 MHz the electrical length of the whip is less than a half wavelength, it can be surmised that the presence of the 7-MHz coil accidentally loads it to make it

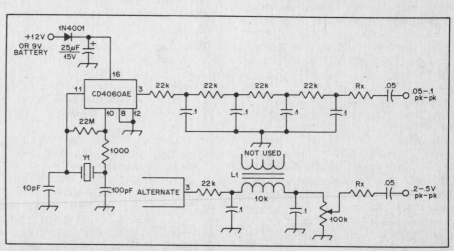

Method for generating a continuous, subaudible tone.

appear to have a length of about 3/4 wavelength. If one is willing to accept a vertically polarized mobile antenna when most stations are horizontally polarized, he is unlikely to find one that is more effective than this one. — *Yardley Beers, WØEXS*

CAR-BATTERY REMINDERS

Always keep battery terminals clean and tight since corrosion reduces the charging current supplied to the battery by the charging system.

Periodically check system voltage with a voltmeter to make sure the generator is developing sufficient voltage. Look for excessive voltage drops caused by loose or high-resistance cables.

Check specific gravity with a hydrometer once a month and recharge the battery if necessary. Add distilled water to the battery as required.

Check regulator setting after regulator has come up to operating temperature. Too high a setting of the voltage regulator is damaging to the radio, light bulbs, and ignition contacts. Too low a setting will allow the battery to become discharged. — *R. Griffin, W1VON*

HIGH-Z TO LOW-Z MICROPHONE ADAPTER

Many commercial and home-built mobile transmitters are designed for low-impedance, carbon-microphone input. The input speech circuit is usually a grounded-grid arrangement as shown to the right in the diagram. However, it is sometimes desirable to use a high-impedance microphone with the equipment, since a crystal or dynamic microphone has better fidelity and freedom from the hiss and "blasting" sound familiar to the carbon type.

The circuit as shown is a matching device which will allow a high-impedance microphone to be used with the original speech circuit in the transmitter without any changes in the equipment. It uses two transistors and doesn't need a power supply. The operating voltage is obtained from the voltage developed at the cathode of the speech-amplifier tubes. It probably could be built small enough to be installed in the microphone case or under its base. By throwing switch S1 the microphone feeds straight through so that it can be used with equipment designed for high-impedance input.

Transistor Q1 is used in a common-collector circuit to step down the impedance of the microphone to match the emitter-follower transistor Q2, which feeds the signal into the low-impedance jack of the speech amplifier. The output voltage from the unit is comparable to that of a carbon microphone but is free from the characteristic hiss sound and nasal quality. — *E. S. Millman, W3WNE*

DIODE-SWITCHING MOBILE BATTERIES

This battery system is useful in mobile work when it is desired to keep the car's electrical system isolated from the mobile equipment. In this plan, an extra battery is installed to power the mobile equipment. Although the car's charging system keeps the accessory battery up to par, the mobile equipment draws only from the spare battery, leaving the car battery to perform its regular duties. All of this is done without any mechanical switching. The system shown in the drawing requires two silicon diodes, D1, D2, and the extra 6- or 12-volt battery. The two diodes are connected so that the car generator will supply both batteries with charging current (through the voltage regulator), but neither battery can feed current back to

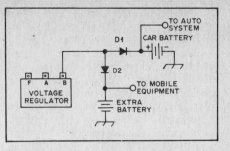

Diodes are used to isolate the extra battery and mobile equipment from the automobile's electrical system, although both batteries are charged by the car generator.
D1, D2 — 70-amp, 50 PIV silicon diodes.

the voltage regulator or to the other battery. The forward voltage drop across the diodes is somewhere around 0.7 volt, so it may be necessary to advance the voltage regulator for an additional 1 volt. Most diodes will operate at temperatures up to 150° C, so they can be mounted right up in the engine compartment. Of course, they must be isolated from ground and mounted on an insulated heat sink. I used a 1/4 × 4 × 4-inch aluminum sink for each diode. — *Robert V. Grater, K6SUB/4*

IGNITION NOISE AND SUPER-NOISY VEHICLES

For a long time it has been recognized that ignition interference from some vehicles is very much more vicious than from others, though little attempt has been made in the past to measure the differences, and there remains a considerable amount of work to be done in determining just why these differences arise. Some idea of the complexity of the individual noise characteristics of different vehicles is indicated in a paper by R. A. Shepherd of Stanford Research Institute, entitled "Measurement of Amplitude Probability Distributions and Power of Automobile Ignition Noise at Hf", *IEEE Trans. on Vehicular Technology*, Vol. VT23, no. 3, August, 1974. The paper is based on a large number of measurements made alongside a busy freeway (motorway) and shows that most of the ignition noise between 24 and 30 MHz is contributed by a small number of vehicles radiating strong interference. It was found that there is a great difference in the noise characteristics of individual cars, particularly different models.

It was found that an engine is a complex noise source and does not radiate a pulse of the same amplitude for each successive firing of the spark plugs; the pulses can vary by up to 30 dB in amplitude, and even successive pulses from the same cylinder vary appreciably. On some vehicles there are two rf pulses associated with each spark-plug firing, the second following the first after an interval of about 1 ms, it being usually about 10 dB lower. It is still not clear whether this dou-

Microphone impedance step-down adapter. Jack J1 is the microphone jack on the transmitter speech amplifier. All resistors are 1/2 watt.
P1 — Plug to mate with J1.
Q1, Q2 — 2N107 transistors.
S1 — Dpdt switch.

ble pulse results from the abrupt cessation of current flow across the spark-plug gap or from the closure of the breaker points.

Generally, the more cylinders there are in a vehicle, the more ignition noise is produced; again, the average noise power increases monotonically with engine speed.

During the investigations a vehicle was deliberately made as noisy as possible (for instance by using copper ignition wire), yet it was found not to be the noisiest vehicle on the road. The super-noisy cars have average powers of 40 dB or more above "quiet" cars, and some parallel investigations in Spain showed noisy vehicles exceeding the median vehicle by 35 dB. — Radio Communication, *March, 1975, RSGB*

PROTECTING MOBILE RELAYS

Old voltage regulator boxes make excellent relay enclosures for mobile applications. The boxes are weather-tight, easy to mount, and usually have a hole or two in the bottom for bringing leads in or out of the box. Discarded voltage regulators can probably be obtained at local garages. — *Rathbun B. Griffin, W1VON*

TIME-OUT WARNING

If you are one of those hams accused of being a clod (or worse) because you always time-out the repeater, this device will help make you one of the good guys — not a bad guy. It can be made from a few parts that provides either a visual or audible warning and can be preset to any desired time interval. Referring to the circuit diagram, when pin 1 of the first NE555 is grounded, the timer starts timing to a preset limit. If the preset limit is reached, pin 3 provides a ground output to the second NE555 which pulses at a 2-Hz rate.

A kit is available from Sharp Co., 23715 Mercantile Road, Commerce Park, Cleveland, OH 44122. — *Fred Sharp, W8ASF*

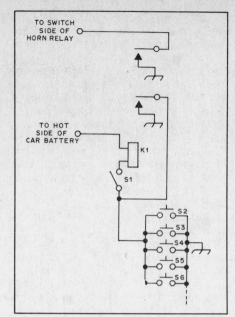

Alarm system for protection against theft of mobile equipment.
K1 — 6- or 12-volt relay dpst.
S1 — Key switch, spst.
S2-S6 — Normally open button switches.

MOBILE BURGLAR ALARM

This circuit is an inexpensive, simple, yet effective alarm for protection against theft of mobile equipment. When switch S1 is closed to the "ready" position, the alarm is armed and opening any of the car doors, hood or trunk will actuate the car horn, which will give an audible alert. The horn will continue to blow, even if the door, trunk or hood is closed.

Switch S1 is a "key" switch that can be located at any convenient spot on the outside of the car. Switches S2-S6 — and there can be as many of these switches as needed — are the normally open button type used as auto courtesy light switches. These can probably be obtained from a local car junk yard or purchased new from an automobile distributor. The switches are installed on each of the car doors and on the hood and trunk lids in such a way that opening any of these will

close the switch contact. Mercury switches could be substituted on the hood and trunk lids if desired.

When S1 is closed, any one of the door, trunk or hood switches can trigger the relay, K1. One set of the relay contacts grounds the horn relay, causing the car horn to sound. At the same time, the other set of relay contacts provides another path to ground for the relay coil which keeps the alarm system going in the event the car door, etc., is closed. The system can only be made inoperative by opening switch S1 with the key. — *G. M. Miller, K5REV and Tom E. White, Jr., K5AUN*

ELIMINATION OF STATIC IN FAN-DRIVE BELTS

Receiver static is sometimes a problem for me when my forced-air furnace operates. I traced the trouble to the fan belt. I had heard that a belt dressing was available that would cure static, but I wanted to eliminate the noise as quickly as possible. Using a rag saturated with alcohol, I cleaned the belt thoroughly and the static completely disappeared. — *James S. Collier, W2QBB*

MOBILE SAFETY

Ian Mant, G8AVJ has drawn attention to the danger of beryllia (beryllium oxide) contained in some silicon planar transistors. At "Communications 76," M. Arrowsmith added to this warning by writing: "Beryllia has a unique combination in that it is a good insulator but also a first-class conductor of heat. It is a hard, clean material which is normally perfectly safe to handle. However, beryllia dust is highly toxic and can prove fatal. Dust or chippings can be formed by accident or even deliberately by someone not aware of the danger. So where is one to find beryllia? How can it be recognized? An experienced engineer is likely to know that beryllia can be found in rf power transistors. On the other hand, exposed beryllia in the form of, say, washers is indistinguishable from ceramic. It is therefore important that all items containing this material be clearly identified in an equipment manual."

This seems a clear indication that beryllia may be found not only in some transistors but also, for example, in the form of washers used in the mounting of power transistors on a chassis or to heat sinks. It is well worth remembering this warning when dismantling or modifying solid-state equipment stemming from the professional market.

A check-list of safety factors for mobile radio designers also appears in this paper, as follows:

1) Fixings on dashboard-mounted equpment should not be likely to break away under impact.

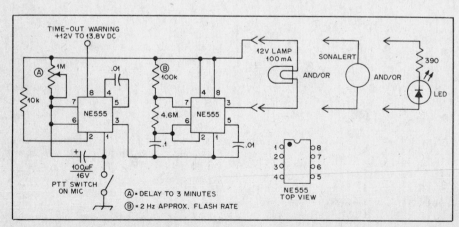

Avoid repeater time-out with this circuit.

2) No sharp edges.

3) Recessed controls behind an impact-absorbing panel.

4) Fire-resistant grades of glass-fiber boards for printed circuits.

5) No exposed beryllia.

6) No components operated beyond their ratings.

7) Adequate installation instructions with special advice to users with electronic fuel-injection systems or anti-skid devices.

In respect of item 7, M. Arrowsmith notes that there have been instances where rf from a mobile transmitter has resulted in the malfunctioning of electronic fuel-injection and anti-skid braking systems on trucks plus other less serious occurrences. In such cases, he points out, it is difficult to categorize either the transmitter or the electronic systems as intrinsically unsafe, though together they may form a potentially lethal combination. — Radio Communication, *July, 1976, RSGB*

NICHROME IGNITION WIRE REDUCES INTERFERENCE

Some automotive-parts distributors carry a resistance type of ignition wire which uses nichrome instead of carbon as the resistive conductor element. This wire appears to be more resistant to aging and more effective in reducing ignition-noise interference. — *Murray Lampert, VE3FXA*

HOMEMADE MAP HOLDER FOR PORTABLE AND MOBILE USE

A useful aid to mobile and portable operation, especially handy during public-service events, is a magnetic map holder. A piece of galvanized steel sheet may be cemented to a sheet of masonite and painted, if desired. Small fasteners with attached magnets, similar to those used on clipboards, will hold the map, as well as any message blanks and slips of note paper. — *Spencer L. McCarty, W2GTI*

KEEPING COOL ON FIELD DAY

Keeping cool on Field Day while pounding brass or keeping up a steady pace before the microphone can be troublesome: This is important when the temperature is high and the sun shines relentlessly on the operating position. Placing one's feet or hands in a bucket of cold water can be very refreshing. This method serves as a heat sink for the human body. — *James W. Milburn, WB5BYK*

A 5/8-WAVELENGTH ANTENNA FOR BASE, PORTABLE AND MOBILE USE

I have made versions of this antenna for my car, for permanent installation at home, and another mounted on a camera

The 5/8-wavelength antenna mounted on a camera tripod.

tripod for use when operating from a portable location. As shown in the photos, the base is a convenient length of a 1-1/4-inch (32-mm) diameter aluminum tubing, with PVC pipe fittings press fitted ino the pipe and acting as insulators. The matching coil is 1-1/4 turns of 5/16-inch (8 mm) copper tubing, 5 inches (127 mm) in diameter. The ratiating element is a telescoping automobile whip, whose length is adjusted to approximately 39 inches (0.99 m); and a sliding tap on the coil is used to obtain a minimum SWR. Adjustment is fairly critical, but once the

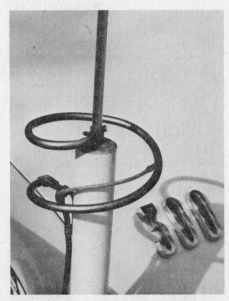

Matching coil for the 5/8-wavelength antenna.

proper length of the whip and correct position of the tap are found, they may be marked by scratching the appropriate metal surface. — *Ralph Netzley, W9WZO*

MOBILE OPERATING AID

Having the mobile rig microphone handy while driving has become a bit of a problem because many present-day cars have vinyl-covered dashboards. Bolted or magnetic hangers are no longer reliable or desirable. A happy solution comes from the boating scene.

Velcro Corporation, Marine Products Department, manufactures a fastening system that becomes very useful for holding everything from microphones and pencils to entire radios. This system suits the inventive nature of radio hams well and it is expected that uses will be found for portable antennas and beams, travel cases, routing wires, holding logbooks and telegraph keys, and so forth.

The Velcro fasteners are made of thousands of tiny hooks on one piece of backed material and tiny matching loops on the second piece. The hooks interlock with the loops when pressed together and release rapidly when peeled apart. This non-metallic device can be cut to shape with scissors and sewn, stapled or cemented in place. It doesn't jam, rust or corrode, and will hold even when wet. It is practically foolproof.

I have applied one piece (the loops are softer) to the microphone of my Drake TR-22 with the other piece attached to my automobile dashboard. Actually, the hooks were placed in both of two cars so the rig can be used with the same convenience in either car. I also applied the hook part to the TR-22 carrying case so the mic would not dangle to the ground or get squeezed accidentally in a pocket.

A visit to most marine stores should turn up a large, floor-mounted display where a variety of sizes are available. For those who are not close to a marina, the product is manufactured by Velcro Corp., Marine Products Dept., 681 Fifth Ave., New York, NY 10022. My wife reports that the sewable variety of Velcro can be found in department-store notion counters. — *Dwight B. Hill, K2KWK*

USING AN AUTOMOBILE BC ANTENNA FOR TWO-METER OPERATION

When an additional transmitting antenna is prohibited or undesirable on an automobile, this simple circuit will permit a 2-meter mobile station to transmit and receive through the bc antenna. Both the amateur equipment and the broadcast receiver may be used simultaneously with no adverse effect on either.

Impedance between the bc antenna and the 2-meter unit is matched by means of

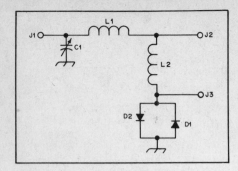

A matching network for using an automobile bc antenna with 2-meter equipment.
J1 — RCA phone connector or equivalent.
J2-J3 — Motorola automobile antenna connector.
C1 — 30 pF, ceramic or air variable.
L1 — Two turns of No. 14 wire, 1/2-inch diameter. May be required for matching.
L2 — Amidon toroid T50 wound with No. 18 wire.
D1, D2 — Silicon diode, 1N94 or equivalent.

L1 and C1. The bc receiver front end is protected from transmitted signals by RFC L2 and diodes D1 and D2.

No deterioration of the bc signal is noticed when the 2-meter set (in my case an Icom IC-22A) is connected to the antenna system. No interference or desensitization of the bc receiver is noticed when transmitting in the high-power position.

The network was built in a Minibox with J1 at one end and J2 at the other. Maximum separation of L1 and L2 was provided. C1 and L1 are to be adjusted for minimum SWR with all connections made and the cover placed on the Minibox. No attempts to measure the SWR should be made without the cover in place or with the bc set disconnected. — *Virgil S. Hinson, W5URP*

COAT HANGER USED TO BOOST SIGNAL

In order to activate a distant 2-meter repeater while operating from a campsite, I hastily fabricated a reflector for my 5/8-wavelength whip. Two coat hangers, a piece of wood and some tape were all that was needed to boost the 10-watt signal enough for "solid copy" at the receiving end. The diagram shows the construction features of the reflector which could easily be made into a director. Maximum gain was obtained with a spacing of 15 to 20 inches (380-508 mm) between the radiating element and the reflector. — *W. H. Collins, W6RWH*

MOBILE BURGLAR ALARM

To protect my mobile equipment from theft, I mounted a normally closed, push-button switch behind the equipment. When the equipment is installed the switch is open and is connected in parallel with the car horn button, so that if the equipment is removed the spring return push-button will complete the horn circuit and discourage the thief from any further tampering! — *Lynn Kuluva, KØIMI*

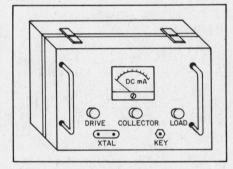

A child's lunch box used as a transmitter cabinet.

EQUIPMENT CABINET

The next time you need a small cabinet for a portable or mobile rig, try a child's lunch box. To protect the components that protrude from the front of the container, handles can be installed as shown. In order to service the unit, it is only necessary to unsnap the fasteners on top of the box. — *Mike Bailey, WB4DCW*

FISHING FOR A PLACE TO STORE YOUR MOBILE ANTENNA?

Here is an idea for those hams who wish they had a place to store their mobile antennas when parked in a lot, or some other area that is not safe for any type of radio equipment (theft). If the antenna in use cannot be stored in the trunk of the car because of the size of the antenna, simply install fishing-pole racks on the inside of the car just above the level of the door tops, when not in use, the antenna can be dismounted and installed in the racks, out of sight. — *Henry G. Eveland, WB2SXD/2*

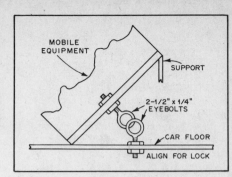

A means of padlocking mobile equipment.

THEFT-PROOFING MOBILE EQUIPMENT

The sketch I provided shows how I theft-proofed my Cheyenne and Comanche mobile equipment. Two 2-1/2 × 1/4-inch eyebolts are used — one attached to the floor of the car, the other to the bottom of the equipment. Any kind of equipment support may be used. The eyebolts are aligned so that when the equipment is installed, a padlock or combination lock can be inserted through the eyebolts and locked. — *Francis Neubauer, K3OKF*

DESK-N-PORT: THE MOBILER'S DESK

One disadvantage of working mobile is not having as much space in a car as is often needed. I wanted to be able to keep my log, equipment manuals and other papers in a compact unit which would provide a small writing desk as well. I used a thick three-ring, loose-leaf binder, and punched all documents I wanted to carry to fit. Important papers such as a band allocation chart and DXCC Countries List, were plastic-laminated before punching. A large spring clip keeps the log firmly attached to the notebook cover. To carry pencils and QSL cards, a plastic, zippered pouch was found to be useful. — *Henry G. Campbell, Jr., WA4DLN*

CAR-RADIO DUMMY ANTENNA

When bench-testing a car radio, a suitable dummy antenna to simulate the fender or cowl-mounted antenna can be constructed from a couple of 39-pF mica capacitors and a small aluminum box. The circuit for the dummy antenna as shown is placed in series with the signal generator and the receiver. Motorola-type connectors are

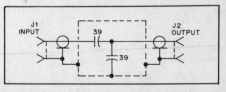

Dummy antenna to simulate a car antenna.
J1, J2 — Automobile antenna connectors (Motorola 1741).

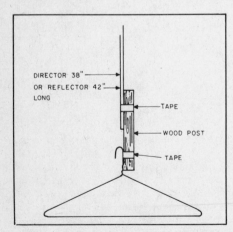

A director/reflector for a two-meter vertical antenna may be quickly made from two coat hangers.

mounted on the aluminum box. A variation on the circuit uses adjustable trimmer capacitors which can be adjusted after the unit is assembled, in which case small access holes must be placed over the trimmer adjustment screws. — *Sol Davis, W3WPN*

PREPARING YOUR CAR FOR WINTER

Amateurs who have mobile equipment should prepare their cars for cold weather. Check the generator for proper operation. Remove the battery cables from the battery terminals. Clean the cables and terminals while using a solution of baking soda and warm water. Avoid getting the solution in the cells. Rinse the battery carefully with clear water after cleaning. The terminals and connectors should be shined with sandpaper. If the cells appear to be low on electrolyte bring them to the proper level with distilled water. After reconnecting the battery, apply Vaseline or axle grease to the connectors and terminals to slow down corrosion.

Next check the antenna system for possible faults. A thin coating of Lubriplate or Vaseline on the threads will make removal easy and will prevent moisture from affecting the contact between the antenna segments. The coating does not interfere with conductivity.

When cooler weather arrives, a change in crystal frequency can be expected. When the transmitter is inside the car, allowing the heating system to bring the passenger area to normal room temperature will in turn keep the crystals operating close to the desired frequency. For crystal-controlled transmitters kept in a trunk it is possible to use a set of crystals which under normally cold conditions will function on the desired frequencies. — *Bruce McCreath, VE3EAR, from the* Bluewater Radio Club Bulletin

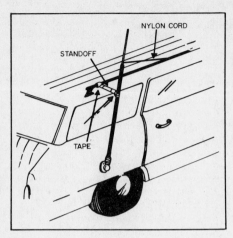
An arrangement for preventing antenna sway.

PREVENTING MOBILE-ANTENNA SWAY

It wasn't very long after going mobile that I had to solve the problem of antenna detuning because of antenna sway while in motion. As many before me have done, a piece of nylon cord tied to the luggage rack eliminated the backward leaning of my Webster Bandspanner. But *sideways* motion caused operating problems.

The 15-cent golf club separator, widely acclaimed for its coil-form shape in the Delta Loop antenna, was again pressed into service. It is easily fashioned into a standoff insulator. The ends are notched to fit both the antenna and luggage rack, and it is held in place by wide, flexible tape. If the tape breaks and the standoff is lost, it can be replaced cheaply and easily. — *Baxter Williams, W5KYB*

WINTERIZING VHF MOBILE ANTENNAS

Winter is once again around the corner, and for those who travel by car, that means driving through snow, sleet and sanded and chemically treated streets and highways. Many hams now have vhf-fm transceivers in their cars, and of course the antennas to go with them. This hint should help save you from possible aggravation later on.

Start by removing the mount from the car; completely disassemble the mount. Remove the coax and rinse the mount with hot water for about 10 minutes. After drying the mount thoroughly (use forced hot air such as that from a "hot comb"), check the antenna with an ohmmeter; infinity should be indicated without the coax connected. Reconnect the coax to the base of the antenna. The most common cause of antenna problems in the winter is salt deposits forming inside the base of the antenna; therefore, some form of sealer should be used to prevent moisture and other foreign material from getting into the base of the antenna. I chose silicon sealer for use in my antenna.

For cleaning the antenna connectors or removing corrosion from the outside of the mount, a common household cleaner of the powder variety can be used. A toothbrush makes a good applicator and that, coupled with some elbow grease, will clean up the connector in quick time. — *Bill Horger, WB8SFZ*

Chapter 8

VHF Band-aids and Tricks

HEATH GR-110 SWITCHING SIMPLIFIED

After I completed the construction of the Heath GR-110 VHF Scanning Monitor, I found the action of the channel selector switch inconvenient. To manually select channels the operator must place the MANUAL/AUTO switch in the manual position and then push the SELECT switch. If a channel is active, the select switch is inoperative until the station stops transmitting or until the channel is locked out. Needless to say this is a lot of button pushing just to advance to another channel.

The procedure was simplified by connecting a jumper between pins 2 and 3 of S3, the select switch. Also pin 1 of S3 was connected to pin 14 of IC101. As a result the receiver will break the lock with any channel regardless of the position of the manual auto mode switch and whether or not a station is transmitting on a channel. I find this improvement worthwhile on

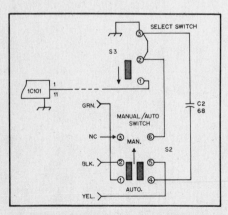

A simple modification of the Heath GR-110 VHF Scanning Monitor to make channel selection easier.

amateur frequencies where the receiver may lock on one channel for some time. When I become curious about the activity on other frequencies, I simply push the select button once to advance the channel in the manual mode or start the scanner in automatic. — *Richard Drew, K9PJB*

PROVIDING A TUNABLE VHF-FM RECEIVER

Here is a trick for providing a tunable vhf-fm receiver. The main station receiver here for the low bands is a Hallicrafters SX-101A along with crystal-controlled converters for 6-, 2- and 1-1/4-meter coverage. This receiver has a double-conversion, i-f strip using a 1650 kHz first i-f.

Also at hand is a Hammarlund FM-50A vhf-fm transceiver, that has a 1650-kHz second i-f. To use the SX-101A as a tunable front end for the FM-50A fm i-f strip, make these simple changes. First, remove V5, the SX-101A second mixer tube (6BA6), insert the center conductor of a short piece of coaxial cable (low-capacitance type works best) into pin 1 (grid) of the now-empty 6BA6 socket base.

Connect the other end of the cable to the grid circuit of the Hammarlund first 1650-kHz i-f amplifier, pin 1 of the 6BH6. Removing the receive crystal or mixer tube will disable the front end of the Hammarlund transceiver.

This lash-up permits me to listen to 29.6-MHz fm and tune in 6-, 2- and 1-1/4-meter fm with the converters. Sensitivity is adequate for casual listening. With a little experimentation, comparable hybrid arrangements for other sets may be feasible. — *John F. Sehring, WB2EQG*

PREAMPLIFIER BURNOUT

Soon after arriving in W1-land I started experiencing random burnout in my preamplifiers, each constructed with transistors and JFETs. Initially, I blamed it on electrical storms. The problem, however, increased dramatically in the winter, a time when electrical storms are usually at a minimum. By then I was even losing my second-stage preamps and multipliers in my LO chain, occasionally.

How could this be? All normal methods for burnout protection failed to improve the problem, including diode protection and input filters. The plot thickened when I left one of the preamps terminated in a 50-ohm load. It still blew out!

Next, a high-impedance battery-operated, digital voltmeter was borrowed and connected to the B+ on the preamplifiers. Everything seemed fine until I keyed my kW transmitter on 80-meter cw (where I spend most operating time in the winter). When I used my east/west-dipole, the dc voltage in the preamplifier went wild. By using the west sloper the trouble disappeared.

Suffice to say, the problem was two-fold. There was rf pickup in the power-supply lines to the preamps and rectifica-

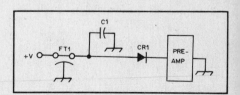

A protection circuit for prevention of preamplifier burnouts.
C1 — 0.1 µF Mylar or ceramic disk capacitor.
D1 — 1N914 or equiv.
FT1 — 0.001-µF feedthrough capacitor.

tion in the "idiot" diode.[1] Eliminating the idiot diode or shortening the power-supply leads was unsatisfactory. However, placing a 0.1-μF Mylar or disk ceramic capacitor ahead of the idiot diode, as shown in the illustration, prevents rf from reaching the diode.

While this cure may not solve all burn-out problems of a similar nature, it should give longer life to those expensive semiconductors where hf operation is prevalent. — *Joe Reisert, W1JR*

[1]Reisert, "Ultra Low-Noise UHF Preamplifier," *Ham Radio*, March, 1975.

MORE AUDIO POWER FOR MOBILE FM TRANSMITTERS

An article in a back issue of *QST* mentioned that a lack of sufficient audio power affected many mobile fm transmitters. To give my set more talk power I added an audio amplifier constructed in modified form from the circuit shown on p. 17 of *QST* for July, 1976. The diagram I have included here shows the changes. In the process of making the addition to my transmitter I also built a squelch system similar to the Johnson Fleetcom system and tied it to my VHF Engineering type receiver.

Because 2N2222 transistors are readily available I used them for the amplifier, but substituted a matched pair of Radio Shack audio output transistors for those shown in the *QST* circuit. They worked well without making any circuit changes. Now my transmitter can really stand up and talk! — *Walter Boller, WØEAH/9*

ABOUT THE *FM AND REPEATER CHARGER*

I have built a NiCad charger from the schematic shown on page 89 of *FM and Repeaters for the Radio Amateur*. I use it to charge all my nickel-cadmium batteries, but there is one problem. The schematic diagram shows that the output is not isolated from the 117-V ac line. When charging hand-held equipment with an external antenna connected, the charger may be grounded through the antenna system, quickly destroying the 100-ohm resistor along with the diodes. Some amateurs may not be aware of this condition.

A useful modification I have incorporated in my charger is the installation of a 117-V neon bulb across the output as a load indicator. The bulb will glow when the charger is on and no load is connected across the output. When charging hand-held devices, the indicator light will go out showing that a good connection has been made at the terminals. — *Joe Felardo, WB6EGW*

HEP S3001 — AN INEXPENSIVE REPLACEMENT

An economical replacement solid-state device for use in the output stage of the Wilson 1402SM and the Drake TR-22 is the HEP S3001 manufactured by Motorola. This silicon npn, rf power transistor is rated at 5-W output and maximum voltage is set at 65 for 1 A of current. Many electronics parts stores carry the S3001, which sells for considerably

less than the price of the equivalent transistors provided by Wilson and Drake. I have found that the S3001s perform just as well as the original equipment. — *Dave Karpiej, K1THP*

REPEATER WALL MOUNTING

The arrangement shown in the photograph has been handy for servicing or removing the equipment for my repeater, WRØAGP.

The transmitter and receiver are mounted in the same fashion by means of GE "Strip for Wall Mounting." I used four barrel bolts, one at each corner of the frame. Each unit may be swung to the right or left by lifting two of the bolts, and may be removed just as easily from the wall. — *Paul Grauer, WØFIR*

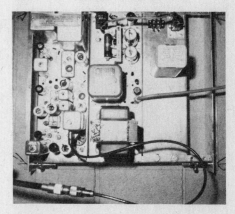

Four barrel bolts were used to mount this repeater equipment. The bolts allow the unit to be swung in either of two directions for easy servicing without dismounting.

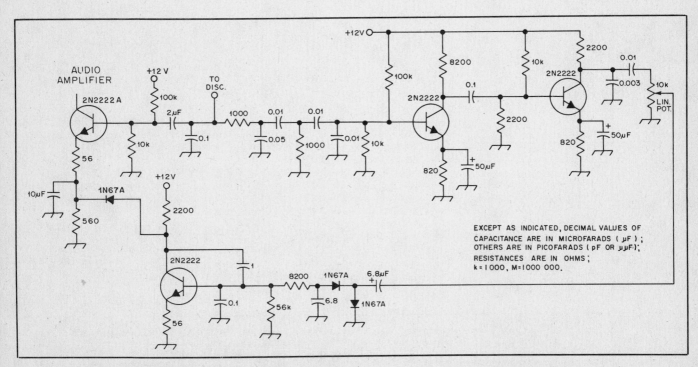

An audio amplifier for improving the operation of mobile fm transmitters.

RECEIVING NOAA WEATHER REPORTS ON 2-METER FM RIGS

Most 2-meter fm transceivers are sufficiently broadbanded to allow reception of NOAA weather reports on either 162.40, 162.475 or 162.55 MHz by installing the proper receiver oscillator crystal. If the operator travels, it might be useful to have crystals for each frequency installed in the rig, allowing one to receive current weather information while in transit. — *Bob Migliorino, K2YFE*

DUAL OFFSET FOR THE HW-2021

With a 147.75/15 repeater going on the air in New Castle, IN, several area amateurs were faced with the problem of installing + 600-kHz offset crystals in our HW-2021 sets without losing either simplex or —600-kHz repeater capability. In addition, I disliked the idea of drilling holes in the case to install an extra switch. This is the solution I came up with.

Prepare and install a new switch according to the illustrations. The extra crystal can be put in any convenient location, but leads should be kept short. My crystal has been placed between the channel switch and the case.

With the original configuration the selector switch offered the choice of one or two crystals. The dual switch (see drawing) provides selection of either plus or minus 600 kHz when the repeat mode is used.

This modification, performed on two HW-2021s in New Castle, has been satisfactory. For this reason, I trust the idea will be beneficial to other owners of the HW-2021 as well as to operators of other sets where an extra switch is needed but space is limited. — *Paul L. Schmidt, WB9BAP*

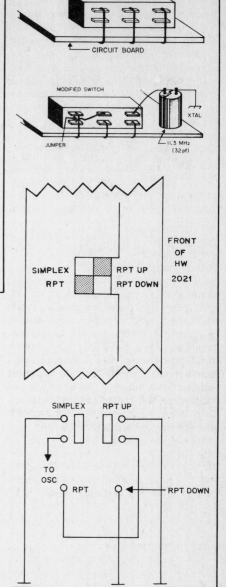

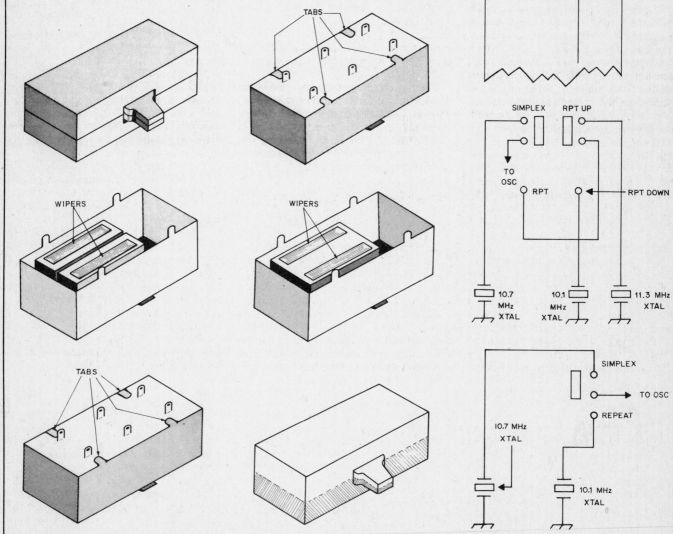

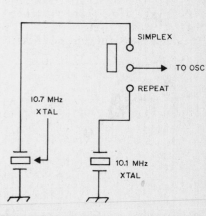

Modification of switches, and circuit changes for providing dual frequency offset for the Heath HW-2021. Steps to be followed: (1) Split two identical switches as shown. Switches must be same size as original. Lift tabs and remove bottom, wipers and case. File switch to one-half original width. (2) Reassemble the two half-switches into one unit. Reinstall combined switch in case, replacing wipers and bottom and bending tabs down. (3) Remove original switch and carefully install new switch and crystal. The new switch functions are shown at the upper right. The original and modified circuits are illustrated at the lower right.

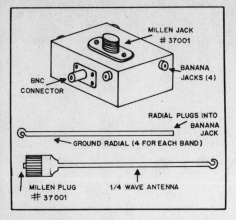

An economical portable antenna for 144, 220 and 420 MHz.

Table 1

Percent of Rated Light	Voltage (V)	Current (A)	Resistance (Ohms)
100	6.2	.150	41.4
60	5.5	.140	39.3
40	4.82	.130	37.1
20	4.2	.120	35.0
10	3.5	.110	31.8
4.5	3.0	.100	30.0

PORTABLE ANTENNA FOR 144, 220 AND 420 MHz

Budget-minded vhf operators needing a portable antenna for operation on 144, 220 and 420 MHz will find this homemade version worth the effort. The handful of components may be mounted conveniently on a Minibox. The antenna and radials are made from No. 12 solid copper wire. Banana jacks are used for connecting the radials. The antenna wire should be soldered to the center conductor of the Millen plug. Prune the wire for an SWR of 1:1. — *Jim Webb, WA6TQA*

PIP SQUEAK MODIFICATIONS

The Pip-Squeak 2-meter fm transmitter, described in *QST* for September, 1972, may be improved by a few simple modifications. Reference should be made to the schematic diagram and the pc-board layout in the original article.

The first item concerns the oscillator circuit where each crystal has a series trimmer capacitor. With the use of high-accuracy crystals as recommended, a single trimmer may be sufficient if the crystals are connected together at the lower end. This also makes crystals interchangeable in the sockets.

The second item is of more significance.

The varactor diode, D1, rectifies the rf voltage present on the crystals and develops a dc voltage across R4. This voltage often exceeds the bias voltage established by divider R3 and R4, causing the operating point of the diode to shift to an area where the capacitance change per volt of audio is considerably less than can be obtained with the bias voltage established by the divider. Since the developed-voltage magnitude depends on the activity of the particular crystal in use, it can also change the effect of the series capacitor. The rectified voltage developed across R3 can be reduced to an insignificant value by feeding the bias voltage from R3 and R4 through RFC1 to the diode. This change is shown in the drawing and assures that the operating bias for the varactor diode is that value set by the divider.

The third item concerns the base biases of the transistors in the IC package U1. The RCA integrated-circuit manual should be referred to for the schematic for the CA3018. Probably because of manufacturing tolerances, I found it necessary to increase base biases to get optimum transistor operation and proper audio, even though resistor values first used were within less than 5 percent of those specified. This point should be borne in mind only in the event of unsatisfactory deviation or audio quality.

The final item concerns unwanted signal output. Because of the small number of tuned circuits employed, and because of the high gain of the transistors used, there is considerable feedthrough in the final-stage output of the oscillator fundamental frequency and second and third harmonics. These can be reduced considerably by a slight change in the base

to ground circuit of Q2. If the high-impedance choke, RFC5, is replaced by a series-resonant circuit broadly tuned to the crystal fundamental frequency, and shunted by a low value of resistance to provide a dc return for the base, frequencies below the desired fourth harmonic are discriminated against. The revised circuit is shown. Suitable values of L, C and R are about 1.5 µH, 49 pF and 470 ohms, respectively. It bears emphasizing that the harmonics referred to are *not* those generated in the Class C doubler and amplifier.

Incidentally, since a no. 47 pilot lamp was suggested as a tune-up load, the characteristics of this lamp may be of interest because it may be used similarly with any QRP project. They are tabulated for a typical no. 47 lamp.

The lamp will actually show color in daylight at 50 mA. Note that at approximately the rated current value the light level changes much faster than the resistance does, so that by using either a parallel or series carbon resistor with the lamp we can make a visual tuning indicator of nearly constant resistance for load purposes. For example, if we wish to approximate the resistance of a quarter-wave whip, a 200-ohm resistor in parallel with the lamp will result in a load which will vary from 31.2 to 34.4 ohms while the lamp brilliance varies from 40 percent to 100 percent. These characteristics are typical of tungsten-filament lamps. The same procedure can be employed with lamps of different ratings for other low-power uses by proportioning the brilliance and currents and then taking measurements of voltage and current to determine the lamp resistance. — *J. H. Ellison, W6AOI*

CONSTRUCTION HINTS FOR VHF CONVERTERS

Quite a few vhf enthusiasts still like to build their own converters. Doing it yourself currently comes close to necessity, with the unfortunate tendency of the larger manufacturers to abandon the converter field — at a time when mixed-band satellite activity brings the need for converters back into focus.

The difficulty of obtaining suitable components, and doubts about one's ability to make satisfactory circuit boards tend to scare off would-be builders of simple equipment. Requiring only elemen-

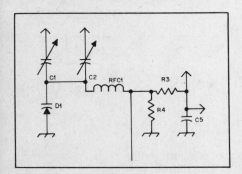

The author found that better varactor-diode performance can be obtained by placing RFC1 between the diode and the bias network. Refer to the original article for component designation.

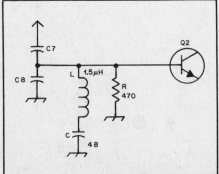

A series-resonant circuit is connected to the base of Q2 to aid in suppressing unwanted harmonics.

The WA3HMK converter is built on circuit board, mounted on a small aluminum chassis. Rf circuits are at the bottom, in this view.

Interior of the 2-meter converter, with components in the same position as in the layout drawing.

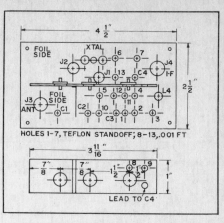

Layout details for the main plate and partition for the 2-meter converter. Both are single-sided circuit board. Hole dimensions and positions, where given, are approximate and may vary with components used, but general layout should be followed.

tary tools, the 2-meter converter shown here, worked out as a joint project by K3HEC and WA3HMK, is simple to build, yet its performance is adequate for weak-signal work. You may find some of its ideas useful even if you don't duplicate it entirely.

Mechanical and Circuit Details

Circuit board is used for the base plate and principal partition, but it is one-sided stock, used as sheet metal, with no etching required. It is 2-1/2 × 4-1/2 inches (64 × 114 mm), mounted on a 1-inch high box of the same dimensions. Push-in Teflon standoffs are used as tie-points, as are

several feedthrough bypass capacitors. Inexpensive Centralab 829-series tubular capacitors for tuning the rf circuits are mounted in an unusual but simple way, to avoid the common problem of loosening lock nuts. Small holes are drilled adjacent to opposite sides of the mounting nut. A Z-shaped stiff wire or thin piece of copper or brass is then soldered to the outer surface of the nut and to the metal film on the underside of the base plate. This locks the trimmer firmly in place and provides a good ground connection.

The layout drawing can be used to duplicate the original if the builder keeps in mind any differences resulting from

component substitutions. The long partition is also circuit board. The small one in which the first rf amplifier transistor is centered is sheet brass or copper, but could also be board material, if desired. It is 7/8-inch square, with a hole in the center just large enough to pass the body of the E-300 transistor. The gate lead is soldered to the shield. The source and drain leads run directly to C1 and C2, respectively. All the other transistors are supported by their leads, which are about 1/2-inch long.

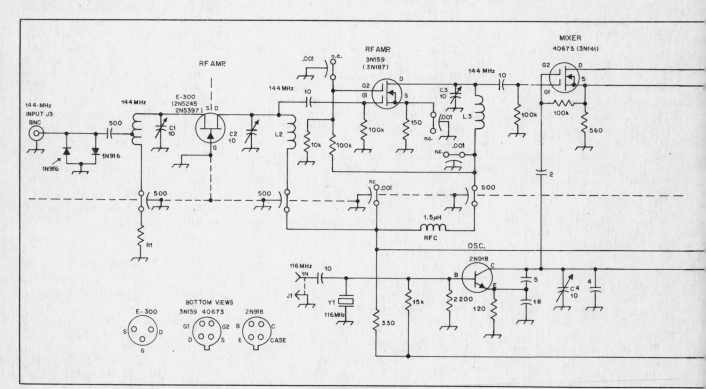

Schematic diagram and parts information for the WA3HMK converter. Decimal values of capacitance are in μF, others in pF. Resistors are 1/2 watt or less. 500-pF capacitors are button-mica feedthrough types (surplus). The 0.001 μF capacitors are small ceramic types (Centralab MFT-1000).

C1-C4, incl. — 10-pF tubular ceramic trimmer (Centralab 829-10).
L1 — 6 turns No. 16, 3/8-inch dia., spaced wire dia. Tap at 2-1/2 turns from bypassed end,

or for best noise figure.
L2 — 4-3/4 turns, like L1.
L3 — 4 turns No. 22, 1/4-inch dia., 5/16 inch (6 × 7 mm) long.

L4 — 2.7 to 4.2 μH, slug-tuned coil (Miller 4307).
R1 — Adjust for 5 mA drain curent, or lowest noise figure. Final value in original unit,

The first rf stage is a grounded-gate amplifier using a low-noise JFET. The second rf amplifier and the mixer are MOSFETs. The oscillator contains a low-cost bipolar transistor. Almost any vhf oscillator type should work. The injection portion of the converter is of interest in that a 116-MHz crystal is used, eliminating the need for multiplier stages and their attendant problems of unwanted frequencies that can generate spurious responses. This is especially desirable in a simple layout such as this. Injection can also be supplied from an external source, merely by removing the crystal, Y1, and feeding 116-MHz energy into the phono jack at the lower left. This provision makes the converter suitable for use in transverter service, an application now in the process of being tried by WA3HMK.

The circuit diagram is drawn in a manner that will illustrate use of feedthrough capacitors as tiepoints and bypasses. All the 0.001-μF capacitors are small ceramics of the FT type. The 500-pF capacitors are button-micas. Both types are often found as surplus. Each capacitor is shown in the compartment or partition in which it is mounted. All parts shown below the broken line are on the oscillator side of the partition. All above are in the rf portion.

The converter was checked in the ARRL lab and used in communication at W1HDQ. Sensitivity and gain were adequate for weak-signal work. Spurious

responses, often a problem in simple converters of the oscillator-multiplier type, were conspicuous by their absence. The value of R1 should be adjusted for a current drain of about 5 mA, or for optimum noise figure. The original is 220 ohms, but higher values may be needed. C1 and the position of the tap on L1 should also be optimized for noise figure. Converter gain can be controlled by varying resistor values in the second stage. — *W1HDQ*

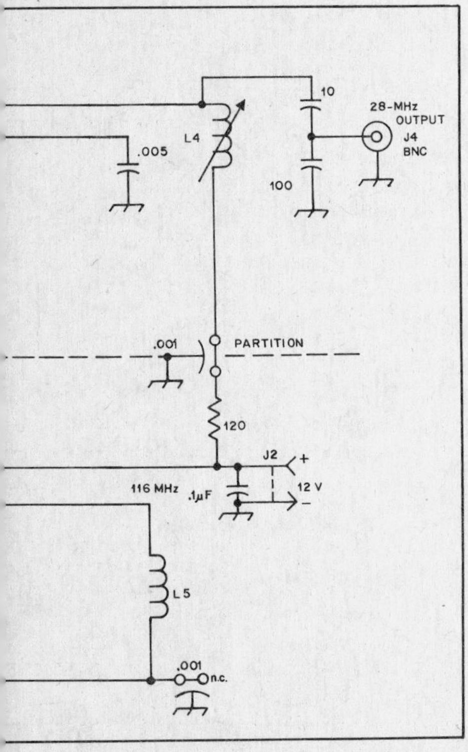

REMOVING GLITCHES FROM THE HA-201 AMPLIFIER

Soon after we acquired our Drake TR-22C, we discovered the joys and drawbacks of QRP operation in the 2-meter band. To upgrade the power we added a Heath HA-201 amplifier only to find unanticipated difficulties. There were large excursions in amplifier stability and a loss of receiver sensitivity. Moreover, there appeared to be less than the rated output even though the amplifier was operating with 13.8 V dc. The difficulty was one of improper interface between the TR-22 and the HA-201, centering mainly around the switching circuit.

Compatibility between the two units was achieved by the use of a carrier-operated relay (COR). After installation of the COR, the HA-201 performed normally with 10 to 12 watts of output across the 146-148 MHz band. Thereafter, there was no sign of instability.

Construction of the COR

Remove diodes D1-D6 (IN4149s), inclusive. Extract C5 (8-60 pF trimmer) and the quarter-wavelength lines for T1 and R2 (RG174/U). Two of the 1N4149s are to be used on the COR board. The rest go to the junk box along with C5. The shielded cable, however, is retained. The components just mentioned are from the electronic switching circuit.

The relay circuit is built on a Radio Shack perfboard (no. 276-1395) with the use of Radio Shack flea clips (no. 270-1392). Dimensions for the Vector Board are 2 × 1-1/2 inches (5.08 × 3.81 cm). A solid-wire jumper is used on the amplifier board in place of D2 and D5. Mount the COR board in the area formerly occupied by T1 and T2. Mounting holes should be drilled just to the right of hole J and hole E on the circuit board, utilizing no. 6-32 hardware. Be sure there are no live traces that are shorted to the ground bus. If necessary, the traces may be trimmed with an X-acto knife.

The shielded cables, originally used for T1 and T2, are now used for the input and output lines and are respectively connected to the input and output connectors of the COR circuit. A connection is also made from the COR board to points A, B, L and M on the HA-201 board. Tie all the shields together at a single point (at one of the flea clips near K1 or the COR). Con-

nect the COR B+ lead to the fused side of the 12-V line on the HA-201 and the COR. Then return the lead to the ground trace on the HA-201. If desired, a small spst switch may be added in series with the amplifier B+ lead for use as a HI/LO switch. This will provide flexibility not found otherwise.

When the installation is completed connect the HA-201 amplifier to the TR-22C, or any exciter capable of providing 1-3 watts of driving power. Apply 13.8 V dc to the amplifier and a 50-ohm load to the output of the HA-201 through a wattmeter. The relay closure should be heard when the exciter microphone button is pressed with an indication appearing on the wattmeter. Adjust C1-C4 for maximum output. The amplifier will run 10-to 12-watts output across the entire 146-148 MHz band with no instability.

Tune-up should be on 146.94 simplex if possible. Use of "94" alleviates the problem of lost output at band edges. Rather than use a VOM as a tuning aid, it is better to employ a wattmeter for all vhf work. — *Dave Karpiej, K1THP and Mark Starin, WA1TZK (from the* Insurance City Repeater Club Newsletter)

THE RIGHT CHANNELS FOR THE HW-202

Some radio amateurs who own the Heath HW-202 find on occasion that their set may be transmitting on one channel while receiving on another. Those operators who line up the crystals so that TRANSMIT is directly above RECEIVE in the push-button configuration can rectify the problem readily.

From a sheet of 1/4-inch Plexiglas, cut four pieces 9/16 inch × 3/8 inch. Cement each piece between a transmit button and a corresponding receive button so that the transmit and receive buttons may be operated simultaneously in corresponding pairs. This system avoids the problem of leaving any one button in the wrong position.

The plastic inserts should be filed sufficiently to prevent them from being so large that the switch arms could be distorted. Before cementing them into place, the Plexiglas pieces should slide easily between the upper and lower push buttons. After securing the pieces with Duco household cement or the equivalent, wait a few hours before operating the equipment to allow the cement to harden properly. This project is worth the effort! — *John Baldwin, W1KUO*

MINIMIZING ADJACENT-CHANNEL QRM

I would like to share with others this procedure that has worked well with my Icom IC-230 to minimize adjacent-channel interference from repeaters operating with

28-MHz
OUTPUT
J4
BNC

PARTITION

J2

116 MHz   12 V

L5

.001 n.c.

220 ohms.
Y1 — 116-MHz overtone crystal (International Crystal Mfg. Co.).

15-kHz separation. With the use of a CFS-455G filter, a weak repeater can be copied even though a much stronger repeater is belting the airwaves just 15 kHz away. Remedies for two situations are described.

Case 1: The interference is equal on both sides of the signals from the interfering repeater. Installation of a CFS-455F (or G) filter, performed in the same manner as recommended by Icom for the CFS-455E filter, will do the trick. The G filter is sharp and if the received signal is off frequency or over-deviating there may be some distortion. The G filter is best for use in areas with strong repeaters.

Case 2: The interference is greater on one side of the frequency used by the interfering repeater. This condition is caused in a receiver that does not have the i-f center on 10.700 MHz. For example, the i-f center frequency may be 10.703 or 10.697 MHz, 3 kHz off center.

These are the steps to take for the second case. Install a CFS-455F (or G) filter. Adjust any one of the LO crystal trimmers to center any remaining interference. If the interfering repeater is on 146.715 MHz, adjust the LO trimmer so that the interference is equal on 146.70 and 146.73 MHz. A strong signal will be required if the G filter is used.

Next, with the aid of a counter, adjust the three mixer trimmers to put the transmit oscillator back on frequency. For example, adjust the set for 146.70 MHz for on-channel operation, 146.10 MHz for − 600 kHz and 147.300 MHz for + 600 kHz. In my case it was necessary to add a 160-pF capacitor in parallel with the mixer trimmers for proper adjustment.

Once the mixer frequency is adjusted, the remaining LO trimmers may be set on transmit. The discriminator coil, L5 (LS-15) must be recentered. With a signal known to be on frequency, set LS-15 from zero with a zero-center meter. That completes the modification. I might add that the filters, mentioned above, may be obtained (at the time of this writing) from Murata, 2 Westchester Plaza, Elmsford, NY 10523. — *Richard Weinstein, W3HSF*

IMPROVED LOCAL-OSCILLATOR PERFORMANCE IN THE K9UIF 2-METER TRANSVERTER

The K9UIF transverter, which appears in *The Radio Amateur's VHF Manual* is one of the most popular and effective designs in existence. One consistent difficulty has been the instability of the local oscillator. The oscillator may drift during warm-up, and its frequency will shift when the oscillator is tuned. The high drive levels required also may result in instability, as a result of the subsequent high crystal current. An OX oscillator module and EX crystal provide an excellent substitute for the oscillator. They are available from In-

ternational Crystal Co., 10 N. Lee, Oklahoma City, OK 73102. The module is mounted in a small Minibox, and a 1000-pF ceramic feedthrough capacitor is used to bypass the 6-volt supply to the oscillator. The oscillator output is connected to a phono connector, and small-diameter coaxial cable joins the output of the module to the grid of the tube formerly used as the oscillator. If the 100-kΩ grid resistor was connected across the crystal socket, it should now be connected directly from the grid pin of the tube to ground. Since the module requires a 6-volt supply, two 1000-ohm resistors are connected as a voltage divider across the 12-volt supply in the transverter. — *Dr. Ralph E. Taggart, WB8DQT*

SOLID-STATE RELAY FOR REPEATERS

The device shown was designed by WØINK to interface with solid-state vhf receiver and transmitter strips. Our 2-meter repeater is now completely solid state and has a current drain of only 400 mA when in operation. The LED, when lit, indicates the transmitter is in operation. The delay of the "tail" can be adjusted by changing the value of C1. For a normal squelch tail, a value of 20 μF is used. The relay is driven by the COR circuit. Several CORs that could be used with this relay are described in *FM and Repeaters for the Radio Amateur.* — *Mike Wisch, WBØLGC/WRØAEN*

UHF-TV AMPLIFIER LOW ON NOISE

I have been unhappy with noise figures for many uhf preamplifiers. Satellite transmissions on the 70-centimeter band as well as other signals seemed to be covered by the noise inherent in many commercial uhf-amateur preamplifiers. All seemed to increase noise along with the signal strength. I was pleased to eventually find that the Winegard uhf-TV preamplifier AC-4990, on the other hand, performed excellently for signals in the 70 cm range. It brought the signals up in strength without noticeable increase in noise. On several occasions no trace of signals was evident until the AC-4990 was switched into the antenna system.

Additionally, the 4990 may be used for the 900-MHz region should any radio amateur bands be allocated there. This preamplifier functions well in the public service band, 450-512 MHz, shared with TV in some areas. A power supply is provided with the AC-4990, making it convenient for antenna mounting or locating near a 70-cm receiver. — *Ronald Marx, WA2CTZ*

A LOW-NOISE PREAMPLIFIER FOR 432-MHZ

This amplifier was developed as part of a low-cost, 400-MHz radiotelescope. Although it does not represent the ultimate in low-noise operation, its performance is much better than many com-

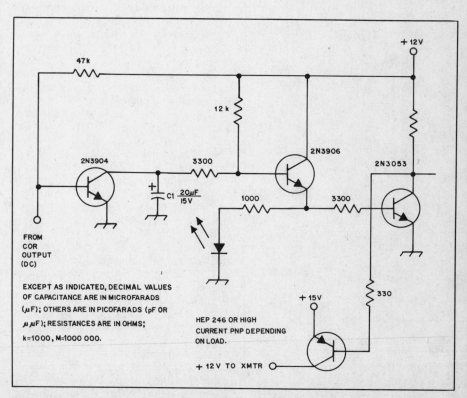

Solid-state relay. The LED is a surplus type, but a Radio Shack replacement should not be difficult to obtain.

The circuit board for the 432-MHz preamplifier.

mercially made units, and the cost and simplicity are hard to beat. The circuit uses a 2N5652 transistor, although a 2N5651, 2N5650 or K6007 can be used for better noise performance. The author's unit has 12-dB gain and a noise figure of less than 2 dB; 1.5 dB has been obtained with a selected transistor.* The total cost can be less than $20.

If greater gain is desired, the amplifier can be modified by changing the operating point of the transistor. According to the manufacturer of the 2N5652, a 5- to 8-dB increase is possible, and greater signal handling ability and linearity is achieved as a bonus. The cost of this gain improvement is an increased noise figure.

Circuit Description

The circuit is a basic common-emitter amplifier, with tuned input and output circuits. It has some attractions that are not obvious from the schematic. Neither neutralization nor shielding is needed, in spite of the high frequency and high gain, because of the low input impedance of the transistor. The amplifier should be unconditionally stable, even when mistuned. Also, because the 50-ohm transmission line is in parallel with the input tuned circuit, wide-band response is obtained. In environments where interference is a problem, the input connection and transistor base may be tapped lower on L1, narrowing the bandwidth.

Power is supplied by a 9-volt source, preferably a small transistor radio battery. Current drain is only 3 mA. A 12-volt Zener diode is connected across the power connection to protect the transistor against excessive voltage and improper supply polarity. The maximum V_{ce} of the 2N5652 is only 20, and the device is not very forgiving.

To protect against lightning damage (if the unit is mounted at the antenna, as it should be) some means should be employed to ground the antenna. The old trick of connecting two diodes across the input will not protect the delicate base junction of the 2N5652, and will appreciably increase the amplifier noise figure.

Construction

The amplifier is built on a 2 × 4-inch (51 × 102 mm) piece of copper-clad printed circuit board, using miniature ceramic insulated terminals. Holes are drilled in the board for all mounted components; where ground connections are needed, the leads are simply soldered to the board. This type of construction results in the shortest possible lead length for all components, and is very simple to do. The amplifier may be fastened to the open side of an aluminum chassis to form a compact, well-shielded unit.

The inductors should be installed so their leads are as short as possible, but keep the coil at least 1/4-inch from the copper surface or from other components. The transistor should be installed last and soldered carefully. Do not bend its leads close to the body, or they may break.

Adjustment

The amplifier is adjusted for maximum gain using a signal generator or a received signal. The collector current should be checked and set to the value which gives best noise figure; this will be very close to 3 mA. The collector current can be varied by changing the values of the base resistors, R1 and R2, or by varying the supply voltage by no more than ± 2 volts.

It may be necessary to trim the inductors in order to achieve a smooth passband response. For best results, the input inductor should be connected from ground to the center pin of the input connector, and C1 should be connected to the same point by a short wire. The bandwidth is also affected by the value of C2; increasing this value by a few pF will broaden the frequency response.

If oscillation should occur, be sure the transistor leads, especially the emitter lead, are well soldered and as short as possible. Oscillation is usually caused by poor construction practices, bad grounds, or poor layout.

To improve the gain, at the cost of noise figure, the base resistors R1 and R2 should be changed, to increase the collector current to a maximum of about 10 mA. R2 may be replaced by an rf choke with a small potentiometer connected in series, to make the bias point variable.

There is no reason why this circuit cannot be used at 220 or 144 MHz, with even better performance. All that would be needed is to change the input and output tuned circuits and increase the value of C2 slightly. — *Steven A. Maas, K3WJQ*

*[Editor's Note: A representative of KMC Semiconductor was consulted about the noise figure obtained by the author. His opinion was that it is not impossible to have a 1.5-dB noise figure if using a selected 2N5652; most are capable of providing 2 dB. For consistent results a K6007 is recommended, which can produce a 1.6-dB figure.]

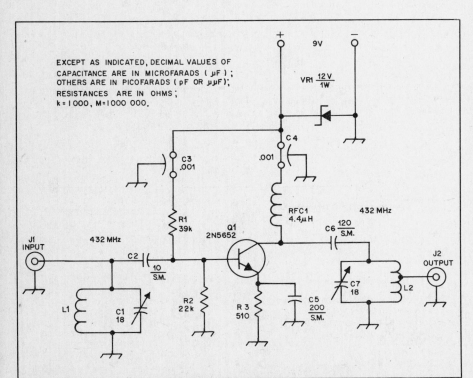

EXCEPT AS INDICATED, DECIMAL VALUES OF CAPACITANCE ARE IN MICROFARADS (μF); OTHERS ARE IN PICOFARADS (pF OR μμF); RESISTANCES ARE IN OHMS; k = 1000, M = 1000 000.

Schematic diagram of the 432-MHz preamplifier. The 2N5652 or K6007 transistor may be obtained from KMC Semiconductors, Parker Rd., Long Valley, NJ 07853, or from their distributors. C1 and C7 are 2- to 18-pF glass piston trimmers (JFD VC-4G or equiv.). L1 and L2 are 1 turn, 3/8-inch dia., no. 16 tinned copper; L2 is center tapped.

A WIDE-BAND PREAMPLIFIER

The wide-band preamplifier I built for use with my frequency counter has a simple

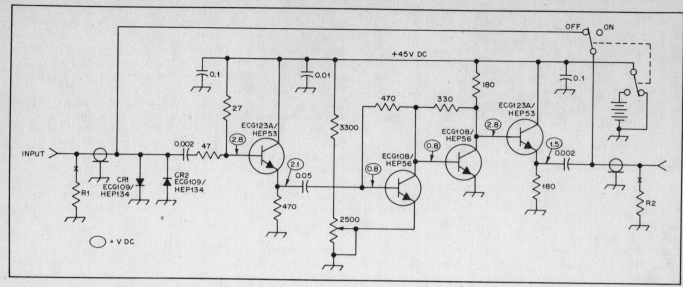

This wide-band preamplifier provides additional gain for effective frequency-counter operation.

design but works well. Tests indicate a gain of 20 dB at 50 MHz. The unit, constructed of commonly available parts, is assembled in a metal box. Input leads must be shielded. R1, the input loading resistor, may vary with the type of probe being used. Where a probe is not used, a length of RG-59/U may be connected to the amplifier input, and R1 should be placed across the input end of the RG-59/U. The value of the resistor should be 270 ohms. The need for R2 is determined by trial and error and will depend upon the input of the counter. I found 100 ohms works well for frequencies up to 45 MHz.

A bias potentiometer is used for gain control. To adjust the amplifier, set the potentiometer for maximum gain but below a point where oscillation may begin. It is suggested that if the unit is used close to equipment that could develop a signal level of 1 volt or more, diodes D1 and D2 should be incorporated in the circuit. — *Ira J. Arnold*

FOR THE VHF ANTENNA

Positioning holes in boom material for vhf beam antennas poses a special problem. The drawing I have provided shows a jig that was built to accurately scribe marks on the boom. Constructed of 0.032-inch brass sheet, the jig can be made with hand tools. The two side plates are made together (for accuracy) and are bolted to the small aluminum hand level. The horizontal bottom plates are soldered in place. A small, long spring can be attached to the jig to go under the boom to help keep the jig in place if desired.

First the boom is secured to prevent rotation. Element positions are then determined along the boom. Place the jig on the boom, marking vertical and horizontal scribe marks. Accurately

center-punch each side of the boom where scribe lines intersect. Drill the holes by working up in drill sizes to the desired hole diameter in order to obtain a smooth round hole. Drill each hole separately. Do not drill completely through the boom. Misalignment will otherwise result.

Mechanically rigid vhf antennas can be fabricated from aluminum rods. Hardware store parts are used for mounting. See the self explanatory mechanical drawing. — *E. R. Angle, WA6GUY*

PROTECTION FOR 432-MHz CONVERTERS

K3PGP has provided this transistor pro-

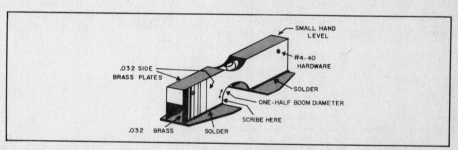

A precision element, hole-alignment, marking jig. The device allows uniform scribe markings in all directions. To use, clamp the antenna boom to avoid rotation. Place the jig on the boom. Make the required marks. Drilling should be done from each side — not through from one side.

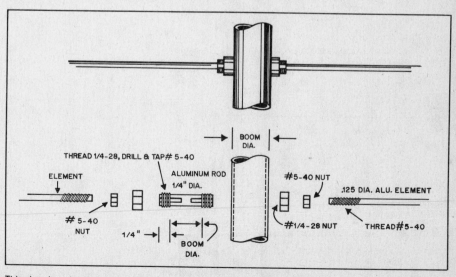

This drawing shows a method of constructing a beam antenna by using aluminum rods.

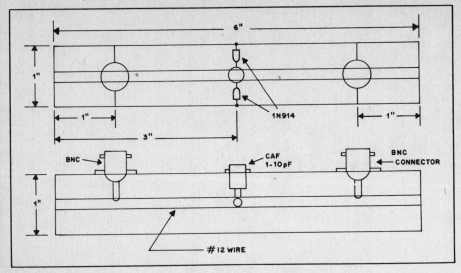

An interference filter and protection device for 432-MHz converter transistors.

tection device which should be of interest to just about everyone. It consists of a low-Q, half-wave filter with diodes located at the peak voltage point. The filter has an insertion loss of only 0.062 dB at 432 MHz and provides the bonus of adequate selectivity to clear interference at most locations. With 400 watts being passed into the filter, less than 80 mW was measured at the output. The diodes chosen are 1N914s but the choice is not critical. — *Allen Katz, K2UYH*

THE 25-CENT MOBILE ANTENNA

The rip-off, the car wash and transferring equipment to a new car present common problems for amateurs who operate mobile equipment. An external antenna on an automobile is an advertisement of the presence of mobile equipment. Without the antenna or mount, a radio thief might well ignore the car.

General Motors had embedded the broadcast radio antenna in the windshield of my 1976 Buick. This triggered a series of thoughts as solutions leading to the installation of a 2-meter, quarter-wave whip just inside the rear window. A steel pan, welded to the body, is located under the trim and insulation of the rear window shelf. The location seemed logical for an inside antenna.

A 1/2-inch hole and two 1/8-inch, self-tapping screw holes were drilled from the inside of the trunk. Location for the

antenna was several inches forward from the center of the rear window. Only a 1/4-inch drill was used for the hole in the plastic-cloth shelf trim. A female auto-radio socket was installed with the solder tab protruding through the trim as shown in the drawing. For the antenna a 20-inch length of No. 32 enameled wire was used, one end being soldered to the connector tab and the other temporarily taped to the

rear window. The antenna was pruned for minimum SWR and the pruned end was taped to the glass.

While the antenna system is a compromise, my mobile transmitter produces full quieting through the local repeater. Performance is good well out to the fringes of the repeater range. My fellow RATS (Richmond Amateur Telecommunications Society) deserve mention for bearing with me during tests on the RATS 28/88 repeater, WR4ACW. — *Arthur Baitz, K4ARE*

REPLACING THE ANTENNA JACK ON THE HW-2021

Owners of the HW-2021 hand-held transceiver made by Heath may have discovered that the soft metal used in the external antenna jack does not stand up well. When mine became troublesome I found that a miniature closed-circuit phone jack (no. 274-253) sold by Radio Shack fits perfectly in place of the original jack. This replacement features a strong return spring which seems to eliminate the problem involved. I might mention that Radio Shack packages these jacks three to a container. The extras could be used as spares for future replacements or shared with other HW-2021 owners. — *Bill Tubbs, WA6FFI*

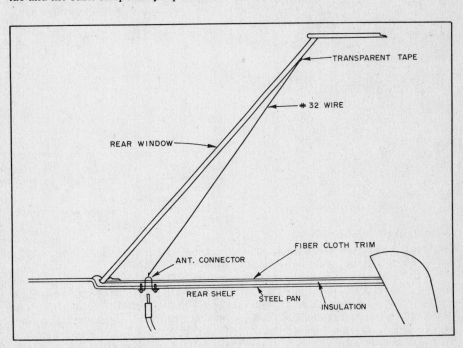

A thin wire that is nearly invisible may be suspended from the rear window of a car to the rear deck as an antenna for 2-meter mobile operation.

Chapter 9

Notions
for Various Modes

RECEPTION OF SSTV SIGNALS TUNED CORRECTLY WITH THIS DEVICE

Tuning in ssb signals for voice reception presents no problem normally. But adjusting a receiver for SSTV is something else because a person would have difficulty trying to determine the correct pitch of the SSTV tones being heard from a loudspeaker. This compact tuning aid solves the problem.

Construction and Adjustments

The circuit may be constructed inside the enclosure of an existing monitor, or it may be housed separately in a small metal box like that shown in the photographs. Component layout is far from being critical.

An unmodified 88-mH toroid should be used for L1, and C1 may be a stock-value capacitor or appropriate combination. Some builders may wish to precision tune the filter to 1200 Hz with the aid of a frequency counter. This is best done after the remainder of the circuit is completed, so the filter is tuned under operational conditions. Before doing this, however, it would be wise to check the receiving monitor, as its own sync circuitry may operate most effectively at a frequency several hertz removed from 1200. Precision tuning is not essential for satisfactory use of the instrument.

The limiter balance should be adjusted first. Ground the audio input connection and, using a voltmeter, perform a coarse adjustment of the balance control by setting the voltage at pin 2 of U1 to exactly equal that at pin 3. If this condition cannot be reached within the range of the control, it is because one or more of the 4700-ohm voltage-divider resistors are somewhat removed in value from

Circuit diagram of the SSTV tuning aid. Both controls are of linear taper. All fixed resistors may be 1/4 watt. All capacitors except C1 may be disk ceramic.
C1 — 0.2 μF Mylar or polystyrene. In the unit photographed this value was obtained by connecting two 0.1-μF capacitors in parallel.
CR1 — LED, Radio Shack 276-041 or equiv.
L1 — Surplus 88-mH toroidal inductor.
U1 — Dual operational amplifier, type 5558, 8-pin, dual in-line package.

nominal. In this case selection of another 4700-ohm resistor or paralleling one resistor with another of much higher value (27 to 47 kΩ) is in order. Next measure the voltage at pin 1 of U1. Slowly adjust the balance control in either direction and note that just a small adjustment causes the voltage to swing from 1 V to 11 V. (This range will be greater for supply potentials higher than 12 V.) Carefully perform a fine adjustment of the control by setting it for a voltmeter reading at pin 1 of 6 volts (or one-half the supply voltage).

If you have an oscilloscope, you can check the balance adjustment by injecting a very low-level audio signal at the input of the tuning aid. Monitor the waveform

at pin 1 of the IC. A signal below the limiting threshold should appear as a sine wave. As the level of the signal is increased, the top and bottom of the sine wave will be clipped symmetrically if the balance is correct.

The threshold adjustment for U1B acts like an intensity control for the LED. Its setting is not crucial, and in operation it almost becomes one of personal preference. With no signal at the input the LED will glow continuously at one extreme setting of this control. Back the setting off until the LED becomes extinguished. Now connect the SSTV signal from a camera, a tape recorder or from a received signal that you *know* is properly tuned. The flashing or flickering of the

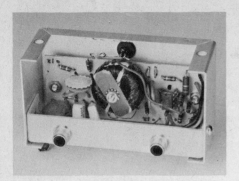

An inside view of the tuning aid. The circuit as constructed here is housed inside a 2 × 4 × 1-5/8-inch Minibox. The LED is supported by its leads and protrudes through a grommeted hole in the front of the enclosure. Phono type jacks are fastened to a bracket for audio and 12-volt inputs, with clearance holes for these jacks drilled in the back cover.

LED will be readily apparent. As the control is backed off farther from the setting obtained earlier, the intensity of the flashes will diminish. You can find a setting for which the LED will glow only during the 30-ms vertical sync pulse, once every eight seconds. The setting should be advanced slightly from this position, so that a flash is observed for every sync pulse. Find the setting you prefer most by tuning around some SSTV signal frequencies on the air.

With a little experience, you'll find that it takes but a few seconds to tune SSTV signals "on the nose" with this handy tuning aid. — *K1TD*

TEMPERATURE COMPENSATION FOR THE *QST* AFSK GENERATOR

Several of us who built the RTTY generator described by WB2RHM on page 36 of the September, 1969, issue of *QST* have experienced problems with considerable frequency changes resulting from thermal effects. Possibly some hams placed their generators on or near other equipment which radiated heat. In my case, the room temperature may vary as much as 25°C.

While the mark frequency held within a few Hertz of the correct value, the space frequency drifted widely with changes of temperature. By simply placing a finger on D1, the 1N914 frequency-shift diode, I found that the diode was sensitive to temperature and that the space frequency would begin to drift rapidly. While experimenting I also discovered that by placing two parallel 25,000-ohm thermistors (obtainable at parts jobbers) in parallel with R15 (the 820-ohm resistor) the thermal effect could be reduced so that the space frequency remained within 6 Hz of the nominal value of 1170 Hz. My generator is designed to operate at 1000-1170 Hz.

Because the thermistors affect the RC time constant of the oscillator, the generator frequencies should be recalibrated. Some experimenting may be needed to find the correct thermistor value for the required frequency and temperature compensation. Thermistors may be used singly, in series, or in parallel. — *Fred Mumma, W3KEK, K3TXG*

UPDATE YOUR OSCARLOCATOR

If you're one of the 20,000 amateurs who have found OSCAR quickly and easily with your own OSCARLOCATOR, you may have noticed that something was missing. You guessed it — beam headings for directional antennas.

Here's an easy way to adapt your OSCARLOCATOR to give approximate azimuth and elevation information at a glance.

Using a permanent, nonwater-base, felt-tipped marker (available at all stationery stores), trace the illustrated design on your QTH/Rangefinder (the small circle that shows the satellite's range) or a separate sheet of mylar, available at art supply stores. The elliptical shape will yield more accurate results for North American latitudes on the polar projection map.

Place the center of the overlay on your QTH. The straight line, now labeled "0" (zero), should be aligned so that the arrows point north. This indicates 0 degrees azimuth.

The lines radiating from the center give azimuth bearings at 30-degree intervals, while the concentric circles give elevation bearings of 0, 30 and 60 degrees. With the relatively wide beamwidth of typical OSCAR antennas (about 60 degrees for a 10-dB gain antenna), estimates between the marks should be adequate; you should have to reposition your antennas only every two minutes or so.

Using your updated and improved OSCARLOCATOR is simple. The "Orbit Finder" overlay still gives the number of minutes after equator crossing (EQX) that the satellite will be within range.

If, for example, the path of a given orbit crosses the 30-degree elevation oval at an azimuth of 180 degrees on the modified overlay, then at that instant the satellite will be 30 degrees above your horizon and directly south of your QTH. With the new overlay, you can jot down the az-el data at two-minute intervals well in advance of an upcoming pass. This will let you devote every precious minute between AOS (when you first hear it) to LOS (when you lose it) to operating. — *Jon Alquist, WA0WYX*

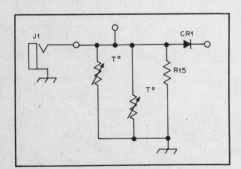

Two thermistors provide temperature compensation for the WB2RHM RTTY generator.

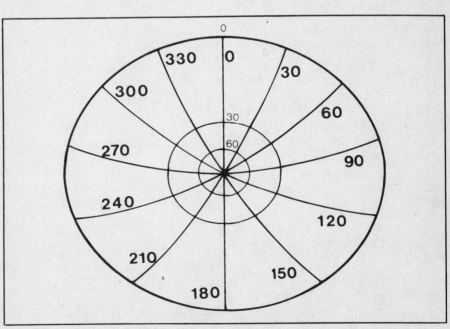

Using this QTH/Rangefinder will provide accurate AOS, LOS and beam headings for all OSCAR passes in the Northern Hemisphere. To determine DX possibilities, center the original (circular) Rangefinder on the area you are interested in working (London, for example). If OSCAR will be within range, the orbital track will fall in the area where the two Rangefinders overlap.

A STABLE TONE GENERATOR FOR REPEATER ACCESS

This circuit was brought forth in an effort to sidestep some of the problems of tone-burst generators, such as instability, temperature effects, difficulty of adjustment, or hard-to-find components. Cost was also a consideration; the unit can be duplicated with all new parts (excluding the pc board) for about $10. Stability is such that drift is less than one hertz after an hour of operation. Potentiometers allow ease of adjustment to the desired frequencies of operation.

Circuit Description

The design is centered around a Signetics NE566V phase locked loop IC.[1] The tone frequencies are determined by C1 and R1 plus R2 through R7. The capacitance remains constant and the resistance is changed to set the various tones. The formula

$$T = \frac{1}{3 \times R1 \times C1}$$

is used to calculate the frequency of oscillation.

The total resistance needed is approximately 28 kΩ for 1800 Hz and 20 kΩ for 2400 Hz. Since the overall resistance, between the extremes, is only 8 kΩ, potentiometers of 10-kΩ value were used to adjust the frequency and a 50-kΩ unit was used to set the range. Shunting C1 with Q1 causes the tone to cease. The values of C2 and R8 determine the burst duration.

In operation Q1 has +12 V applied to the base and is in full conduction, shunting C1. When the PTT line is grounded, Q1 will cut off and allow the PLL to oscillate. C2 will begin charging through R8 and again force Q1 into conduction, shunting C1, and stopping the oscillation. The 0.05-μF capacitor and the 1-MΩ resistor provide isolation and a high impedance to the audio line.

Construction

Since the NE566V is a voltage-controlled oscillator, it is very sensitive to voltage changes and a Zener-diode regulated supply is a necessity. The HEP724 (Q1) must be removed from the circuit in order to adjust the tones; therefore, a socket should be used for this transistor.

The circuit is constructed on a pc board measuring 1-1/4 × 2-7/8 inches (32 × 73 mm). A single-pole, 6-position switch is used to select the desired tone. Don't forget to provide an ON-OFF switch. Some people get upset if you are using tone-burst and the repeater doesn't require it.

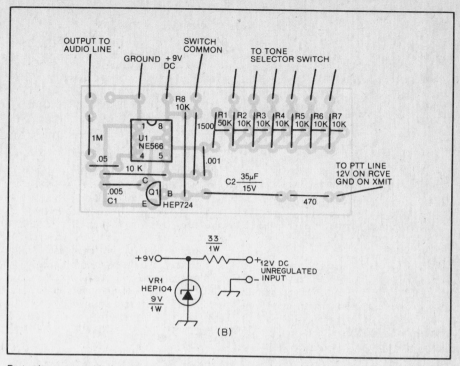

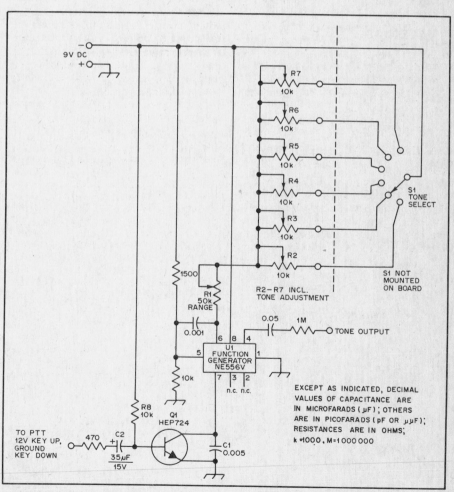

Parts-placement guide for the generator. View is from the component side; shaded areas are copper foil. A method of obtaining regulated power for the generator from a 12-volt source is shown at B.

Schematic diagram of the tone-burst generator.
Q — Motorola HEP724 or equiv.
R1 — 50-kΩ miniature pc-mount control, Radio 271-219 or equiv.
R2-R7, incl. — 10-kΩ miniature pc-mount

control, Radio Shack 271-218 or equiv.
U1 — Function generator (PLL) IC, Signetics NE566V.

[1]Phase-Locked Loops Applications, Signetics Corporation, 811 East Arques Ave., Sunnyvale, CA 94086.

Adjustment

Remove Q1 from the circuit. This will allow the oscillator to run continuously. Connect a counter to the junction of the 0.05-μF capacitor and the 1-MΩ resistor.

Set R2 through R7 to minimum resistance, then adjust R1 for 2500 Hz. Set the selector switch to position 1 and adjust the corresponding control for the desired frequency. Repeat this with the rest of the potentiometers.

After setting all of the controls replace Q1 and check the burst duration. Using a value of 35 μF for C1 will give a burst duration of 0.4 second. If a different duration is desired change the value of C1. Do not change the value of R8.

Comments

During the testing of this circuit one unexpected advantage of using a range control (R1) came to light. If you should change power sources and a different supply voltage results, the tones will need to be reset. Remove Q1 and select a tone with the switch. Adjust the frequency of that tone using R1. You will find that the other tones will be correct and need no further adjustment. — *Glenn Dickenson, WB5BAF*

TV BACKDROP

With more amateurs using SSTV and fast scan (regular) television, the need for a white backdrop becomes important for the production of high-contrast pictures. The installation of a white roll-type window shade hanging from the ceiling, mounted a few feet behind the subject, provides a suitable background for this purpose. — *Robert W. Gervenack, W7FEN*

ANTENNA SWITCHING FOR RTTY

My main interest is RTTY. For this mode I have a separate transmitter. When I planned my present installation I wanted to avoid damage to my other equipment through a moment of forgetfulness that would allow a mixing of coaxial cables when bringing another receiver on the line. Many ham stations have multiple

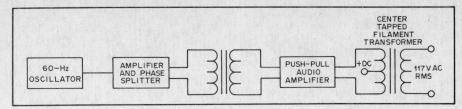

A 60-Hz oscillator, an amplifier and a 12.6-V center-tapped filament transformer provide 117-V ac for teleprinter motor.

receivers and transmitters and it is not uncommon to hear of a receiver being damaged by rf when a mixup occurs.

The circuit I have shown will prevent such accidents and also eliminate the inconvenience of having to change cables manually. Any receiver or transceiver can be used in conjunction with a main transmitter. Also, any antenna or dummy load can be used with any rig or receiver, while the SWR bridge, as well as an oscilloscope, may remain in the line, ready for use.

No receiver can be damaged by the misapplication of rf, but misapplication of an antenna could cause damage to a transmitter if not spotted quickly by observing the SWR indicator.

Features of the switching arrangement are shown in the illustration. Coaxial-switch no. 1 selects the receiver or transceiver to be used. It also provides a bench-testing jack where a transmitter or receiver may be tested. Switch no. 2 selects the antenna to be used or a dummy load if desired. Any equipment connected to switch no. 1 is disconnected from the antenna line by the action of the antenna relay controlled by the main transmitter. The ssb transceiver is available for use when not transmitting RTTY as is receiver no. 1 (for receiving RTTY on the ham bands only) and the general coverage receiver, no. 2. The latter may be used for Navy MARS phone or RTTY reception. — *Melvin Leibowitz, W3KET*

FOR MOBILE RTTY

A number of years ago mobile RTTY was a topic for discussion here in Minneapolis, MN. Frequently these discussions turned to dc-regulated motors for the teleprinter.

While the thought of such dc-regulated motors has merit, I have made a qualitative investigation of the use of a special ac supply for machines with synchronous motors. The circuit for the supply is not complex, but certain points had to be considered when the unit was being built, namely the battery supply voltage, the frequency, and the current/voltage ratings of the transformer.

Fundamentally, the power supply consists of a 60-Hz oscillator driving an amplifier and a phase splitter. The best output device would be a push-pull audio amplifier used in conjunction with a center-tapped filament transformer. When one considers the 12.6 volts available from an automobile storage battery, plus rms and peak voltages inherent in the situation, a 12.6-volt rms center-tapped filament transformer being driven by a push-pull audio stage is the best means of obtaining 117-V ac (rms) from 12.6-V dc produced by the battery. These stipulations required the device to be solid state.

The 60-Hz oscillator can be calibrated with an oscilloscope and a WWV receiver. Using Lissajous figures, one can compare the 60 Hz with the 600-Hz signal. If the unit is operating properly, the two frequencies will produce a 10:1 scope trace. This supply could be very useful in emergency vehicles. — *Rodney B. Maas, KØCAZ*

FACSIMILE TRANSCEIVER FOR WEATHER-SATELLITE PICTURES

Considerable interest in adapting the plentiful Western Union Telefax unit for satellite pictures has seemed evident. W4NK's antenna and desk-facsimile picture in the October, 1973, *QST* (p. 69) has also stirred considerable interest. Since Essa 8 has deteriorated to a "flying phantom" of its original state and with both NOAA 1 and 2 pumping out excellent pictures in both infrared and visual modes, a means of converting the Telefax for the reception of the 48-line scan of these and future satellites is in order. Using weather satellite bulletins from W1AW, the writer was able to catch pictures from NOAA 2 on the day after launch with equipment similar to that described.

The reception of the satellite signal, approx. 137.5 MHz, is the first step. Here

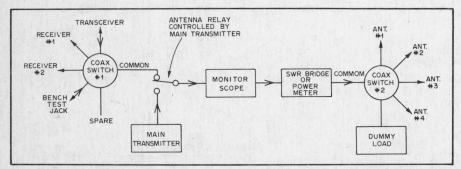

A "no-smoke" antenna switching arrangement for the RTTY station.

the articles by K2RNF,[1] W4MKM,[2] and 2-meter information in *The Radio Amateur's VHF Manual* are the starting point. Hand-held dipoles operated in the shack or the backyard with a little experience will often outperform some of the complex antennas now in use, so keep it simple, at least at first. A good converter is a must, and remember, the receiver must be fm and have a 20-kHz bandwidth or more.

The second hurdle in the project is the construction of a standard-frequency generator putting out exactly 16 Hz. This is best done by dividing down from a 1.6-MHz crystal oscillator with five decade counters. The oscillator must be exactly on frequency or skewing of the picture will result. Use of compression type crystals which can be adjusted by either loading with a pencil or solder, or by grinding with kitchen cleanser such as Ajax, is desirable.[3] The need for the 16-Hz frequency will become evident shortly.

Driving the drum at the correct speed is the third problem. The drum of the desk FAX, when driven by 60-Hz line voltage, turns at 180 rpm, which is near four times the satellite's 48 lines per inch. An exact multiple of four would be 192 rpm. In order to speed up the drum from 180 to 192 rpm we just feed in a higher frequency of ac. To find the correct frequency we use simple ratio and proportion of $60/180 = x/192$. Solving for x we get 64 Hz, or four times 16. Restating all this, if we record 16 Hz on the left channel of our stereo tape recorder and the picture information on the right simultaneously at 1-7/8 ips, and then play back at 7-1/2 ips, we will multiply both the outputs by four. The 64-Hz output should be fed into the voice coil of a reversed output transformer. The 5000-ohm winding is tuned to resonance to help shape the 48-Hz output to a sine wave. This output is fed into the input of a 15-watt audio amplifier to feed 130 volts under load into the drum motor. This will turn the motor at 192 rpm in synchronism with the video at 192 lines per minute which is being fed into the stylus through the Telefax amplifiers. The only changes necessary on the Telefax are those of King[4] to make it functional for amateur facsimile, and the addition of a dpdt switch to transfer the motor, including its capacitor, from the ac mains to the new line from the 64-Hz amplifier.

Since the pictures which are now produced are negatives, some means of inversion is necessary. The writer used a dc inverter already at hand and would recommend for simplicity's sake the system used by W7UGV,[5] which lets one use the original stylus amplifier of the Telefax. The frequency of the subcarrier has been multiplied from 2400 to 9600 Hz in the tape recorder and one must reduce the value of the 0.08-µF filter capacitor that

W7UGV shows, designed to smooth 2400 Hz (4800 Hz after demodulation), to approx. 0.0033 µF for the 9600 (19200) Hz. The time required for printing a ten-minute picture has also been reduced to about three minutes. — *Lindsay R. Winkler, W7AVE*

[1] Anderson, "Amateur Reception of Weather Satellite Picture Transmissions," *QST*, November, 1965.
[2] McKnight, "Evolution of an Amateur Weather-Satellite Picture Station," *QST*, April, 1968, and Feedback, *QST*, July, 1968, p. 67.
[3] An alternative arrangement is to use a circuit with provisions for trimming the crystal frequency, such as described in "A TTL Crystal Oscillator," *QST*, February, 1974.
[4] King, "Conversion of Telefax Transceivers to Amateur Service," *QST*, May, 1972, and Feedback, *QST*, Nov. 1972, p. 33.
[5] Spillane, "ESSA II," Technical Correspondence, *QST*, December, 1966.

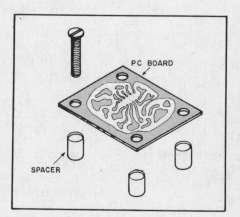

Spacers may be made from the body of a ball-point pen.

PC-BOARD SPACERS FROM BALL-POINT PENS

The bodies of empty ball-point pens make good pc-board mounting spacers, as indicated by the illustration. They may be cut to any desired size. I used Bic ball-point pens because they have straight walls. — *Jose M. Armengol, WA2BNM*

SELECTABLE NONOVERLINE FOR THE TELETYPE MODEL 28

Nonoverline is a valuable function for most amateur radio teletype applications. However, the trend toward higher baud rates, coupled with poor operating habits of some amateur and commercial stations, makes correct copying of these stations impossible with the nonoverline function. The authors have yet to find a Model 28 typing unit that will complete the carriage return function in the "less than one character length" required when a printing character follows the line-feed character at 100 wpm. Thus, when nonoverline is being used annoying black "blobs" appear roughly one third of the way across the page. These blobs are

caused by the print hammer striking the character which follows the line feed — which also causes carriage return — before the carriage has completely returned. There are three possible remedies for this problem:

1) Only copy stations which use a non-printing character code after the line-feed code.

2) Do not use nonoverline when copying offending stations.

3) Use a machine that can complete the carriage return before the next character is struck.

This article explains a simple modification which allows the carriage return on receipt of the carriage return code to be optionally selected in addition to the nonoverline function without removing the typing unit from the cabinet.

The modification consists of using a part of the on-line backspace-function mechanism to perform the carriage-return function. In order to do this a carriage-return-function bar along with the associated function lever, function pawl, function-pawl clip, spring plate, and springs must be installed in slot 9 of the stunt box. The rest of the modification consists of adding a back-space slide arm along with its retaining plate and a back-space bail. Many Mark III machines already have the back-space bail installed, so you only need to add the back-space slide arm and retaining plate. The back-space bail is installed on the same shaft as the carriage-return bail as shown in the drawing. A carriage-return slide arm may be used in place of the back-space slide arm if one is available and if either the two-slot extension on the rear of the arm is removed or slot 8 of the stunt box is not

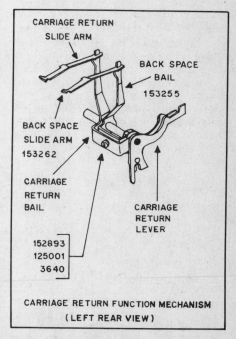

The modified carriage-return mechanism for nonoverline operation.

Table 1

Parts for Model 28 Nonoverline Operation

Teletype Corp. Part No.	Description
153254	Bracket. Retaining plate for back-space slide arm.
151657	Screw. Used with 153254.
2191	Lock washer. Used with 151657.
152127	Clip. Function-pawl clip.
152642	Function lever.
152653	Function pawl.
152660	Plate, spring.
157240	Spring.
72522	Wick.
90517	Spring.
4703	Spring.
152667	Function bar (carriage return).
153262	Back-space slide arm. A modified carriage-return slide arm may be used.
153255	Back-space bail.
152893	Screw. Used to couple back-space bail and carriage-return bail.
3640	Lock washer. Used with 152893.
15011	Washer. Used with 152893.

used. There is a screw in each end of the carriage-return bail shaft which may be removed allowing the shaft to be pulled away from the machine so that the back-space bail assembly can be placed on the shaft. This operation requires some twisting and turning, but it can be done. Once the parts have been installed, the carriage-return adjustment should be checked. Note that the screw in the carriage-return bail extends through a slot in the back-space bail to couple the two. They are not screwed together rigidly.

With the modification completed, the function pawl in slot 9 can be disabled with the pawl clip and the nonoverline will operate in the normal fashion. The clip can also be set so that slot 9 is active and the machine will carriage return on receipt of the carriage-return code with the following line-feed character interval providing the time needed for completion of the carriage-return function.

We have found this feature to be extremely useful when copying 100-wpm press stations, some amateur stations, and certain types of teletype art where overlining is used on purpose. The required parts necessary for nonoverline operation are listed in Table 1. — *Lenox Carruth, Jr., WA5OVG and Dick McDonald, K5WOR*

AN ELECTRONIC FAX CONVERTER

Amateurs who have the model 6500 facsimile machine may be interested in the positive FAX converter that I have designed and built. The circuit shown here also has provision for sending electronic sync bars.

In my installation all components are mounted on a pc board. the 10-kΩ potentiometer in the output circuit is a

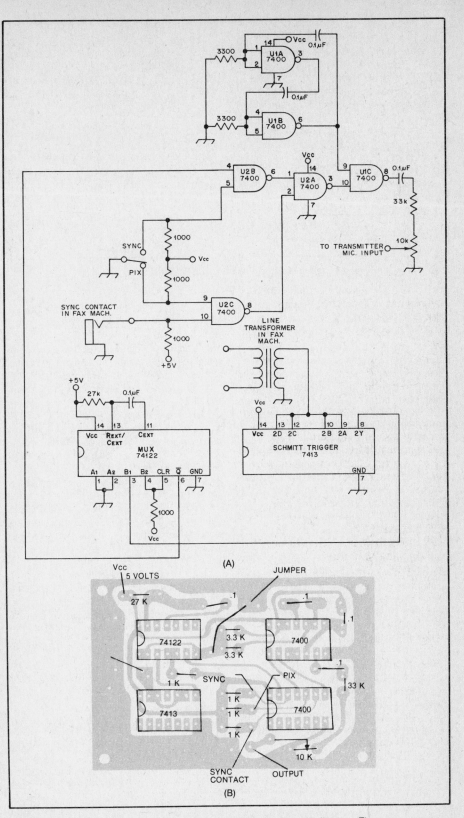

(A)

(B)

An electronic, positive FAX converter. Part A is the basic schematic diagram. There are no connections to pins not shown in the schematic diagram. Part B is the component layout for the printed circuit board, shown from the component side.

multiturn type. It should be set for the input level to the transmitter. R2 on the facsimile machine must be adjusted carefully for proper operation of the converter. The output frequency ranges between 1500 and 1600 Hz. I found that best results

were obtained with the pc board mounted within the machine. All resistors are 1/2 watt. They are mounted vertically. The pc type of capacitors used are obtainable from Radio Shack stores. They work well. — *Robert A. John, WBØFVL*

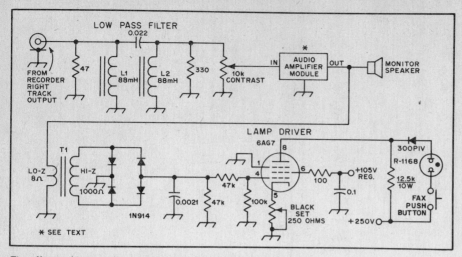

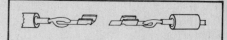

The effects of hum and noise are reduced in the Deskfax with this filter.

Small disconnect junctions made from parts of old tube sockets.

A NOISE AND HUM FILTER FOR THE DESKFAX

In the process of modifying my Deskfax APT equipment for use with photographic paper, I found that this filter circuit and audio amplifier improved the operation by reducing the effects of noise and hum. A Radio Shack 1-watt audio amplifier compensated for insertion losses through the filter. An equivalent amplifier could have been made from tubes and components contained in the FAX unit. This circuit may be of help to others. — *Lindsay R. Winkler, W7AVE*

SCR RELAY CONTROL FOR RTTY, VOX, AND COR

One would expect to find more extensive use of SCRs in present day relay-control circuits, given the desirability of economy, reliability, simplicity, and state of the art. Often an SCR can replace up to several transistorized or tube stages in RTTY, VOX, COR, and other relay-control circuits.

The threshold triggering effect of the SCR can be used to advantage here, triggering being automatically suppressed on low-level noise and similar interference. Because of its turn-off characteristics, ac is easier to control with an SCR than is dc.

Some experimenters may wish to take

the final step: Replacing the relay with an SCR or, if an ac motor is being controlled, with a TRIAC. (SCRs conduct only on half cycles.) Caution: When replacing relays with solid-state devices, always avoid circuits which present potential hazards, such as an ac primary chassis ground.

Here is a representative circuit for SCR relay control which has been used with excellent results in RTTY auto-start/motor-delay sections of homemade RTTY demodulators at WB8DKX and W8KDC. Pick-up/drop-out times can be varied by the combination R1/C1, and also vary considerably with the SCR type (in this circuit the times are 1 second and 3 seconds respectively). It is virtually immune to cw, voice, etc., and keys only on a RTTY mark tone (2125 Hz). D1 and D2 are silicon diodes, 50 PIV or greater, if needed, for the ac relay — the contacts of which should be capable of handling the load being switched, plus a safety factor, of course. — *Dick Weeden, W8KDC*

TUBE SOCKET YIELDS MINIATURE DISCONNECT JUNCTIONS

Need a few disconnect junctions for wiring between pc boards or from circuit board and panel controls? Use a pair of side-cutters to shatter a moulded phenolic

7- or 9-pin miniature tube socket to obtain two individual pin sockets. Solder stranded wires to the pins, using the holes just as you would if the socket were intact. Push a piece of No. 18 wire into one of the pins and after soldering, nip it off, leaving about 3/16 inch. Two short pieces of spaghetti, about 5/8 inch long, slipped over each pin, will insulate the bare metal. This small pin and socket will allow for easy connection and disconnection when required for modifications. — *W. Conley Smith, K6DYX*

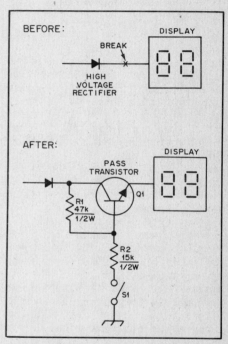

This circuit shows how a high-voltage, pass transistor may be used to turn gas-discharge display lights on and off.

FOR READOUT OF DIGITAL INSTRUMENTS

The readout of such digital instruments as clocks, panel meters, multimeters and others using Nixie lamps or seven-segment, gas-discharge displays, may be turned on and off by means of this simple circuit. High-voltage transistors such as MJE345, ECG154 or MPS A42 may be used. One should note that the display will be on when S1 is in the off position and vice versa.

Some commercial digital instruments employing the early type seven-segment, gas-discharge displays, such as SP751 and SP752, may show anomalies which show up as display flicker. This effect may be eliminated by means of the simple

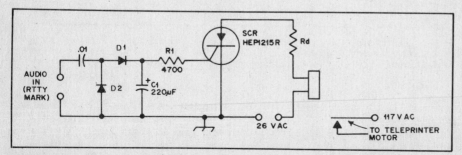

A representative circuit for SCR relay control for auto-start/motor-delay sections of RTTY demodulators.

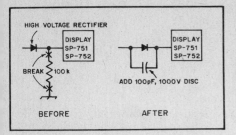

Display flicker, occurring on some commercial digital instruments, may be corrected by means of this modification.

modification shown in the schematic drawing. This modification was effective on a series of Weston no. 1230 units and should provide good results for other devices. — *Jose M. Armengol, WA2BNM*

ANOTHER ANALOG/DIGITAL CONVERTER

In developing a system to expedite field readings for geophysical surveys, I employed an analog-digital converter. The converter is a voltage-to-frequency type, for which the output is stored on a cassette recorder. The recorder is played back to the input of a digital frequency meter to recover the information. The converter input is 0-1 volt, and the output frequency is 0-10 kHz.

The converter, when connected directly to the frequency meter, becomes a digital voltmeter. With the availability of digital frequency meters, the converter becomes a useful accessory for the ham shack.

The circuit is conventional. My requirements were dictated by the frequency response of the aforementioned recorder. It should be possible to change the range

of the converter by changing the value of the input resistor. For example, a 1-megohm resistor yields a basic 10-volt range. Ohmmeters and milliammeters can be adapted. One should be aware of the possibility of over-range readings when there are a limited number of display decades in the frequency meter. A polarity indicator could be added just as well.

For stability of calibration, the positive supply should be regulated to a percentage equal to the accuracy of the least significant digit. Cost of the converter was less than $20. — *D. K. Trueman, VE4AY*

References
Dance, *Electronic Counting Circuits,* 1967.
General Electric *Transistor Manual,* 1964.
Malmstadt, Enke and Couch, *Digital and Analogue Data Conversions,* 1973.

MAKING CIRCUIT BOARDS WITH AN END-MILL CUTTER

A method I use for making copper-clad, circuit boards may be of use to other amateurs. Instead of using etched printed-circuit boards, I use a drill press with an end-mill cutter to remove unwanted copper. With this process, I have successfully made several boards described in *The Radio Amateur's Handbook.*

To adjust the tool for proper depth of cut, the end mill is placed in the drill press and set for a depth that is just below the bottom of the copper. Drill-press speed should be approximately 3000 rpm. The diameter of the cutter I use is 1/16 inch. After adjustment is made, the circuit board can be moved very carefully in any direction. — *Joseph Schnipper, K3RFL*

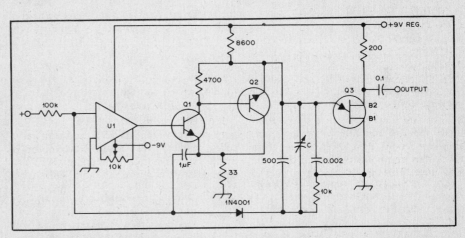

This diagram shows a voltage-to-frequency analog/digital converter.
U1 — 741 operational amplifier.
Q1 — Silicon npn transistor, Hitachi 2SC281, or equiv.
Q2 — Germanium pnp transistor, Hitachi 2SB77, or equiv.
Q3 — P-N, bar-type, silicon unijunction transistor, Texas Instruments 2N1671-B or equiv.
C — 7-45 pF ceramic trimmer capacitor.

Chapter 10

Data for PC Boards and Solid State

THE UBIQUITOUS NE555 TIMER

Recently I wanted a timed-alarm circuit but did not want to bother researching past issues of electronic magazines to look for one. The solution was the NE555 timer and a simple negative-pulse arrangement. This IC combined with a simple low-cost circuit provided an alarm that could be set for a given period of time, then automatically turned off. With the components shown in the diagram the ON time is about three minutes. Increasing R or C lengthens the ON time and vice versa. One must remember, when building this circuit that electrolytic capacitors vary widely from their marked ratings. This can result in timing variations from one timing circuit to another.

The device is particularly useful in connection with an intruder- or theft-alarm signal to limit the time the alarm operates, to conserve battery power and to limit annoyance to neighbors should the alarm be activated. — *Charles L. Shaw, K8ET*

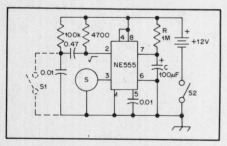

A solid-state, timed-alarm circuit.
SW1 — Remote, hidden trigger switch, N.O.
SW2 — Remote, hidden arming switch (close to energize or arm the system).
S — Mallory Sonalert SC616N. Rated 80-95 dB at 2900 Hz, 6-16 volts, 4-16 mA.
Note: Builder may choose switch type for SW1. When closed by action of an intruder, a negative pulse is delivered to pin 2 of the NE555 turning it on to drive the Sonalert through pin 3.

NPN OR PNP WITH A VOM

A simple outline is offered below to determine the base configuration and type (npn or pnp) of a transistor. The only test equipment required is a VOM.

The first step is to set the VOM in the proper mode. Place the meter in the R × 100 position. The black meter lead is connected to the COM. meter terminal, and the red lead is connected to the VΩA meter terminal (on some VOMs it is just Ω).*

The next step is to find the lead on the transistor that shows about the same resistance to each of the other two terminals. This is the base. Note the color of the meter lead. If red, the device is npn, if black, it is pnp. At this point, the base lead is known and the type is known.

Now set the meter to the high-ohms scale (R × 100k). Place the meter leads across the other two leads on the transistor. Reverse the meter leads to locate the lowest meter reading. Note the polarity of the meter leads. If the device is npn, then the black lead is on the collector and if it is a pnp type, then the red lead is on the collector.

The last terminal on the transistor, by the process of elimination, is the emitter. In a power transistor the case is generally the collector. It should be noted that although these tests are quite helpful in locating the different elements and types of transistors and will work 95 percent of the time, not all transistors can be identified in this manner. — *G.D. McKechnie, W4IKB*

*[Editor's Note: Not all ohmmeters have the same polarity (red +, black —) when in the ohms position. In some instances, black may be the positive terminal. Confirmation of the test lead polarity may be found by placing the milliammeter across the leads while in the R × 1000 position. Proper meter movement will determine the ohmmeter polarity.]

A SIMPLE ANALOG/DIGITAL CONVERTER

There are times when an analog/digital conversion is desirable. I designed this circuit for that purpose, so that it may be used with any counter having a one-second time base. I use a Heath IM-1102.

Section 1 of the schematic diagram shows the basic integrating circuit consisting of an operational amplifier and a unijunction transistor along with a few components which form a linear voltage-to-frequency converter. The only problem is that the input voltage has to be referenced to the ± 12-V line. Also, the output pulse (negative) is of very short duration, creating a possible problem for some counters.

Section 2 shows an input amplifier that inverts the input, thereby referencing the input voltage to ground. Section 3 includes a second operational amplifier which changes the output pulse to a square wave, clearing the way for use with any counter.

An option is shown in Section 4 where an NE555 timer is added operating with intervals of one second on and one second off. With this time base, it is possible to connect the output of the converter directly to a type 7490 counter and have a direct readout. Three 7290s and decoders, however, would be needed.

The upper limit of the basic converter is

Table 1	
Voltage	Count
0	0
1	100
2	200
3	300
4	400
5	500
6	600

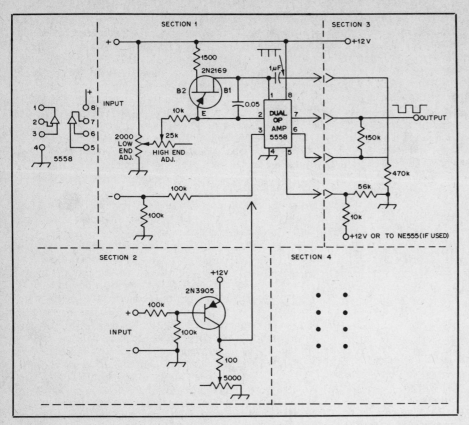

Circuit for a simple A/D converter.

Like the original tube version, the agc line must be of very high impedance. This would be the case with an FET i-f system. If this circuit is to be used with an integrated-circuit or bipolar i-f amplifier system, a low-impedance driver would be necessary. — *Dick Stevens, W1QWJ*

A HIGH-CURRENT, LOW-VOLTAGE REGULATOR FOR TTL CIRCUITS

While many amateurs are now using integrated-circuit voltage regulators, an external current-boosting (a series-dropping element) pass transistor is usually required to increase the regulator current capacity. Normal current-controlled regulator schemes, however, require additional active devices to duplicate some of the worthwhile safety features of the regulators — i.e., short-circuit protection, safe-operating-area protection and thermal shutdown.

Here is a regulator circuit which retains these safety features through a current-sharing design. This regulator, intended for TTL circuits, has an output of 5 volts at 5 amperes, and typical load regulation of 1.4 percent.

R1 and R2 provide the necessary current division (assuming the transistor base-emitter voltage equals the diode drop). The voltage drops across R1 and R2 are equal, and the currents through R1 and R2 are inversely proportional to their resistances. In this circuit, R1 has four times the current flow of R2.

For reasonable beta values, the transistor emitter current will approximately equal its collector current, while the cur-

approximately 6 volts. A resistive type of divider can be used at the input to increase the limit to any value needed. Also it is possible to add a rectifier at the input to measure ac voltages. Ohmmeter ranges may be included.

Construction notes: The output may not follow the input below the 1-volt level because of operational-amplifier offset. Preferably, check the operational amplifier and UJ separately to observe the range and linearity. The 5000-ohm potentiometer in the collector circuit of Q1 must be adjusted for the transistor used. There is interaction between the two potentiometers. — *Robert D. Corbett, W1CH*

SOLID-STATE HANG AGC

I converted Goodman's hang-agc circuit[1] from a tube to a solid-state system. It works as a hang-agc system should — very fast attack time with no agc "pop." Q1 and Q2 function as audio amplifiers. D1 is the agc diode, with C7 and R9 serving as the charging network. Q2 output is stepped up through the 2- to 10-kΩ audio transformer. D2 charges R10/C8 to a higher voltage than that across R9/C7, which keeps the FET (Q3) cut off. A 2N5716 was used because of its low pinch-off voltage. When the voltage across R10/C8 decays to a lower voltage than

that across R9/C7, Q3 conducts and clamps the agc bus to ground. D2 is the charging diode for the 0.01 μF agc capacitor. Agc threshold is determined by the value of R_T. The value should be between 100 kΩ and 470 kΩ depending on the agc threshold desired.

[1]Goodman, "Better A.V.C. for SSB and Code Reception," *QST* for Jan., 1957, p. 16.

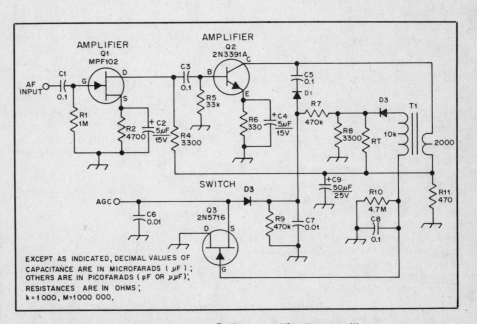

Schematic diagram of the hang-agc system. Resistors are 1/2-watt composition.
C2, C4 — 5 μF electrolytic, 15 volts.
C9 — 50 μF electrolytic, 25 volts.
D1-D3, incl. — Silicon diode, 1N914.
Q1 — MPF102FET
Q2 — 2N3391A transistor.
Q3 — 2N5716 FET.
R_T — See text.
T1 — Audio transformer, 10,000-ohm primary to 2,000-ohm secondary (Radio Shack 273-1378 or equiv.).

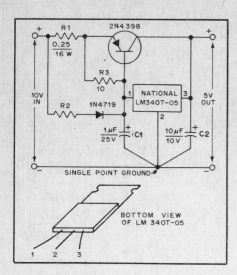

A regulator for TTL circuits.

rent through R2 will equal the current through the regulator. Under overload or short-circuit conditions, the protection circuitry of the regulator not only limits its own output current, but that of the external pass transistor, too.

Thermal overload protection is extended to the external pass transistor when its heat sink has at least four times the capacity of the regulator (this is because both devices have almost the same input and output voltage and share the load current in a 4:1 ratio).

For optimum current sharing between the regulator and the transistor as a function of temperature changes, the diode should be located physically near the pass transistor so its heat-sinking arrangement keeps it at the same temperature.

If the National LM340T regulator is used and mounted on the same heat sink as the transistor, the regulator should be electrically isolated from the heat sink, as its case (pin 3) is at ground potential while the case (collector) of the transistor is at the regulator output potential.

C1 prevents unwanted oscillations, while C2 improves the output impedance of the overall circuit. R3 is used to "unload" the excessive charge in the base region of the pass transistor when the regulator suddenly goes from full load to no load. The single-point ground system allows the regulator sense terminals (pins 2 and 3) to monitor load voltage directly, rather than at some point along a possibly resistive ground-return path which may be carrying up to 5 A of load current. — *William R. Calbo, K9ASL/8*

AN ALTERNATIVE TO HIGH-WATTAGE ZENER DIODES

High-wattage Zener diodes, the type used to develop bias in some linear amplifiers, are often hard to find. While they are not terribly expensive, not many distributors

stock Zener diodes of the 50-watt variety. The accompanying diagram shows how a 1-watt Zener diode, an inexpensive 50- to 90-watt audio transistor along with a half-watt resistor, can be connected to perform the same function. Circuit A uses a silicon or germanium pnp transistor. The voltage rating of the Zener diode should be approximately 0.3 volt less than the desired bias voltage for a germanium transistor and approximately 0.7 volt less for a silicon unit. The circuit at B uses an npn transistor. Again either a germanium or silicon transistor may be used, and the Zener-diode voltage rating is the same as that for circuit A. The transistor should be bolted to the chassis, using the chassis as a heat sink. In circuit A the transistor

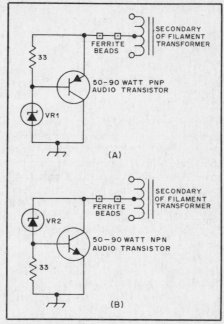

Use of high-wattage Zener diodes may be avoided by these circuits.

can be bolted directly to the chassis, but the circuit at B will require a mica insulating washer because the collector (case) is above ground. Ferrite beads are placed on the transformer center-tap lead to discourage parasitic oscillations — adapted from a circuit in the article "The Amplified Zener," which appeared in the September, 1970, issue of *Electronics World*, copyright 1970 by Ziff-Davis Publishing Company. (All rights reserved.)

[Editor's Note: Many thanks to J. F. Dunten, K5DQT, for calling this circuit to our attention.]

DESIGN OF PRINTED-CIRCUIT COILS

The fabrication process of printed circuit components results in essentially fixed-device parameters. Considerable variation in the inductance value of coils occurs as a

result of spacing, plating thickness, and the physical relationship of the component placement and the location of the circuit ground plane. The fixed printed coil must be trimmed in order to obtain the desired inductance value.

One solution of this problem is shown in the diagram. A spiral-like coil is printed with several extra turns which increase the realizable coil inductance; shorting connections are also included to reduce the inductance. The shorting connections not only short the extra turns, but also short out several turns of the main body. Coil tuning is accomplished with relative ease by removing the shorts until the desired inductance is obtained.

Approximate printed coil lengths and fabrication parameters are obtained by calculation from circuit models or experimentally determined design curves. After the approximate coil dimensions are obtained, the printed-coil layout is constructed with the several extra turns and shorting bars. Shorting connections are then removed from the coil until the exact value of inductance is obtained. This procedure calibrates the layout and subsequent photoetching process.

Once the exact coil geometry is obtained, the designer has several options. If there are a limited number of active devices in the circuit, the existing printed circuit art work may be modified by removing the appropriate shorting connections. On the other hand, if the circuit contains a large number of active devices, individual coils may be trimmed to account for differences in active device parameters. The former approach was used in a phased-array receiver. Nineteen coils of values from 0.05 to 0.1 mH were used in a variety of circuits such as delay lines, hybrids, and amplifiers. For the larger coils a tolerance of plus or minus two percent was obtained, and a tolerance of plus or minus one percent was obtained for the smaller coils. The cost per coil was very competitive with commercially available fixed or tuned devices. In addition, the other advantages of the printed wiring approach were obtained at minimal cost.— NASA Tech Brief 69-10665

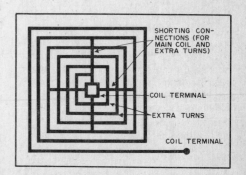

A spiral printed-circuit coil.

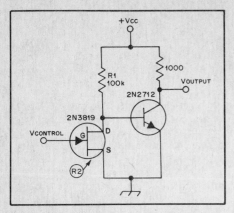

An FET and transistor combination used to provide the equivalent of a voltage-controlled Zener diode.

VOLTAGE-CONTROLLED ZENER

The use of two complementary bipolar transistors to form what is in effect an adjustable Zener is fairly well known. A variation of this approach is noted in *Practical Electronics* (January, 1976) suggested by I. D. Evans. He uses a junction FET (2N3819) and bipolar npn transistor (BC169/2N2712) to form the equivalent of a voltage-controlled Zener. This is based on the so-called "amplified Zener" arrangement but replaces the Zener diode with a resistor (R1) and the usual resistive branch of the network with an FET whose resistance (R2) varies in accordance with an applied control voltage: see the diagram. The FET resistance controls the voltage at which the transistor turns "on" and can, if required, be readily controlled remotely. — *Radio Communication, March, 1976, RSGB*

WORKING WITH IC COMPONENTS

When working on a project using ICs and double-sided pc boards, one may find it necessary to solder IC pins on both sides of the board. Although the IC may be soldered directly to the board, a more practical approach is to install a socket. Use of the IC socket facilitates component replacement and may save an IC from damage caused by excessive heat while soldering.

Mounting the socket on a pc board may be difficult because of the short pins on the socket. An easy solution is to use a single conductor of stranded hookup wire to make pin extensions for the socket.

Place the end of a strand through the hole in the board for each IC pin which must have soldered connections on both sides of the board. Bend one end of the wire against the board on the side opposite the IC. Do not let the end pass beyond the edge of the foil to be soldered. Solder this end.

Next, turn the board over. Cut the end of the strand to a length equal to that of one of the socket pins. Do not let the tip touch the foil beyond the point of soldering. Bend this end away from the IC socket. Prepare each of the necessary solder points on the board for each socket. A "Z" pattern will make holding the wire against the board easier when soldering: That is, bend the wire one direction on one side of the board and in the opposite direction on the other side.

Now, bend outward each socket pin which must make electrical contact on both sides of the board. These pins should correspond to the wires just soldered. Be very careful with them since they may be easily broken. Solder each socket pin to the proper place. Soldering wires on both sides of the board may be necessary for mechanical support. This should be done if the majority of socket pins make electrical contact only on the IC side of the board. Tinning both the socket pins and the foil on the top of the board can be helpful. That's all there is to it. — *Tony Stalnaker, WA4LPJ*

SOLID-STATE RELAY FOR REPEATERS

The device shown in the diagram was designed by WØINK to interface with solid-state vhf receiver and transmitter strips. Our 2-meter repeater is now completely solid state and has a current drain of only 400 mA when in operation. The LED, when lit, indicates the transmitter is in operation. The delay of the "tail" can be adjusted by changing the value of C1. For a normal squelch tail, a value of 20 μF is used. The relay is driven by the COR circuit. Several CORs that could be used with this relay are described in *FM and Repeaters for the Radio Amateur*. — *Mike Wisch, WBØLGC/WRØAEN*

MARKING ETCHED-CIRCUIT BOARDS

Etched-circuit boards can be neatly marked with component designations and polarities by using waxy rub-on transfer letters. Alphabets of various sizes can be bought at art supply stores. The waxy letters act as a resist, leaving the marking in the copper after the board is etched. I always include W9IWI in a corner of the board to show who made it. — *Julian Jablin, W9IWI*

LOW-COST ETCH-RESISTANT PENS AND A NEW SLANT ON ETCHANT BATHS

Less-expensive etch-resistant pen substitutes are Sanford's Sharpie permanent ink marker for narrow lines, and Sanford's Impact with a wider tip.

For etching printed-circuit boards, I use a one-gallon mayonnaise jar. Place the board to be etched face down on the inside of the jar, with the jar resting on its side in the sink. Pour in enough etchant solution to wet the surface of the board, and put the cover on the jar. A plastic grill reduces the chance of breakage and the irritating noise of the glass rolling in the sink as the etchant is agitated. The etching process may be hastened by placing the jar in hot water, keeping the water level below the mouth of the jar. By holding the jar up to the light, it is possible to determine when etching is completed; and when it is, the solution may be poured down the drain or back into the jar. The board may be rinsed while still in the jar. With this method, it is never necessary to handle the etchant directly, reducing greatly the chance of spills and stains. — *John H. Bordelon, K4JIU*

Solid-state relay. The LED is a surplus type, but a Radio Shack replacement should not be difficult to obtain.

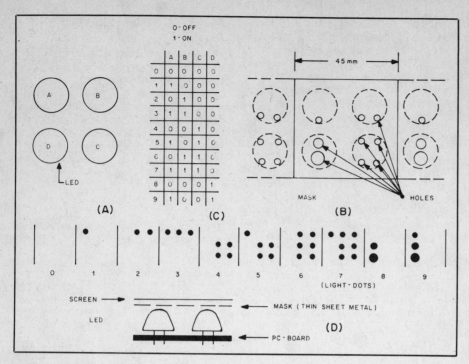

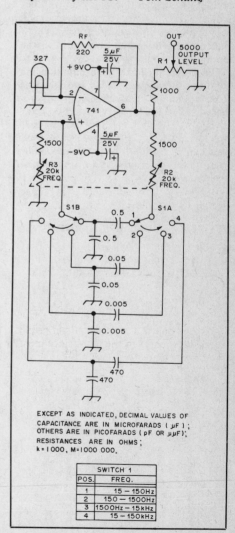

An arrangement for a simple BCD converter and readout.

A SIMPLE BCD CONVERTER AND READOUT

The arrangement shown will take a binary input and convert it directly to a decimal readout using four clamps (or LEDs). This eliminates the need for decoder/drivers, Nixie tubes or neon lamps and provides the ultimate in a low-cost readout.

Each decade digit consists of four lamps in back of a mask as shown in the drawing. The lamps correspond to the binary positions for 1, 2, 4 and 8. One hole is drilled in the mask for the "1" position, two holes for the "2" position, and four holes for the "4" position. A small hole over a larger one is drilled to represent the "8."

In reading the display, one could merely count up the lighted dots (except for 8 and 9). But with a little practice, the digits can be read on sight. The figures for 1, 2, 3, 4 and 6 resemble the numbers themselves (with a little imagination). Only 5 and 9 are new but can be learned with little difficulty. — *Peter Hansen, DK4YD*

ETCHING METAL PANELS

Decal labels on radio equipment often wear and peel off quickly, particularly on test equipment subjected to constant use. Etched labels, on the other hand, provide permanent identification of control knobs and dials.

To etch a steel panel, pour hot paraffin over the area to be labeled. When cooled, letter the label into the paraffin with a sharp pointed instrument, scraping the metal clean to form the letters or numerals. Neat lettering can be insured by using a lettering guide from a stationery store. Remove any wax shavings with a fine brush and place a drop of hydrochloric or nitric acid on each letter with a medicine dropper. Several applications of acid may be necessary to obtain the desired depth. When etching has been completed, wash the panel with cold water and peel off the remaining wax. The etched characters can be filled with paint or nail polish.

The necessary acids can be obtained in small quantities at most drugstores, but are highly corrosive and should not be brought in contact with the skin. Containers should also be properly labeled and have tight plastic or rubber caps. — *Joe A. Rolf, K5JOK*

SEMICONDUCTOR CIRCUIT REPAIR HINT

When a diode or transistor "blows," knowing why is a help in order to eliminate the cause and to prevent further occurrences. If the failure was caused by too high a current, the semiconductor would be open because of the overheating and melting of the pn junction. If a voltage spike or high voltage was the cause, the device will be shorted inasmuch as holes will be punctured in the pn junction. This hint has proven helpful and reliable for me in troubleshooting transistor and diode circuitry. — *Rick Liftig, WA1ISD*

AUDIO OSCILLATOR

A wide-range audio oscillator that will provide a moderate output level can be built from a single 741 operational amplifier (see diagram). Power is supplied by two 9-volt batteries, from which the circuit draws 4 mA. The frequency range is selectable from 15 Hz to 150 kHz, although a 1.5- to 15-Hz range can be included with the addition of two 5-μF non-polarized capacitors and an extra switch position. Distortion is approximately one percent. The output level under a light load (10 kΩ) is 4 to 5 volts. This can be increased by using higher battery voltages, up to a maximum of + and — 18 volts, with a corresponding adjustment of R_f.

Pin connections shown are for the TO-5 case. If another package configuration is used, the pin connections may be different. R_f (220 ohms) is trimmed for an output level about five percent below clipping. This should be done for the temperature at which the oscillator will normally operate, as the lamp is sensitive to ambient temperature. Note that the output of this oscillator is direct coupled. If you are connecting this unit into circuits where dc voltage is present, use a coupling capacitor. As with any solid-state equipment, be cautious around plate circuits of tube-type equipment, as the voltage spike caused by charging a coupling capacitor may destroy the IC. — *Tom Schultz*

EXCEPT AS INDICATED, DECIMAL VALUES OF CAPACITANCE ARE IN MICROFARADS (μF); OTHERS ARE IN PICOFARADS (pF or $\mu\mu$F); RESISTANCES ARE IN OHMS; k=1000, M=1000 000.

SWITCH 1	
POS.	FREQ.
1	15 – 150Hz
2	150 – 1500Hz
3	1500Hz – 15kHz
4	15 – 150kHz

A simple audio oscillator that provides a selectable frequency range. R2 and R3 control the frequency and R1 varies the output level.

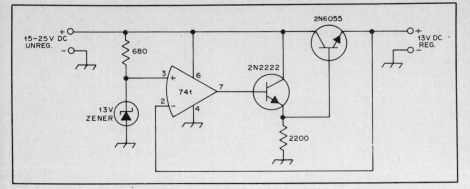

This circuit provides voltage regulation of better than 0.1 volt from no-load to 8 amperes.

STANDARD COMPONENTS PROVIDE EFFECTIVE REGULATION

The standard voltage regulator circuit which uses a pass transistor referenced to a Zener diode often fails to provide sufficient regulation under widely varying current demands. Perhaps this is true because a higher current demand translates into a lower-ohmage emitter load for the pass transistor, hence, a lower input impedance appears at the base with a rise in base-to-emitter voltage, resulting in a consequent drop in output voltage from the supply.

The diagram illustrates a circuit using standard components. This provides far better voltage regulation. The 741 operational amplifier compares the output voltage of the supply to the 13-volt Zener reference, and with nearly an open loop gain, adjusts the pass via the 2N2222 emitter follower for essentially 0 differential voltage. I use this circuit to power my Kenwood TR-7400A and experience regulation of better than 0.1 volt from no load to 8 amperes! — *C. R. MacCluer, W8MQW*

EASY PRINTED-CIRCUIT LAYOUT

After reading the article on printed circuits in January, 1970, *QST*, some procedures that I use came to mind. On laying out the board, I use Clear-Print graph paper, ten squares to the inch, since most solid-state components use 0.1 inch or multiples thereof, for lead spacing. The lines on the graph paper are handy references for drawing interconnections. Crossovers are placed so they cross at the gap formed by a component.

After laying out the circuit, the graph paper is trimmed to size and affixed to the board with a transparent tape. A No. 60 drill is then used to cut mounting holes through the paper layout. The layout can now be used as a schematic (or wiring) diagram when painting the etch-resist material on the board. I use nail polish for this. The brush tip should be cut at an angle to allow the lines to be made finer. — *Ross W. Stevens, W6FRE*

LONGER LIFE FOR CIRCUIT-BOARD ETCHANT

Storing ferric-chloride etchant (the type used for etching printed-circuit boards) in a refrigerator will prolong the usefulness of the solution. Chilling the etchant causes precipitation of free copper to the bottom of the container as "mud." The clearer liquid can be poured into another vessel and the "mud" then washed out of the original container with clean water. — *W. H. Fishback, W1JE*

BEWARE OF PROTECTIVE DIODES

A word of caution regarding the use of protective diodes across the antenna input terminals of solid-state receivers is in order. If separate antennas are used for transmitting and receiving, severe TVI can be created by the diodes rectifying the transmitted signals and reradiating them on many frequencies in the rf spectrum. I discovered this while experimenting with my solid-state receiver. I was attempting to see if the diodes really protected the front-end rf transistor stage by leaving the receiver connected to its own antenna while transmitting with a 350-watt rig nearby. I was impolitely informed by the XYL that I was raising havoc with the television set. As soon as the receiver was disconnected from its antenna, the problem disappeared. If the same antenna is used for transmitting and receiving such a problem should not exist. — *Glen Benskin, K6UH*

PULSE-DETECTOR CIRCUIT FOR THE VEST-POCKET LOGIC PROBE

I have built the vest-pocket logic probe described in *QST*.[1] I used LEDs as indicators, instead of the incandescent lamps, with a 220-ohm resistor in series with each LED. It is a wonderful test instrument to check logic circuits, and handy to use. What I would like to know is if it could be modified so that it will indicate

[1]Rogers, "The Vest-Pocket Logic Probe," *QST*, August, 1972, p. 46.

pulses. Then the logic probe could be used by those who have no high-speed oscilloscopes to trouble-shoot clock circuits, pulse generators, and the like. — *Ray Dagenais, VE3ARJ*

[Editor's Note: There are several ways in which a pulse-testing feature can be added to the Rogers logic probe. The circuit of the drawing is suggested as a simple approach. The circuit may be constructed as a separate module, and is used in conjunction with the logic probe without requiring any modifications to the original device. U1 is a quad 2-input positive NOR gate, type 7402, half of its sections being unused. S1 is a momentary-push normally open switch. C1 may be disk ceramic, and its value it not critical.

With no connection or with a steady-state dc level (either a logic high or a logic low) at the pulse-test input, depressing and releasing S1 will cause the "0" indicator of the logic probe to light and remain lit. As soon as a positive going logic pulse of 3.5 V or more is applied at the pulse-test input, the "1" indicator of the logic probe will light and remain lit. After connections are made to the circuit under test, S1 may be depressed and released repeatedly, and a train of pulses will be indicated by the "1" indicator becoming lit each time after the reset switch is released. With a relatively small value for C1, as shown, the circuit will not respond to any wave forms except fast-rise-time pulses and rf.]

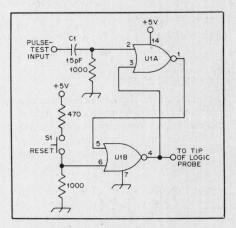

Suggested circuit for adding pulse-testing feature to the Rogers logic probe. See text for parts description.

A HIGH-FREQUENCY INDICATOR WITH LED

The use of a light-emitting diode as a low-cost indicator is noted in a short item by F. Maters, PAØFMY, in *Electron* for May, 1975. This appears to be a useful gimmick to have around. — Radio Communication, *August, 1975, RSGB*

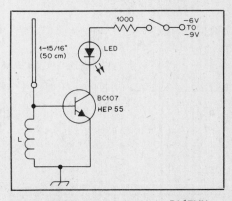

Simple high-frequency indicator by PAØFMY using an LED as indicator.

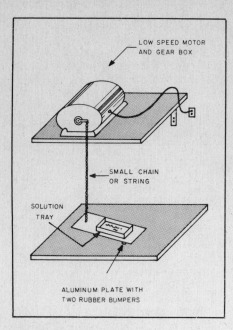

When mounting the motor above the tray, the level of agitation can be adjusted by moving the chain on the rotating arm.

PRINTED-CIRCUIT AGITATOR

After reading about etched-circuit boards, a different method of agitating the tray came to mind. I took a fairly heavy piece of aluminum, and on the underside of one end, mounted two rubber bumpers. These bumpers, or feet, allow it to rock without moving around on the workbench. A small chain, as shown in the sketch was added to the other end of the piece of aluminum and was attached to a rotating arm mounted on the output shaft on the motor/gear assembly. The amount of tray motion is adjusted by properly placing the chain on the moving arm. The assembly can be moved, cleaned or stored by just removing the chain. — *Harold D. Mohr, K8ZHZ*

ZENER + DIODE

Frequently, while experimenting, the need arises for a Zener diode of a slightly higher voltage than is on hand. An easy

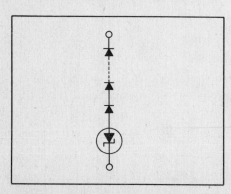

An alternative for higher-voltage Zener diodes.

way to achieve this higher voltage is to add silicon diodes in series with the Zener diode. Each diode will add approximately 0.5 to 0.7 volts to the regulated voltage amount (see diagram). It is considerably cheaper to stock a couple of Zener diodes and a handful of silicon diodes than to stock a Zener diode for every voltage that might be required in the course of an experiment. — *Robert A. Sullivan, WØYVA/4*

A THIRD HAND

Here is a hint that could be a great help for kit builders and homemade equipment builders. When soldering or working with pc boards often one has need for more than two hands. This device can serve as that "third hand."

Obtain a small block of wood, 4 × 4 inches. Fasten rubber grommets to the bottom of the block to prevent scratching the worktable. Screw cable clamps to the block for holding pc boards, wire or components while working on a project. Extra clamps may be added to hold additional pc boards. — *Rick Cole, WD4CTA*

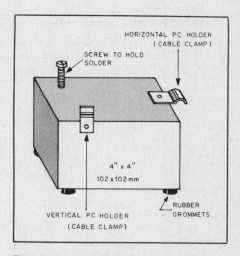

This simple wood block with clamps makes a useful tool for holding circuit boards.

ETCHED-CIRCUIT BOARDS WITH NO FUSS

In the course of making a considerable number of circuit boards during the past few years, I have arrived at a style, which though not suited for many commercial requirements, is sufficient for most amateur needs. Instead of etching an elaborate pattern of lines, circles, dots and curves, I have designed all of my boards in a mosaic, or floor-tile pattern. I find three distinct advantages to this method of layout. First, there is less copper foil to be etched away; second, there are no fine lines of foil to pop off the board when extra heat is applied; and

third, there is a much greater latitude available in the placement of parts.

Anyone who has access to a Dremel type drill can make his own boards without resorting to chemical etching. After laying out the desired pattern on paper and transferring the design to the copper foil, it is a simple matter to cut through the foil with a fine rotary saw, or a small emery-saw wheel.

Shown is a typical circuit and the board that I would etch, drill, place components on, and have in operation in about 30 minutes time. Although this is a simple design, I have made more complex circuits in about the same time and they have remained in operation a long while without foil failure. — *F. T. McAllister, W8HKT/4*

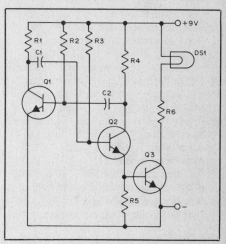

Shown is a light-flasher board and the pattern for the etched circuit board to build it on.

DIG THIS DIGITAL CLOCK HINT

I constructed several digital clocks which contain the MM5314 chip described by Kelley in *QST* for November, 1974 and as described in the 1974 edition of *The Radio Amateur's Handbook*. I experienced some difficulty with stability with both the ac and mobile models. My solution to the problem may interest other amateurs.

With the ac model, I bypassed pins 13, 14 and 15 with 0.01-μF capacitors. I also placed a 0.01-μF capacitor across the filter capacitor. In the mobile unit I installed 0.01-μF capacitors as described above and changed the multiplex circuit as shown in the diagram. After these changes were made both clocks appeared quite stable. — *Robert S. Putman, K7ACP*

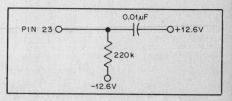

Stabilizing circuit for digital clock.

INDEX